# BY HAN SUYIN

DESTINATION CHUNGKING

A MANY-SPLENDORED THING

# A Many-Splendored Thing

# A Many-Splendored Thing

## BY HAN SUYIN

AN ATLANTIC MONTHLY PRESS BOOK

LITTLE, BROWN AND COMPANY · BOSTON

1953

The author is grateful to Henry Holt and Company, Inc., for permission
to quote four lines from *Last Poems* by A. E. Housman, copyright 1922
by Henry Holt and Company, Inc., 1950 by Barclays Bank, Ltd. She also
thanks Charles Scribner's Sons for permission to use four lines from "In
No Strange Land" by Francis Thompson.

ATLANTIC–LITTLE, BROWN BOOKS
ARE PUBLISHED BY
LITTLE, BROWN AND COMPANY
IN ASSOCIATION WITH
THE ATLANTIC MONTHLY PRESS

PRINTED IN THE UNITED STATES OF AMERICA
BY THE HADDON CRAFTSMEN, INC., SCRANTON, PA.

# *Foreword*

Han suyin, the author of this moving book, is a Chinese woman. Born in Peking, she was educated at a Chinese university and then toured Europe for two years. In 1938 she returned to China with her husband and lived in the interior during the Sino-Japanese War, where she wrote her first book, *Destination Chungking,* in collaboration with an American woman missionary. It presented a vivid picture of Free China, of the sufferings of the Chinese people and of life in the old feudal provinces of Western China. In its last chapter Han Suyin foreshadowed prophetically the coming struggle between the Chinese Nationalists and Communists.

At the end of the war fate took her back to England. There, after the death of her husband — killed in the civil war now raging in earnest in China — she finished her medical studies and qualified with honors at London University. At the same time she supported herself and her child by supplementing her scholarship with the income from a job. She could not, however, stay long away from her own people, and soon left England again to plunge into the turmoil of contemporary Asia.

*A Many-Splendored Thing* is a book about that post-war Asia, shaken from end to end by stupendous, revolutionary changes. Future historians will regard this mid-twentieth century upheaval in the largest and most populous continent on earth as one of their grandest themes; and they will no doubt be able to assess it with the cool judgment of men observing great events in retrospect. For us who live in the middle of the earthquake it is more difficult to appreciate dispassionately and exactly its significance. Many petty and ludicrous prejudices on the part either of those who regard the whole upheaval as unnecessary, and who long for "the good old days" in Asia, or else of those who so despise those days that they wish the new Asia to make a complete break with them and so to become entirely uprooted from its own historical past, are apt to blur clear vision. Yet the fundamental explanation of what is happening is simple. The feudalism which gradually, over centuries, disappeared from the Western world as a result of "modern" material progress and intellectual evolution persisted virtually unaltered everywhere in Asia until the other day. Then Western practices and notions began to invade the East, following in the wake of the enterprising European traders, soldiers, administrators and missionaries who, by their superior material power, established themselves as rulers in large parts of Asia. Now these ideas have germinated; and a process which occurred gradually over a long period in Europe is being attempted with revolutionary haste in Asia. Feudalism is being swept away; and incidentally the "Western Imperialism" which was either the last phase of the old feudalism or the first phase of the new liberalism — according to which way you look at it — is being swept away, too.

That historic transformation is common to almost every country in Asia, although it takes different shapes in different countries and produces at present such varying regimes as Nehru's in India, Mao Tse-Tung's in China, Soekarno's in Indonesia and others elsewhere. At the moment, the great change is only in the process of occurring. Its pace varies from place to place. The story of *A Many-Splendored Thing* is set in two lands, one small and the other vast, which — though they lie side by side as close physical neighbors — are at the opposite extremities in this political process of change; first in Hong Kong, which is a little-altered relic of "Western Imperialism," with its good points and its bad; and then in China, where a full-blooded Communist society is now being rapidly established. One need only refer in passing to the fact that this new China is in danger of falling under a later imperialism far more sinister than that of the liberalizing West — the harsh Russian tyranny which is the same cruel, reactionary influence whether it masquerades under the crown of a Tsar or the cap of a Commissar.

A vivid feature of Han Suyin's book is the contrast in her brilliant pictures of Hong Kong and China. These two clashing settings make dramatic back-scenes for the stage on which her actors play their parts. In their conduct these people — the Christian missionaries and old-school Chinese refugees from China, the enthusiastic young Chinese Communists and serene, imperturbable non-Communist elders inside China, the foreign observers of various types in Hong Kong and, above all, the Eurasian girl, Suyin, and her English lover, Mark — represent other clashes which disturb Asia today. These conflicts are the stuff of contemporary human history, and must be understood sympathetically by people in the West and the East alike if a world disaster is to be avoided.

Han Suyin describes them with deep intuition. They intrude constantly like a full orchestral accompaniment to the duet of Suyin's and Mark's intense and gracious, troubled but harmonious, ill-fated and yet triumphant love affair.

One conflict which Han Suyin describes is the internal one being waged in the hearts and minds of many intelligent Chinese, between their passionate, elemental desire to be associated with their own people, "right or wrong," and their distaste for the excesses of the Communist Revolution; between their sympathy for the generous impulses which have prompted that Revolution, and their recognition of the intolerant cruelties which it has introduced; between their love for a multitude of their young fellow-countrymen, who in China are devoting their enthusiasm to try to create a reformed and revitalized Chinese nation, and their doubt, to say the least, about the Chinese leaders who seem to be organizing mass misguidance of that enthusiasm; between their approval of the liberation from old bonds which the Communists have achieved for scores of millions of Chinese, and alarm that these same Communists now proceed to bind with new chains those whom they have freed from the old.

Although the girl Suyin is a Eurasian she is mostly Chinese, and her reactions to events in China and to foreign criticism must be typical of countless educated Chinese both inside and outside China. Parts of her feel a compelling urge to return to China, to help her people in their struggle; but other parts bid her stay away, sympathetic yet aloof in Hong Kong, watching events from that semidetached observation tower. The account running through this book of her thoughts and feelings is of profound importance, for by reading it we foreigners understand better the motives which have led so many good, non-Communist Chinese to stay in China and associate themselves with the Communist effort. Such understanding will help when the time comes — as come it surely must — for reconciliation between China and the West. Although many of the individual Chinese concerned will then be dead — murdered by their Communist masters — large numbers still alive will probably retain a similar frame of mind.

Another conflict hovering perpetually over the episodes of *A Many-Splendored Thing* is that between the white races of the West and the colored races of the East. No doubt various circumstances contribute to the unhappy antipathy which plays such a dominant part in Asian politics today, and which bedevils good relations between the peoples of the Occident and the Orient; but the chief cause is the recent rule by several European nations of various Asian peoples. "Western Imperialism" brought many benefits to Asia which one day, in more dispassionate times, will be recognized with a measure of gratitude. Chief amongst them was perhaps that introduction of liberalizing ideas which are the very weapons for destroying Asian feudalism. But Western rule unfortunately also brought some evil consequences; and chief amongst them was the creation of a superiority complex amongst the whites and of an inferiority complex amongst the colored peoples, neither of which was justified, each of which did untold damage to the characters of the two respective peoples, and both of which have for the time being made natural, unprejudiced and truly friendly relations between them extremely difficult.

I must not misuse this note to moralize pompously on these themes, for it is a brief Foreword to Han Suyin's lovely story, not a protracted political treatise. In any case she writes with an insight far deeper than any that I command about these all-important problems of contemporary Asia and of relations between the East and the West. As she herself has said: "European and American authors write with great beauty and perception about Asians. I write as an Asian, with all the pent-up emotions of my people. What I say will annoy many people who prefer the more conventional myths brought back by writers on the Orient. All I can say is that I try to tell the truth. Truth, like surgery, may hurt, but it cures."

Something at least as drastic as a surgical operation is needed to create new, healing relations between the peoples of the West and the East. It is a change of heart, a complete abandonment of old superiority and inferiority complexes, a meeting together of the renewed nations of the East and the old nations of the West on a footing of equality, as glad, mutually devoted partners in the struggle of all humanity to attain peace and enlightenment. Han Suyin's book should help to accomplish that.

Such vast matters form the ever-intrusive background of her story. In the foreground occurs the incident of Suyin's and Mark's love. It is best that I leave the author to tell that narrative in her own beautiful way — a tale of one of those perfect unions between a man and woman which is somehow doomed, and which yet possesses imperishable, deathless quality. Han Suyin writes it with a beauty of feeling and language, and with a passion and poetry and philosophy which need no comment beyond the homage of silence.

MALCOLM MACDONALD

*Commissioner-General for the United Kingdom in South-East Asia*

# Preface

*April 1950*

Will you write a book about me?" asked Mark. It was the hour after love. We lay in the long grass of the hill slope, in the abundant sun. Above us the sky stretched widely to an undefended horizon. Around us was granite rock, grass, bracken and small myrtle. Below the hill lay the wrinkled blue sea, all alone without a sail in the endless spring afternoon. We spoke quietly, detached from ourselves; careful, deliberate words. We spoke of things which at that moment no longer hurt to think about. Lucidly, we speculated on absence, separation from each other, and the splitting of our worlds into ever more irreconcilable fragments. Our voices were disembodied and calm, voices which we only achieved in the hour after love.

"I may write something about you," I replied. "But not now. Now I am too full of joy to do anything but to live, with the ever-present knowledge of you within me, filling me with gladness. Perhaps if you leave me, and I grieve, or for some other good reason, I may write a book about you."

"What other good reason would you have?" asked Mark.

"Food. I'd sell my love for food any day. The rice bowl is to me the most valid reason in the world for doing anything. A piece of one's soul to the multitudes in return for rice and wine does not seem to me a sacrilege."

"If you wish to sell red-hot passion, dear one," said Mark, running his finger along my eyebrows, "you must do it before you forget all about me, since you hate so much the embalming odor of memories."

"That is why I'll do it. I shall exhume all my memories, for I was born irreverent. And I'll do it before the love of you recedes from me as surely as the sea's tide, leaving a sea-wet shore littered with meaningless fragments. I shall write how we loved in the fashion of all lovers, and strove not to let the little things of existence destroy us. How they did, and how we forgot. Just like everyone else. For we are, no more nor less than anybody else, transient, imperfect lovers in a world of endless inconstancy."

"What rhetoric," said Mark. "Do you really think, then, that other people get as much pleasure and happiness out of their bodies as we do? Do you really think that this love will not last forever? I do not believe it." And he looked round him for confirmation. But there was only myrtle and long grass and bracken, hill slope and sea, and ourselves all golden with lying in the sun.

"Dear love, even the paunchy, ugly people of this world believe they love as much as we do and forever. It is the illusion of all lovers to think themselves unique and their words immortal."

Mark said: "It may be an illusion, but it is the only truth that you and I possess, therefore let us enjoy it while we can. For after all, my dear one, we may have only little time, so little time to love."

And those words of his were the only true ones which we said on that afternoon.

# Contents

*PART TWO*

# Progress

*PART THREE*

# Crisis

*PART FOUR*

# Conclusion

PART ONE

# Onset

# CHAPTER I

# Exodus from China

*March 1949*

Mrs. PARRISH PATS HER NEW SILK DRESS INTO PLACE ROUND her hips and her tongue clicks with approbation against her small white teeth.

"You are getting slimmer, there's no doubt about it now," says Mrs. Thrale, crocheting away. "Thanks to you, Doc," she flashes at me.

"You were an answer to my prayer, Doc," says Helen Parrish, twisting in front of the full-length mirror to inspect her back. Three weeks of dieting have produced admirable results. Her husband, Alf, is coming down from the Mission in Hankow. He may arrive in Hong Kong any day. The communists are closing in from the north and from the east. Every city falls to them without resistance, whole armies surrender complete with general. Hankow will fall. Helen Parrish does not think that Alf will be able to stay in Hankow when the communists start taking over the school where he teaches. She and the children came to Hong Kong four months ago. Here the abundant food, ice cream, lack of exercise, added twenty pounds to her bulk. She was quietly desperate about it until I arrived at Church Guest House in February, fresh from England, where I had completed my medical studies. For weeks I stood over her at meals, brandishing under her nose a written list of forbidden items. "It's such a relief to know that you are going to stay at Church Guest House for a while," she says. "So nice to have a doctor at hand, when one's got children."

Mary Fairfield knits, her pale lips shift against each other, counting the stitches. This morning, after long and earnest prayer, she has been told by God to go back to China, with the children.

"You'll be liberated by the communists," says Helen Parrish, "and I don't think that will be good for you or for the children."

But to Mary Fairfield, as to many another missionary, China is the field, the chosen land for the spreading of the Word. In this hour of darkness and danger, salvation must be propagated more than ever before. "My father and my mother were missionaries in China. I was born there, and spent my early childhood there. My children were born in China. Somehow I cannot imagine life without China."

Mrs. Thrale, who does not knit, is also sad, but for other reasons. She is not a missionary of long standing. The Thrales had arrived from America a short while ago, and furnished a house; then their town was threatened and they left for Hong Kong. "You should have seen the curtains in my bedroom. Yellow chintz, with a lily-of-the-valley pattern. I feel brokenhearted when I think about our house and all the furniture we had to sell. I feel sure that God means us to go back one day."

Mrs. Jones is English. She belongs to the group that sit in Helen Parrish's bedroom, and knit, and talk. But she says very little when we are all together. I roomed with her during my first week at the Guest House, and we used to talk in whispers, at night, when we lay next to each other in our iron beds. That was before I moved to the basement. "Henry and I don't agree about leaving China. He wants to stay."

If he leaves he will have to resign from the Mission, and find a job in England. He has been away from home a long time, and does not know how to set about finding a job. Mrs. Jones is scared, there are no heroics about her. "If Henry were a medical missionary the communists would let him get on with his work. But he is an evangelist. He prints and distributes religious tracts. They're bound to stop him before anyone else."

In the first impulse to get away from the sweep of the advancing armies, many missionary families have come to Hong Kong. Once here, their fears subside, and they want to go back. Very few want to return to America or to England. A good many are second-generation missionaries, with a China tradition in the family. The Word of God was preached by their parents in the heathen land of China, and must now the good earth go back to the heathen? After so many years of toil, have they failed to make a Christian impression on the Chinese soul? "I love China. I have always loved the Chinese people. China, my China," they say. "I just cannot understand so many people going over to the communists. Even among our best Christians. Why, I knew these people as the back of my hand; I cannot understand what has happened to them."

Church Guest House, a rectangular yellow building with two rows of green shuttered windows adorning its front, stands opposite the Botanic Gardens on the island of Hong Kong. The hall with its rattan chairs, white settee, potted palms, dark polished floor and cream walls combines simplicity with shabbiness in a halfhearted attempt towards home comfort. It is always crowded with missionaries from China, mostly Americans, with a sprinkling of English missionaries and of Chinese pastors. Nonmissionaries are not supposed to stay here more than a few days. The Guest House costs sixteen dollars, an English pound, per day, for board and lodging. It has modern sanitation. There is no running hot water, but two pails of warm water for a bath are available every day for each adult. At the time I was staying there, the average number of people in each room was five.

"The housekeeper is hovering again," says Helen Parrish after a glance outside her bedroom door. "The *Capsicum's* just come in. There's bound to be plenty of our folks on board. I wonder how many more they're going to pack into each room."

"I think it's unfair having people who are not missionaries staying here. This is Church Guest House, after all. I don't mean you, doctor. You're in the basement, anyway."

In the midst of these exchanges, to which I submit mutely, the housekeeper materializes in the doorway. Gentle and shy, she resorts to pantomime to make her meaning understood. Throughout the day her features contort to express sorrow, pleasure, surprise, interest, astonishment and delight. With consummate ease and rapidity she passes from one emotion to its exact opposite. She does not tread the ground, but hovers two inches above the floor, an ever-ready smile wreathing her mouth. All of her, complete with smile, now stands in the doorway of Helen Parrish's bedroom. She beams at us, then her face warps with anguish, and Mary Fairfield, startled, drops a stitch.

"So sorry, dear Mrs. Fairfield," she whispers, "but we must, we really must put a little boy with his mother in your room. A very nice child, dear sweet little boy," she coaxes, and her face expresses delight at the thought of the dear little boy.

"Well" — Mary Fairfield struggles blatantly between Christian charity and human distaste — "of course I wouldn't dream of refusing. We must all help each other in these crowded times. Suzie and Clare do have such bad colds, I wonder, I most certainly wonder whether it's fair to have another child in the room. And my husband may be coming down any day, you know. The baby hasn't been well either. It may be measles. She's had whooping cough and pneumonia, but she hasn't had measles yet. I took her temperature four times today. I wonder whether an enema would help her. It's wonderful what an enema does to bring down a baby's temperature, Doctor Han."

I say: "No enema."

Mrs. Jones, Mrs. Thrale, Mrs. Parrish, are blind to the housekeeper's facial entreaties. We are all thinking of the water supply. More people, less water. Or colder water. Schemes run through our heads. Getting up half an hour earlier, or tipping the boy, might be helpful. . . .

Hong Kong is crowded. There are two and a half times as many people as there were a year ago. Every day more arrive, by train, by ship, on foot across the border. It is impossible to get a room without the expenditure of a great deal of cash. Before getting a sniff at a room, there is key money, foot money, stairs money, feeling money to pay. There is furniture money for nonexistent furniture, and then the preposterously high rental. Each one of these expenditures to the innumerable middlemen through which rooms are available represents a small fortune in thousands of Hong Kong dollars, sixteen to the pound.

I am not a missionary, yet I am staying at Church Guest House, a favor and a concession to the Medical Service which employs me. However, my salary is paid at the local Chinese rate since I am a Chinese, but I am living at the Guest House on a European (or nearly European) standard. The money is not enough for board and lodging for myself and my daughter, let alone incidentals. Nothing can increase it, for it includes already the maximum high cost of living allowance which I, as a widow supporting a child, am entitled to receive in Hong Kong. By the second month I am rapidly falling into debt. Then Mabel Chow, the receptionist at Church Guest House, and Lucy Koo, a school teacher, together rescue me.

Mabel sits in the hall, reads the paper, gives out misleading information on the location of shops and the whereabouts of streets, and interprets for the missionaries, who cannot speak the dialect. "You don't speak Chinese," she informs me on the second day after my arrival at the Guest House.

"Of course I do." I look down upon Mabel, four foot nine, who already has six children, and whose seventh is very evidently in the offing under her tight Chinese gown. "I don't speak Cantonese dialect, because I come from the North."

"Ah, Shanghai," she says.

"No, not Shanghai. Shanghai is not North China to me. I am from Peking."

"For us Cantonese," says Mabel, "all North is Shanghai. And here Cantonese is Chinese. We don't speak Northern language. So you don't speak Chinese."

After these elucidations we become friends, and soon Mabel knows of my financial troubles. She helps.

"I have talked with Mrs. Koo about you," she announces one day. "Mrs. Koo says she take you in her room. She old friend with manager. You pay half only."

"But Mrs. Koo does not know me."

"She does not know you, but she likes you all the same."

I meet Lucy Koo that evening. Tall for a Cantonese, slightly stooped, a widow with two children to support, she teaches at a school. She has a basement room, cold and rather damp. She has stayed at the Guest House for years. Her husband, a Chinese Protestant pastor, was killed by the Japanese during the war.

Lucy Koo is pious, but she never tries to convert me. We have in common our widowhoods, our children and our penury.

"You and your daughter can come in my room with me, my two children and Soosee my dog. I hope you won't mind."

I don't mind at all. Lucy has arranged that I should pay only half price, and thus I become solvent again. This is important to me, for I have no money left after paying our passages from England.

Thus I will stay four months at Church Guest House, until I move to the Hospital in June to live there as a resident. Meanwhile I go up to the Hospital every day by bus, come back at night to Lucy Koo's bedroom. Mei my daughter, aged nine, goes to a Chinese school, starts to forget her English, and to learn Cantonese.

During these four months I meet more missionaries out from China than I have ever dreamt there could be. "The Exodus," they call it themselves, jokingly. And certainly that is what it looks like.

# CHAPTER II

# The Kingdom of God

*March 1949*

I HAD ALWAYS THOUGHT OF MISSIONARIES AS "SUPERIOR persons" in the Confucian sense; that their fund of goodness, benevolence and knowledge must be greater than the average person's. It was with relief that I found they were just ordinary people. Well-meaning, earnest, hard working, not endowed with more wisdom, knowlege or virtue than anyone else. Not gifted with more vision, and not always more tolerant. Teaching the Bible was their *métier,* just as medicine was mine, although I suppose both professions deluded themselves into calling it a vocation. They were concerned, as all normal, healthily self-centered people are, with family, children, home, security, life insurance, salaries, pension and furlough, all the mechanics of existence.

In those early months of 1949, they seemed bewildered, confused and indignant. What was happening in China?

Some averred that it was only a passing phase of violence, similar to those previous eruptions of xenophobia which flare up from time to time in China. Some were inclined to think that the Kuomintang government would make a stand and win in the end "if only it would carry out reforms instead of just proclaiming them." The fact that the Chiang Kai-sheks were Christians seemed to them a guarantee that the Kuomintang government might still turn over a new leaf and that all would be well again.

Perhaps those who understood the irreversible change which was taking place remained in China until they could do so no longer, but those I met in Church Guest House showed much bewilderment and hurt.

It was a little like unrequited love. "After all we've done for them," they implied, "look at what they are doing to us."

How difficult it must be to become a missionary! In order to convince others, one must be so completely indoctrinated with the superiority of one's own brand of belief. To understand, to tolerate, to condone, is incompatible with the very idea of being in possession of a higher truth, a better explanation of the spiritual life.

There were two types of missionaries in Hong Kong. The first, those that had not been long in China, were still under the spell of their narrow denominational fanaticism. They carried with them a sulphurous aroma of hell-fire and damnation to the heathen. They were spiritually intolerant and physically bigoted. They were inclined to gloat over the possibilities of martyrdom and to emphasize the persecutional element in the pressure against them. But they were very few. The larger group was eminently likable. They had been converted and mellowed to humanity, tolerance and a sense of humor. They had quietly jettisoned the belief in the infallibility of their own theme of salvation, together with the more wrathful aspects of the Deity they professed to love. They were far more interested in the social and practical aspects of Christianity. They were humanists, sociologists, and for them religion became the building of hospitals and schools, the creation of Christian Associations, and picking up abandoned waifs. But they were the ones who were the most hurt, because they had loved their work, and they had been selfless in their devotion to it. "What is going to happen to our Christian communities? Many of our Christians seem to have gone over to the new regime, some have not. Will these be persecuted? What is going to happen to our churches, our schools, our hospitals?" They wanted to help China. And they found that their motives were suspected, and their efforts towards conciliation and understanding misunderstood. They were no longer wanted. China was throwing them out.

\* \* \*

It was the jolly round man whose name I never knew who discussed all this with me one evening. He was stopping at Church Guest House for a week, on his way to America. He had the brisk Christian-jocular manner of the extrovert type of preacher. We had a long talk over some walnut and chocolate ice cream at the Dairy Farm. It developed that he had been a missionary for years before he became an agricultural expert.

"How many converts did you make?" I asked. "Genuine converts."

"One, I think. The others were rice-Christians or seemed to revert only too easily."

The jolly round man was dying to talk to someone who would listen, and I am a good listener. "I feel," said he, "that although some of us may know Chinese, and some may even acquire what may be termed intellectual knowledge of China, yet we remain forever ignorant of the emotional structure of your people, and of the reactions we evoke. The very fact that we have a missionary upbringing insulates us against acquiring what you Chinese call 'the understanding heart.'"

I protested. "It is a question of language, I think. You are so convinced that all men mean the same things by the same words."

He nodded. "Perhaps. Very early I felt that I did not quite know what I meant by God and the Word of God. I knew when I was in my own country, but when I was in China the meaning began to go out of the words. I was never sentimental and romantic about China, as so many Americans and Europeans are. I never liked my Christians as much as I did the heartily heathen. That is why I had to give up preaching.

"It did not come easily, demolishing my own faith. It took me a long time before I saw the truth, and left the mission. I think I am right, for I am one of the few who are neither hurt nor puzzled by what is happening now.

"How could we expect anything else from our teaching but what is happening now in China? We combined Christ with the emancipation of women, social reform, and the building of hospitals. We prepared the soil and watered the seed of that tremendous power which is going to rule China and perplex the world. We, the missionaries. Not Marx, not the Russians. We did it, through our mission schools and universities and our Young Men's and Women's Christian Associations. Communism came in afterwards, took the strength and power that we had reared, and gave it a name and a shape, because we had nothing else to offer you.

"We gave your Chinese youth the habit of collecting themselves into groups. We derided and broke down your introvert tendencies and your loathing of the masses. We turned your aesthetic scholar away from versifying, and made him use pen and tongue for the good of the million instead of the delight of the few. We built large universities in the midst of or near the busy, populous cities, with their agitation and their discontent. We took you away from your homes and herded you into modern, sanitary dormitories. We developed in you a community spirit, made you play community games, relax with community singsong. We drilled into you your duty towards your country till you acquired a savior complex about your country.

"The education we provided for you cut you off from your old traditions and made your uprooted spirits fertile soil for the reception of the grandest and vaguest humanism with which humanity comforts itself. We taught you a lot of abstract words which were not in your language — democracy, freedom, equality — without bothering to find out what they meant to you, or even to ourselves. We talked of mass education and the abolition of injustice. Your political ideas may be Marxist now, but the fervor and the faith which pushed you forwards are rooted in our social-Christianity.

"Our Christian Associations were in the forefront of all movements for freedom and social justice in China. All your revolutionaries have had some contact with our teaching. Many of your communist leaders are Christians. We taught you group-power and armed you with social ideals. You made the Revolution.

"Communism aspires to a paradise just as Christianity does. It wishes to have in life what the Christian hopes to enjoy in heaven. It wants to create a perfect mechanism of existence, banishing need and insecurity and want. The Christian provides himself, through works and prayer, with a guarantee of happiness and security after death. Communism replaces the word 'eternity' by the word 'future,' and 'sin' by 'imperialism' or 'capitalism.' The communist lives on belief in the worth of man and hope in the future, as the Christian lives on faith in God and love of his neighbor."

The jolly man's round face and blue eyes stared into the future he disapproved of. "Yes, we talked to you of the Kingdom of God, and you are trying in your turn to make it come on earth. You found us out, how we kept our Christianity safe and private, how much importance our Christian nations attached to wealth and to material success, while we preached to you about treasures in heaven. You found us out a long time ago.

"Missionaries will never go back to China. Missions are as anachronistic there today as bound feet. We belong to the same dying world as colonialism does, and we are just as putrefied. It's no use deluding ourselves; we have done our work, and now we must go. Some will be clinging on until one by one they too drop off. The China Inland Mission will probably stay a little longer. And the Catholic Church will hang on."

"What do you do besides agriculture?" I asked.

He understood my meaning.

"I am trying," he replied, "to find out what the Word of God means to me. It's such a big thing. And now it seems to me that the most important thing is to find out about myself. Not to teach others."

He was reticent about his soul, and so we talked of me, for it is bad to come too close to the center of a man's being.

"What are you going to do?"

"Go to China, do medicine. Not because I am a communist, but because I am a Chinese."

"Take care not to fall in love and get married, if you are going to stay in Hong Kong for a while."

"No fear. I'm going to be shut up in the hospital in two months time. Besides, I'm only interested in medicine. I was married for eight years and that ought to be enough time, in this world of war, for any woman. One must not be greedy."

"But you are young, you've got a long time in front of you."

"But I'm a widow, and in China, you know, we are not supposed to get married again. Besides, I see no point in having anything to do with another human being. I am altogether above temptation," I laughed, "for my heart is dead."

"Well, it makes life simpler for you, with a career. But I would not be too sure. Hong Kong is a funny place; like a ship, and you never know what is going to happen to people in a ship. All the best to you."

I never saw him again, and I wish I had, for he tried to make sense for himself, and he was right about Hong Kong.

# CHAPTER III

# Rich Man, Poor Man

*April 1949*

"LET US TAKE A WALK," SAYS LUCY KOO TO ME. HER IDEA is to wander into the department stores on the two main shopping streets of the city, and finish off the afternoon with a film at one of the air-conditioned movie theaters.

It is a beautiful warm day, pouring sun, the air like fine frenzy about one's body. I say: "Let us walk." From Church Guest House, where on the sun-drenched porch Helen Parrish and Mrs. Thrale watch the children play, we drag ourselves, our three children and Soosee the Alsatian to the Botanic Gardens. There the children stand underneath the giant ferns, and Lucy photographs them. We toil on the higher road, ascend the path which meanders up the hill slope. Below us the University scatters its brick and stone buildings up and down the hillside. Parallel to the shore the town spreads its gray roofs. Further lies the blue gap of the harbor with its ships, between the island and the town of Kowloon on the mainland. And in the distance the bare hills of Kowloon prop themselves like a barrier between the Colony and unseen China beyond them.

The children count the ships while Lucy, Soosee and I pant for breath. Large ships asprawl like cockroaches on their backs, their masts and funnels and cranes projecting like limbs from their bellies. Sampans cling to their flanks like red ants swarming round a dead insect.

Skiffs like small spring butterflies skim the top of the water. A white yacht slides lazily past a gray destroyer. Squat ferries ply their shallow furrow between the island and Kowloon. The cream-colored Macao boat cuts straight through the pliant water like scissors going through silk. Large junks with ribbed purple and tan sails plough the blue sea as they push steadily forwards. "Eighty-four ships," says Mei, my daughter, "I count eighty-four." And begins to count the junks in her newly acquired Cantonese.

Lucy is tired, so she takes the children down for lunch and to see a movie in the afternoon. I am left alone to roam, wrapped in the warmth of the sun, covered by the sky, cradled in the hills, thoroughly happy to tramp by myself and look at Hong Kong.

Everywhere building is going on. Hong Kong's population is nearly three times what it was, and new arrivals from China stream in at the rate of ten thousand a week. Day and night, blasting, drilling, hammering is heard. The quiet hills are not exempt from the clang of human agitation. On the promontories, slopes and hillocks jutting from the high center of the island, the rich erect their habitations. Before any building can be done, an approach road has to be cut deep into the hillside to reach the projected residence. The top of the hill must be taken off to obtain a level surface large enough for the foundations. Work is going on at a dozen places in the hills. Scores of black-clad Hakka women, wearing their crownless straw brim fringed with black cloth, carry off, in antlike procession, basket after basket of soil. The top of the hill is slowly eaten off, and the earth appears, a bright ocher patch amid the surrounding green bush. Here and there on the surface of this patch the women leave conical masses of earth, like fingers pointing skywards. Their height determines the amount of soil taken away and the pay of the women. Finally the earth is stamped flat with their bare feet and wooden hand paddles, and the foundations are laid.

Because so many trees have been cut, the slopes are bare, and in the summer rains large chunks of hillside slide away. The exposed rock, waterlogged and sun-baked, decays and crumbles under pressure. So that the house may stand firm, a large pyramidal base of stone or concrete must be built. This massive structure is often two or three stories high. Its top is a terrace, paved, or laid out as a garden, upon which the house is built. A parapet runs round the edges of the terrace, supporting dozens of large flowerpots which are changed with the seasons. Chrysanthemums and red coxcombs in autumn, caladiums and dahlias, hibiscus and poinsettia in winter, camellias in spring, pinks and carnations and lilies in the summer.

The houses of the rich, set upon their ponderous bases, high above one's head among the palms and frangipani and bamboo of their gardens, protected by their flowered battlements, have the remote, enchanted look of castles. The older ones, round-arched and many-pillared, mellowed and grayed by damp and mold, merge in the structure of the hills about them. The new have no such gift of time and weather to soften them, but stand crudely white and pink, unsullied and unblended in the strong sun.

Here and there rise the blocks of government flats, erected for European government servants. Monotonously regular, studiously undecorative, biscuit boxes six to eight stories high, their gaudy whiteness dominates the gray city below them. Similar blocks, but of more flimsy aspect, rise by the score in the newly built areas of the expanding town. They are destined for the merely affluent Chinese, mostly from Shanghai, who have turned these districts into small bustling replicas of their own city.

In the outlying districts, on the slopes above Causeway Bay, round Mount Davis, and among the hills of Kowloon, are the squatters' wooden shacks, grouped into camps. The huts have low sloping roofs touching each other. The lanes between them are five feet across. They have no water, no sanitation. In one agglomeration of two hundred huts the only water supply is one tap a quarter of a mile away on an uphill road. Untidily stacked above each other, clinging to the crumbling hill slope, huddling beneath large threatening boulders, in danger of being washed away by the rains, in danger of being pulled down for health's sake, in danger of fire every time a meal is cooked, many thousands of huts house many tens of thousands of people. The government of the Colony cannot do more, for new thousands cross the border every week.

The squatters' camps root, extend, and spread across the Colony. Kept away from the center by demolition, they nestle at the foot of the hills in the outlying districts; crouch at the doorstep of the hilltop mansions of the wealthy; insinuate between the layer-cake blocks of government flats and the busy main streets; line the orderly roads along which the latest Buicks glide to the swimming beaches. One camp huddles next to the luxurious stables of the racing horses, near the Happy Valley Race Course.

Seldom is there such close proximity of squalor and wealth, misery and ostentation. Here, within sight, sound and smell of each other, rich man and poor man live, intimate neighbors and brother refugees.

There are two kinds of street in Hong Kong. The smooth level main streets parallel to the shore, lined with shops, crowded with the newest cars; and the narrow, staircased climbing streets which cut across them. In the large level streets can be found all the world's finished goods in profusion, for everything comes to or goes through Hong Kong, and the harbor is full of ships unloading more. "You can buy anything here," is the Colony's motto. Anything from a fighter airplane to the latest perfume. There are no restrictions. And now that the rich have come from Shanghai there is plenty of free capital floating about, and there is a boom on.

There is a boom on. Hong Kong is dazzling with prosperity. The rich have brought their money, and they build and banquet and buy. The shops are crammed full with everything that the rich can desire, and what do the rich like best but American things, slick and stream-lined and colorful? Cameras, bathing suits, lipsticks, perfumes, watches, shoes, nylons, silks and brocades, perfumes and stockings, all in great heaps on the shop counters. Hong Kong is a shopping paradise.

Like battalions of sea gulls, the idle rich Chinese women walk from shop to shop, their voices raised above the din of the street, their brace-lets tinkling on their wrists. Their scarlet-taloned hands dig into the silks and velvets, the brocades and the satins. Cantonese shopgirls and

Indian salesmen unfold roll after roll of iridescent satin, drape shimmerings silks round themselves for the inspection of their clients. The rich women crowd into the jade and gold shops, congregate at beauty counters, eddy among the lipsticks glistening in their gold cases, the strapless bathing suits, the Chanel perfumes, the "falsies" spread on the counters. They buy and buy, noisy, rapacious, and bored.

Around the Hong Kong Hotel, in the English business section of the city, American sailors amble, hail taxis, have their shoes shined by little boys. On their arms hang shrill Chinese prostitutes. Tourist women in off-the-shoulder dresses gaze at embroidered silk underwear and ornate Chinese coats. Shanghai bankers and businessmen in twos and threes, all in natty sharkskin suits, flamboyant American ties, with fountain pens in their coat pockets, talk business in earnest sibilant tones. Wounded lost soldiers of the Kuomintang, dirty and ragged, some on crutches, stand against the walls of the shops, and watch the street with an angry scowl on their dark faces. Under the covered archways of the sidewalk glide, flow, rattle and clatter the anonymous common men of Hong Kong. Each man, despite his air of belonging, a transient, claiming as his origin a village back in South China, refusing to belong to the Colony, maintaining his status of passer-by even when he works here all his life, even when his children are born here, sometimes even when he is born here. This is the most permanent fact about the Colony: with few exceptions, those who come regard themselves as on the way to somewhere else.

In the narrow, vertical, staircased streets of the Chinese district abide the poor, and few go to look at them. The streets are dirty, the houses smell. The tenements are four-storied. Their insecure rotting wood balconies are draped with washing. These structures have no bathrooms, no latrines, no courtyards, and only one communal kitchen for anything up to twenty families. The floors are divided into cubicles. Each cubicle is eight by eight feet and houses a family of five or upwards. The beds in these cubicles are in tiers. At night the pails of human excreta are placed outside the door for collection. Up and down the staircase of the street the innumerable children of the poor play in the dust. Here are the street sleepers, the human scavengers that live off refuse from the hotels. Here a family spreads a mat between a cobbler's stall and a congee man's table and calls it a home. Here between the feet of the passer-by the offal of the markets — two rotting tomatoes, a handful of beans, one broken egg — is offered for sale by the poor to those poorer than they.

As beings from different planets, invisible to each other, unconscious and indifferent, these people move, walk side by side, jostle each other, sidle to avoid contact. Their glances skid over each other and rest nowhere. Absorbed in their preoccupation, aware only of their own perils and opportunities, riveted to their individual search for safety and survival, each is filled with the illusion of entireness, moves in his world and denies the others, for to acknowledge others would breach his own tenacity in the struggle for existence.

And here on the pavement, I run into my friend Anne Richards, American free-lance writer, met in Chungking ten years ago, met in London at a cocktail party five years ago, and met here again, in Hong Kong where I was to meet so many people; she is lost, as I am, in contemplation of the streets.

"Come to the Immigration Office with me. I must renew my permit for staying in Hong Kong," says Anne.

The Immigration Office is housed in an old baroque building on the Praya, the broad avenue which runs along the waterfront. The walls have not been painted for years, and the ceiling drops flakes of plaster quietly on our waiting heads.

"It is one of the lovable things about the English," says Anne. "Unlike us Americans, their important administrative offices are not lodged in steel and reinforced concrete, furnished with imposing desks and comfortable chairs, guarded by soundproof doors, connected with the outside world by a battery of modern telephones. Their government departments function, as this one does, in two or three dim, shabby rooms, with worn floors, doors that cannot shut properly, with one antiquated telephone inconveniently placed, just out of hand's reach, on the desk of the Head of the Department." We laugh as we note the one single wooden bench for the waiting crowds, and along the wall at its back the oily gray band where sitters have rested their heads. Files marked *Urgent* and *Not to be Removed* lie in careless heaps on the marble top of the chimney mantelpiece. Chinese clerks in shirt sleeves tap meditatively on archaic typewriters. Two unruffled young men in police uniforms talk in low voices to the visitors. This is self-reliant security, authority without pomp to make it bullying and inefficient; this is how government should govern, it seems to me — casual, good-tempered, human among its ramshackle desks and rickety chairs and insecure file boxes with broken bottoms. Anne and I are delighted with the Immigration Office.

The blond young policeman comes back with Anne's passport between his fingers and a large stamp dangling from his left hand. "You're not a missionary, are you," he half states.

"No, I'm a writer," says Anne.

"That's all right then. We'll renew you for six months. We only give three to the missionaries, there are so many of them. Seven hundred on our books."

"Come to Church Guest House and meet a few of the seven hundred," I say to Anne.

The evening in gray and gold strides across the sky as Anne and I walk to Church Guest House. In the hall Mabel Chow grins feebly at me. Her face is tired-looking. "I have a pain in my back, I think maybe Baby is coming," she says to me. "Good luck," I answer. "Hope it's another boy." Lucy Koo and the children are back from the cinema. Mei says to me: "It was all about love again. Aunt Lucy likes love. Love, always love." The dinner gong sounds, and we file into the dining room with the first lot of diners. There is great excitement, and Helen Parrish rushes up to us.

"Dr. Han, meet my husband, he's come this afternoon on the train from Hankow."

I shake hands with Alf, tall and fair and very quiet. Back in China, Hankow fell today. Mr. Parrish left a week ago, just in time. He has brought some news from Mary Fairfield's husband. Mr. Fairfield is not going away, he has decided to stay, and so Mary Fairfield is going back to China, just as God told her some time ago. Her face is beautiful with serenity, and as I look at her I am a little awed, because I never thought that she was beautiful at all. "Well," she says in the New England drawl that used to irritate me, and which now has dignity and resonance for me, "I think we'll stick it till we're thrown out. Perhaps we'll understand what it's all about when we go back to China. I only feel at home there, and I think, yes, I believe, that we must have faith in the Chinese people."

After dinner Anne, Lucy and I sit in the common room and look at Hong Kong, where we are, and then beyond the hills at the darkness that is China, unseen, but always felt, the China which is the reason why we are here.

We are all here, bankers, businessmen, rich women, missionaries and squatters. Those that take off half a hill to build themselves a home and those that crowd on a mat on the sidewalk to sleep. Wanderers against our will, we are the refugees. And to me, a transient among so many transients, that is Hong Kong in April 1949: a refugee camp. Harbor of many ships, haven of people out from China, squatters' colony, fun fair, bazaar and boom town. Hong Kong, where people come and go and know themselves more impermanent than anywhere else on earth. Beautiful island of many worlds in the arms of the sea. Hong Kong.

And China just beyond the hills.

# CHAPTER IV

# Gay Encounter

*June 1949*

BECAUSE I HAD BEEN A BRITISH COUNCIL SCHOLARSHIP student, Evelyn Walsingham asked me to dinner. It was her job to look after those of us who had come back from England, and to help us in our difficulties. Evelyn is always extremely punctual; I had had an urgent cut-throat case to stitch up, and though her pleasant voice, pitched to an impersonal elegance, as if poised on high heels, informed me on the telephone that it would not matter, it was in some confusion that I arrived three quarters of an hour late.

Evelyn lived, during those summer months of 1949, on Conduit Road, once the fashionable residential district. Conduit Road is lined with large old houses perched on massive fortresses of stone, gay with flowers and graceful with trees. The house belonged to James and Fiona Manton, but Fiona was away in Europe and had asked Evelyn Walsingham and her husband to stay there during her absence, with James Manton.

So many times afterwards, when I lived with James and Fiona Manton, I was to enter, to sit, to spend hours in that same drawing room; but I shall always remember it as on that night. Spacious French windows opening on the star-studded night; the cream walls bespattered with soft light, the camellia-pink lampshades, the green and the pink armchairs, the Chinese carpets, fawn with blue designs, a Persian rug glowing like a ruby under the sieved lights; the slow revolving fans, the massed flowers. And Tattybogle, most beautiful of grey-hounds, a very dignified dog, seated on' *his* settee, allowing no intrusion on it; Tatty, planted in front of the guests, barking at them when he thought it was time for them to depart; a gentle, thoughtful soul who nurses his own feelings closely all day, and sleeps on his back after lunch with his limbs sticking straight up, somewhat indecorously for such a gentlemanly dog.

There were a number of people sitting about the room. Evelyn looked beautiful in turquoise linen, with her spun silver hair in impeccable curls round her smooth white forehead. She steered me competently round, covering my shyness with a spate of introductions, her technique so efficient that I heard no names at all. Evelyn said: "Correspondent for . . ." and I shook hands with Mark without knowing his name or that of his paper. We then went in to dinner.

I remember . . . a most futile occupation. What does one remember, and why does one remember one thing and not another? Of this dinner I do not remember anything except, in a visual flashback out of the corner of my eye, the left hand of my neighbor, with a gold signet ring on his finger, and a good deal of black hair on the back, darting a fork about his plate. I was quite unaware of Mark.

There were irises, jasmine and roses in a silver basin near the pink chairs where James Manton and I sat having coffee and talking about China. China so near, and yet so far, so far from the Colony, another world. James is charming, handsome, with dark Spanish eyes under straight eyebrows. He was born in the North of Scotland. "You must come to see us often when my wife is back from Europe. She is keen on dogs and birds, as you are on cats and butterflies." We then talked about the communist advance, and how the business people were all in favor of hanging on through the hard times, believing that it would settle down, and that they would be able to trade with China again, for trade with China means everything to the Colony. "When everything calms down, it will all be just the same as before," James said. "I don't think the Chinese can ever really be communists. They aren't born that way. The family system has gone on with them for thousands of years. They won't give it up."

Someone crossed the floor to the empty chair on my right. I looked up. The man was not very tall. He was slim and deceptively frail-looking in his white suit. He stepped delicately, in a prehensile manner, as if his feet were hands, lifting his leg a little at the knee, as a deer does. And suddenly I was intensely aware of the texture of the carpet beneath his shoes. As if I lay on it and each hair on it was sharp against my skin. I felt, rather than saw, the blue designs on the fawn background, the emblems of Happy Augury woven onto its surface, the bats and the peonies, the lotuses and the endless knots, the peaches, and the ramparts of eternity bounding its edges. It was as if something had suddenly turned in its sleep within me, and sighed. As a shy finger stroking, within my heart, and like a sleepy bird that fluffs its wings and then goes to sleep again, so I stirred and moved within me, and then was quiet. Unexplainable, an immediate direct knowledge of texture, of the stuff that things are made of, in this case the carpet, without the interposition of words. For a moment I lost touch of that which we call reality, the chair I sat on, the coffee cup I held, James's words, as I felt the stranger walk across the room towards me. Then the world jerked back into place, and I was seated, calm, as Mark sank in the armchair on the other side of mine.

He smiled back. I thought: "How blue are his eyes. Just like sapphires. With eyes like that he will have to be careful not to drink too much, because then they'd turn rather white, like a fish."

His smile was leisurely, disarmed, not the earnest, rather painstaking grimace which some foreigners inflict on themselves. It was what we call an opening-the-heart smile.

"I believe," said he, "we have a mutual friend in Peter Dixon."

"Oh, Peter." I was pleased. "How is he, still with the Indonesians?"

"Still. As usual irritated by them, yet loving them," said Mark.

"He thinks they will never grow up, in spite of his efforts. I stayed ten days in his house in Bangkok on my way to Hong Kong, and he took me round, and I discovered how much he loathed the Chinese."

"That's because he loves the Malays, the Siamese, the Indonesians, and does not feel entirely sympathetic towards your vital, go-ahead race. You crowd out the easygoing peoples of Southeast Asia."

"Peter is so English in his desire to rush around doing good to the weak and the downtrodden. It's a kind of sport with your countrymen. But he doesn't know why the Chinese have to get ahead."

"I should imagine it's congenital with your people," said Mark. "Built and then conditioned that way. Grinding poverty at home; and from abroad the endless remitting of comparatively large sums for the support of extensive family trees in the mother country."

"You should not condemn this."

"Of course not. One should never condemn what one cannot understand. I don't think we can claim to understand other peoples. I mean, East and West don't really ever mix, do they? They'll always be apart. You can't be both East and West at the same time. You have to choose between the two."

"Oh, do you think so?" I said, and turned my face away, and smiled. He was staring at me when I looked again, but politely averted his glance. He began to tell me about himself.

"I've been nearly fifteen years in the Far East, all over the place. I am going to Europe next year. Rome, I think."

"That will be a nice change," I said.

He gave me a graspless stare. "I don't really want to go. I hate the thought of leaving all this. But my wife misses Europe a great deal. She would like to live in Rome."

"She is quite right. I'd hate to live permanently in Europe or in America; but then I am Asiatic. It's different for you, of course. It will be much nicer for you there. As soon as China is under its new rulers there will be a great deal of upheaval and turmoil all round here. All Southeast Asia will be heaving and bursting. You're sitting on top of a volcano now. Oh yes, much safer away."

"You seem very sure that the communists will win in China."

"Of course. There is no other way. This release of energy was inevitable. The people are for the communists, not because they are communists, but because the Kuomintang is so hopeless and corrupt. This is going to be one of the world's biggest revolutions."

Now I know that I could not have said anything more calculated to make him resent going away to Europe. But I did not even know his name as I spoke to him. I thought that all Europeans should go back to their own countries, and he was just another European, a foreigner, to me.

It was time to leave. Tatty was getting agitated and barked with relief as we rose. We stepped into the night with all its stars, the lights climbing the hills skywards, the green and red neon shop signs like a riot of fireflies zigzagging the streets below us, the ships like diamond brooches pinned onto the dark velvet of water. I turned to Mark, who was walking near me. "Hong Kong," I said, "look, no one knows where heaven with its stars ends, and the earth with its lights begins."

We walked down the long winding path from the house to Conduit Road where the cars were parked. It was steep and slippery. On one side the wall rose, sheer, overgrown with moss and ferns. Overhead, bushes and trees stooped over the walls of gardens staircased along the slope of the hill. On the other side a low broad parapet of white stone followed the path all the way down to the road. At the end was the lamp post. In the warm June night, squadrons of mosquitoes, gnats and night moths hurtled against it, colliding noisily with the glass bulb. They fell on the ground with a limp snowball plop, and still the incandescent fascination drew fresh victims from the night. We said good-by, and James Manton drove me back to the Hospital. Mark bent forward in the car he shared with two other people and aimed another smile at me. I waved, charmed with his friendliness, and forgot him immediately.

# The Mind's Conjunction

*June 1949*

CONTIGUITY BRINGS INTO SHARPER FOCUS OUR ESSENTIAL separateness. In Hong Kong I was more homesick for China than I had been in London. Mei was now a weekly boarder at her school, and I lived at the Hospital as one of the residents.

When Anne Richards moved to a minute and expensive flat two hundred yards from the Hospital, I used to go across for tea and a talk about Peking, Chungking, and the old war days. For Anne and for me, China was the center of the world. I met, scattered about Hong Kong, a few men and women like Anne, Americans and English, bitten by the bug of China, cast under a spell by the country beyond the hills, whose talk invariably turned to the years they had spent inland. "It was awful in Chungking," they said. "But it was fun. We were alive then. There is no country in the whole world so alive as China."

Anne was chewing her cigarette holder when I came in. I had Mark's first letter to me in my pocket. "Dear Han Suyin," it said, "I thought you were charming, and I would like to see you again."

"How's the Hospital?" asked Anne.

"Very busy. I miss Church Guest House and the missionaries. I want to find out what happens to them. What does a missionary do when he cannot missionarize any more, Anne? It's like a doctor having no patients to cure."

"Oh," said Anne, "they go home, and they're given some small church in the backwoods of South Dakota. They teach, or go into business. I suppose some will be used as "experts" because of their knowledge of China. And if there's going to be a war they'll be drafted to teach Chinese, or into information services."

She gave me a cucumber sandwich. "How was your party last night?" said she.

"Very nice. I met a reporter and he has written to ask me to dinner next Wednesday, which is my half-day off. I don't feel I should go."

"What's his name?" asked Anne.

I scanned the letter. "Mark Elliott," I said.

"Oh, I know him," said Anne, "he's nice. He's a foreign correspondent, you mustn't call him a reporter, although I don't suppose he'd really mind. Why don't you want to go?"

"Well, I'm Chinese, and he's English. In China, a girl doesn't go out with a foreigner. I mean, a good family girl."

"Don't be archaic," said Anne, "this is Hong Kong, you know, not Chungking. Times have marched on. It'll do you good to go out with a man, for a change."

Wednesday came, and he was outside the Hospital, waiting near a small green Morris. It was a beautiful June evening. The sea was pink and turquoise, spangled with the gold and pink sails of fishing junks, swaying dreamily, gently, as if smiling to itself. All the land was pink and emerald, and blue shadows curled round the tree trunks and at the foot of houses. The islands of the sea, Lantau, Cheungchau, Nikuchau, were dappled with purple. A small nimbus of gold cloud wrapped up a theatrical orange sun. It was all very colorful, artificial and gay.

"Where shall we go?" said Mark.

"I don't know," I said, "I've only been here five months."

"Where would you prefer to have dinner?"

"I don't know any restaurants. I've only been to parties at friends' houses." And, ashamed of being so unpopular, I added: "You see, I'm a widow."

We rounded Pokfulum Road and left Mount Davis, blue with dusk, on our left, and he said: "If you don't mind I shall take you to the Parisian Grill. The food is good there."

The Parisian Grill has walls painted with scenes reminiscent of a French ballet. A buxom barmaid, a gendarme swirling his baton, an apache, some absinthe drinkers, two ladies in bustles, a newspaper kiosk complete with mustachioed seller, a child with a hoop. We sat on the red leather bar seats and were greeted by the manager. Mark had a pink gin and I asked for a Martini.

"I hope my letter did not offend you," said Mark.

"I was surprised, it was so direct, but not offended. It was the best way to put it, if you wanted to have dinner with me."

"You might have thought me impertinent."

"It was the truth, so that's all right."

He laughed suddenly, a light, attractive sound. "Shall we order dinner?" he said. "I myself rather like messes. Let's have asparagus cocktail and sweetbread *financière*."

"It sounds terrific," I muttered. The Martini was having a benevolent effect on me. "Have you been to China too? For me there are three species of human beings: Chinese, non-Chinese who have been to China, and others."

So Mark started telling me about himself. He told me first about his trip to Sinkiang, and his visit to the Tun Huang caves and the Crescent Moon Lake, and eating watermelon there. He had hitchhiked from Peking, going on the local buses, carrying his bedding like any other Chinese traveler. We had more pink gins and another Martini, and he talked and talked. Suddenly I too was talking. We moved to the table, and, fork describing arabesques on the table cloth, I explained to him the structure of Chinese words, and spoke of song poems. I spoke of things I had thought vaguely, but not completely formulated, and the right words came to me. And Mark spoke about public schools in England and the ties they created, and how life was made easy when you met a chap anywhere in official position who'd been to the same school as you.

"It's the same in China," I said. "We have the old school tie habit

to an even greater extent, but with us it's a university tie. I am preju-
diced in favor of anyone who has been to my university. Even our marriages are often concocted in our coeducational universities. Because of
the similarity of your public school code and our Confucian upbringing, I have always found Englishmen predictable."

Mark told me about that two-year period in his life when he was a
"financier," as he put it, with headquarters in Shanghai. He went round
China, up to Mukden, down to Hankow, Nanking and Canton, fixing
business contracts, sometimes smoothing out disputes. "It was always
easy; I could not speak, read or write Chinese. The great thing was to
have perfect trust, not to be suspicious or resentful just because something was strange and different from my own way. I did not worry
about getting things down in writing, as so many foreigners seem to do.
I couldn't add, subtract, or multiply properly, and division I never attempted. But it made no difference to being a financier. I didn't even
have to tell lies."

"But do you usually speak the truth?" I asked, bending forward to
scan his face.

He looked a little *ahuri,* but he replied without a trace of feeling,
"Yes, I suppose I do try. Do I? Yes, on the whole I do speak the truth,
as I know it. Have a Drambuie. I'll smoke a cigar if you don't mind."

So we had a drink to his financier days, and then liqueur brandies to
toast the world, our oyster, as Mark called it. Both he and I, that evening, felt that our past lives had been very satisfactory. Assured with
gathered experience and wisdom, I forgot the occasional sorrow and
remembered that I was a career woman with a full life, marriage, a
child, and a profession. Mark was telling me how well life had treated
him . . . travel, success in his work, many friends. Replete, we talked
of foods. All the foods we had eaten. Chinese, Siamese, Indian, American, French, English . . . "When I was traveling in China as a hitch-
hiker, a 'yellow fish,'" he said, "I often had watermelon, which I
loved. In the evening, very hungry when the cold air starts nipping
one, pinching one's nose with sharp frosty fingers, I used to eat flat
hot baked cakes, seasoned with parsley and onion, sprinkled and fra-

grant with sesame seed, split open and stuffed with thick smoked ham. And congee, hot and steamy and redolent with water-lily seeds."

"Oh, stop, stop," I cried, "you make me so homesick. I think of moonlight nights in Peking, in autumn, with small cups of hot wine and thin slivers of ginger and pickled liver and sausage, and the moon swinging huge in the tree above us, and the last faint cicadas. . . ."

Behind this evening were different pasts. But at the moment they had resolved into a comparison of amusing episodes. "In 1933," said Mark, "I was in Japan, making a tour of the sacred temples." — "Oh, I was at the University in Peking," said I. — "I went to Peking in 1936," he replied. — "I had left on a Grand Tour of Europe. I was in Italy." And so it went on. Apart from having been born in Peking, at an interval of some years, we had nothing in common, we had never yet been in the same spot at the same time, until now. Mark seemed elated by this. "We couldn't possibly have met before," he repeated. "Destiny never put us anywhere together at the same time."

We mellowed and glowed. His months in New Guinea, spent in a plaster cast for fracture of a vertebral process, seemed a comic interlude in a life full of interludes, like a banquet of hors d'oeuvres. My years of emptiness of feeling were the years of the ant, a hoarding of knowledge in the granary of my mind, a preparation for the career I enjoyed, through which I would play a part in the building of China. "Doctors," I said, "are granted the veneration and treated with the awe once reserved to seers and priests. As a consequence our lust for power is phenomenal. Imagine how corrupting it must be to hold sway over life and death. We are all megalomaniacs."

"But so are journalists," said Mark. "Think of the delusions we spin for the hordes of our readers. We are the great dispensers of up-to-the-minute unrest to the millions. *Folie de grandeur* is our occupational disease."

At this moment we believed ourselves Fortune's favorites. There was so much we had seen, heard, felt and lived, that others had not.

"Oh, dear," said Mark, sighing with content. "What a pleasant evening. I did not think it would be so pleasant. When Peter told me about you over the telephone in Singapore, I thought: Another one of Peter's intelligent career women. I was certain that you wore spectacles. When I saw you at Evelyn's party, I was surprised, and distrait all through dinner, and decided that you were someone else. I'm afraid I've told you the history of my life, and a lot more about my inner self than I remember."

"You have," I said. He really had told me everything. Later on he filled in the details, but I knew him well from that day on.

## CHAPTER VI

# Destiny's Puppy

---

*July 1949*

Summer is the least attractive of Hong Kong's seasons. The island's beauty is obscured by the harsh, unblinking light. Everything is blanched in the reflected glare from steely sea and wan sky. It is too bright to see anything well, too hot to smell the earth, too damp to feel the texture of things. However early one gets up in order to enjoy the dawn, one finds it cluttered up with cloud and fog. A bean-curd landscape, the Chinese call it, because the fog and the cloud lie in slabs like bean curd, over the hills and the sea. And yet there is a moment when night removes itself and day comes. But it is difficult to seize it: dawn, morning and day run into each other.

The slight dawn breeze stirs faintly under the gray clouds heaped on the land and the sea, rasps some banana leaves, fingers the flames of the forest, sighs through the casuarinas. It sidles down into the harbor, prowls round the poised ships swathed in gray mist on a leaden sea. Towards the east, where the aircraft carrier anchored yesterday, a strip of lighter, paler gray widens slowly, turns white and opalescent like the belly of a fish. The ships are now clear, like pencil marks against the gray silk of the water. Land smoke from uplifted chimneys can be seen looping sluggishly skywards. Here a wall, there a roof, the glimmer of a window alight. The aircraft carrier, a bristly black hedgehog, is now surrounded by a widening primrose patch, the sun. One moment all was gray and night-still, the next it is light, and in the hills the birds go mad.

The light streaks the water with magenta, sweeps the mist away from the green hills, turns the ships black and red and white. The last cobweb cloud vanishes. Cars honk, boats hoot, ferries churn, trams ring wild bells, magpies call impatient names at each other, the cicadas tune up, and all is heat and toil, for day is here.

It is hot in my Hospital room, for the warm-water pipes run under my floor. The cockroaches wax enormous, fight great duels, and leave quivering, half-consumed carcasses amidst my clothes. They thrive on DDT and Gammexane, so I leave them alone. It is a week since my last afternoon off and Mark rings up in the morning just before our surgical operations start.

"Perhaps it is the place and the weather, but your company gives me more pleasure than that of anyone else in Hong Kong."

I reply: "Perhaps it is the weather, but I like to know that you want to see me again."

"Then may I come and give you a lift wherever you are going? It's your evening off. Wednesday."

We are setting up milestones on the road towards each other. I say: "Do you want to?"

I can hear him waiting at the other end. Waiting before he replies: "Yes, I do want to."

Why should it mean something? It does not. Yet I am suddenly very gay. Suddenly I feel, with what intensity, the telephone grasped in my hand, the excoriated floor of the common room beneath my feet. A little heady, I reply: "Some Chinese friends of mine from Shanghai have asked my daughter and me to dinner. Can you give us a lift to the ferry? They live in Kowloon across the harbor."

I should have known. But the eyes and ears of my heart are stoppered up and I do not wish to know. I am safely dead. Nothing will happen to me. This is the first man I want to talk to. I want to see him again.

He was at the foot of the front steps, and beyond him was the afternoon sea. A sea like a full-throated song, knocking at one's spirit with its swagger. His eyes sea blue. A few restless waves sparkling on top of the water, towards Dumbbell Island. The gravel of the drive was speckled with gold.

"What is a hysterectomy?" asked Mark. "I've been reading the surgery notices."

We climbed into his borrowed Morris, and I introduced my daughter, Mei, who was going with me to the party. Again, we drove down Pokfulum Road, and then turned left through the gay uproar of the Chinese shops in the Saiyingpun district, past the opera houses, and the slums, to emerge on the Praya. At this hour the Praya was crowded. Crowded with junks on the water, and lorries and trucks and cars standing on the quays, raucous with loud Cantonese voices, restless with shuffling feet and the horns of cars. Mark's face was happy. "How alive it is," he said. We slowed down to watch duck eggs for Manila, packed in crates, taken to the square-fronted junks; and litchi nuts in round baskets going with them. Sudden shouts and the quick trot of two carriers, and slung on the bamboo pole between them a large basket full of leaping fish. Conical plaited hats, painted with yellow rainproof varnish, stacked like soup plates, on a waiting truck. Flour sacks, one to each man, unloaded from a junk with two large blue eyes carved on either side of the prow; the men, white with flour, handing a number stick to the tallyman who sat on the quay and collected them as they filed past. Crates of Campbell's chicken soup. Boxes of Sunkist oranges. Boxes labeled Made in England, Made in U.S.A., Made in Norway, Made in China. And between and around all this the black-clad, agile Cantonese men and women, clambering onto boats, pushing crates, starting motors, shouting their way clear. A sprinkling of solemn waddling children, rice bowl and chopsticks in hand, miraculously unhurt and completely unperturbed by the vociferous din. The speed of everything beneath the apparent confusion, and the soft smack of water rubbing against the quayside, lapping against the junk flanks, smack and suck like the damp nuzzling of a child. "Charming, fantastic, so alive," repeated Mark.

Traffic was slow, and we were one in a procession of many cars, when suddenly, in the *désinvolte* way of Hong Kong drivers, the car in front of us swung without warning to the right and just as quickly a small tan puppy ran in front of us from a junk on the left. Mark braked and a rumbling procession of crashing sounds, shouts, and grinding noise of brakes took place behind us. The first sound was explosive and there was with it a jolt of our own car, the last of the series sounded like the soft roar of thunder behind a hill. "Oh," said Mark, "I think something has happened."

A thin, agitated young Englishman in khaki with black shoulder tabs and leather belt sprang to our right, gesticulating and talking. He was obviously pleased with himself and the event. He started shouting in self-conscious but good Cantonese. "Oh dear," repeated Mark, showing faint traces of perturbation. "This is rather terrible. I am sorry to have landed you in such a mess. How terrible. How awful."

I said: "Don't worry. This is very funny." When one has been driven in China by homicidal maniacs, and in London in diplomatic cars that occasionally shoot through red lights and cut across corners with impunity, one retains no conscience about driving.

A large crowd of women, children of various ages, and men began to fill the space at my left between the car and the sea. The young man ran back and forth, returned to shout long explanations in Mark's ear. Mei and I abstracted our spirits from the momentary annoyance, and sat happily gazing at the onlookers, who stared back at us in a similarly detached manner.

Mark got out of the car and followed the young man to contemplate the damage.

He came back unobtrusively ruffled. "Oh dear. There are about six cars behind us which have piled into each other. This policeman is in a van, the third in the queue, and he says I must now go to the station with him. It will take me hours. I'm terribly sorry. It's a mess."

"Well," I said, not understanding his European attitude towards traffic, "it isn't a mess. Nobody was killed, not even the puppy."

Mark looked at me suddenly, and then away, and said colorlessly, "It's nice to be with someone as calm as you. You unfuss me."

Mei pulled my arm, said loudly and hopefully: "Will he go to prison?" And stared at Mark with interest.

"Maybe," I replied, to please her. We got out with difficulty, the crowd had now grown to accident proportions, and part of it jammed the car doors tight.

"One moment," said Mark. He too got out, pulled his pipe from his pocket, filled it from a yellow oilskin pouch. The crowd oozed and swayed round him while he stood still, looked at the sky, then at me, and said: "You remember the last time we met we talked about destiny. Do you think that, by any chance, you and I have any sort of destiny together?"

I was delighted. Such a charming, absurd thing to say, standing in the middle of a large crowd, on the Praya, with cars stuck to each other like a dilapidated concertina, and the last of all a truck full of Watson's orangeade bottles!

So I lifted a laughing face to his, feeling suddenly very tender, thinking it was all so comical, that he was talking, in jest, of omens and portents, and I replied:

"Oh no, I am quite, quite sure, that we have no destiny together. Of that I am quite sure."

# CHAPTER VII

## *Shanghailand*

*July 1949*

PAST THE KOWLOON RAILWAY STATION, THE YOUNG MEN'S Christian Association. Past the Peninsula Hotel, its dusty fountain and its geraniums. As we walk, Mei and I, towards my friend's flat, the blue twilight smears the street, precursor of the heavy daub of night which blots it out. One moment each object is sharp and clear, the next it is beveled into dusk. Color goes, volume and dimension change as well. Objects recede as they merge, distances alter. The lighted street lamps plunge the world beyond their glazed circle into deeper shadow. The blank houses sprout sudden glimmering windows. I love this mobile moment, the fluid passage into another world, because with it comes a lightening of the heart, a relaxation of the body. The warm night diffuses security, as if within the deep velvet crack of darkness fear went to sleep. Like night flowers, faces unfold and open, and the spirit of man, ensconced within the careful taut body, peers out in the safe gloom, like a diffident sea spider waving a small claw from its shell.

Like all the flats of my Chinese friends from Shanghai, Robert and Nora Hung's flat is bright with neon lighting and shining modern furniture. There is of course an air conditioner, and two radios and a frigidaire. Some of the people who have come down from Shanghai are wealthy. Some are very wealthy. And since Shanghai has fallen, all the wealthy are here.

On the walls hang old paintings and photographs of friends. On the floor are Peking carpets. Robert is very happy that he has saved something from his house in Shanghai. "People are selling their embroideries for nothing," he says, "valuable old books go by the pound. No one wants them now."

"When I think of my beautiful house," he says, "I feel very sad, not because of the loss, but because we had so many happy times there, and all our friends loved that house."

"Who is looking after it now?"

"My servants. They have been with us for years. They are staying to look after our things. Afterwards, we shall see."

Nora appears, in pale blue French silk. She is so lovely — I say it every time I see her. Her hands are most beautiful, nearly unhuman in their loveliness. I think of orchids and magnolias and willows. Her fingers curve, like a Siamese dancer's; she often moves a hand when she talks, and her fingers sway back and forth as it moves. They hypnotize me, and I sit making small talk for an hour or two in order to stare at them. Although she is beautiful, her hands are more so, and I believe that she is there only to bear, on her ivory arms, the tender marvel of her hands.

"How are you, Nora?" I ask, "and how is your urticaria?"

For we are Chinese, and acknowledge the necessary flaw in our constitution, that snag of imperfection which makes and keeps us human. Instead of having our physical and mental liabilities harped on behind our backs, we discuss them without vapid discretion with our friends. Nora has allergy, the fashionable disease.

"I'm very much better," Nora says. "It's my new doctor. My old doctor, F. K., died last week. I was in a terrible fix. Ten days ago, at the Palmer-Jones's cocktail party, I ate a tiny little bit of shrimp. They had concealed it in salad, I didn't know it was there. I swelled up so much, I thought I would die. I rang F. K., and the amah told me he was ill and couldn't see anyone. "What! not even me? I am very ill too," I said. Luckily I got another doctor, a specialist from Boston, because F. K. died the day after. Just imagine, if there had been nobody else to treat me! My new doctor has some marvelous special injections. They made me much better. Now I've only got a little bit under the ears."

"You are very lucky, Nora."

"He's terribly expensive," she says. "But of course, he's a specialist."

We circulate among the bridge and mahjong tables, set up in the drawing room and dining room. Charming, well-dressed men and women play, smoke, talk, laugh and fan themselves. How comfortable and unstrenuous life is. We are one and all refugees. Some have lost their homes and others will never go back. But there is no feeling of tragedy, for good and bad times come in cycles. At the moment Hong Kong is not at all a bad place. If you have capital you can double or treble it in three months in Hong Kong.

A little group in a corner listens to a gentle and dreamy man, with a fine small beard, who is telling them how his wife was drowned last year when pirates attacked the boat to Macao. They have seven children, the youngest four. He tells about the premonitions his mother had, and how the youngest child's nurse screamed, the night before in her sleep, that two green-eyed devils were throttling her. He speaks of the sound of gurgling water which filled his own ears as he woke up on that fated evil morning.

Another group is discussing the price of passports and visas. Passports are for sale, in Hong Kong and in Macao, although the Kuomintang government threatens to punish severely those who go away. The South won't hold. The communists have crossed the Yangtse River when no one expected them to do so, as they had no boats. Their ingenuity evokes our admiration, for they used rafts made of rice stalks tied in bundles, three bundles to each man floating across, one by one.

"South America is a good place. Safe. Put your money in South America."

"I'm going to New York in a few months."

Hong Kong is, at the moment, a fine place for people with money. Business is good, and business means everything to Hong Kong. The levelheaded, experienced traders here, English and Chinese, are not panicking. They are hanging on, waiting for events to settle, waiting for the dust to clear, waiting to begin trade again. For who cares about a nation's politics if one can trade with it? "We have never refused to trade with anyone," is the Hong Kong businessman's comment on the situation.

"If Hong Kong falls, Nora, where will you go?"

"I am tired of moving about," says Nora. "Before the last war, Nanking, then Hankow, then Chungking, then back again to Nanking, then Shanghai, now Hong Kong."

"The government is in Canton now. I expect they will be going back to Chungking one day," says Robert. "Poor government."

"Poor Chungking," I retort. And we all laugh.

Robert looks at Nora. They have been married twenty years. Behind his thick-rimmed glasses his love for her still shows very clearly.

"All we wanted from life," he says, "was a nice home and peace. And we have had twelve homes, but no peace. I wanted to be a doctor like you, but I had younger brothers to look after, and I became a businessman instead. Now my life has passed, and I know that I shall never be a doctor." For a moment he looks like a mournful sparrow, but soon his smile is back.

"You'd have been a bad doctor," says Nora. "You're so fussy about your health."

We all laugh. I say: "I always wanted to be a doctor. Now I am one, and I am going back to China at the end of the year when my job here comes to an end."

No one objects. It is different if one is a doctor. The communists are good to doctors. They get preferential treatment. Businessmen do not, in July 1949.

"Robert," I say, wanting a serious talk with him. "A lot of you Shanghai people are putting your capital in Hong Kong."

Robert obviously does not want a serious talk. "Look at all the new building that's going on," he says. "Why, you can buy a site and build for two lakhs, and two months later sell for four lakhs. Factories, too. There is a lot of money to be made here. Yes, good investments. Quick profit. Double your capital in three months."

"Do you think Hong Kong is safe? The English are jittery."

"They are always jittery. They've got to be. But, personally, I don't think Hong Kong is safe," says Robert. "Because it cannot be defended."

"The English think it can. They are moving in troops and building tank roads, and look at the new police stations they're planning to build. It will all cost a lot of money."

"Of course," he says, "but I don't know. I wouldn't like to say. I don't think the communists will last, mind you. But even if they win, they may not invade Hong Kong. What for? It's worthless to them. And if they want it, then it will fall from the inside, and all this defense is not worth much."

"But of course," he adds, "it is a question of prestige. If the communists attack, the English may fight for Hong Kong."

"Oh yes," says young Mr. Luk, who has only heard the last bit. "England will fight for us."

We both look at him as if he has said something extraordinary. He is a Hong Kong Chinese.

"Well," says Robert, skidding away from serious talk, "there is a boom on now. We Shanghai people are going to change Hong Kong. Brighten it up a little."

I see my friend Maya Wong and wave. We were in a Chinese school in Peking together twenty years ago. She has three children in Shanghai with her husband's mother. Her husband died of tuberculosis last year. She has come to Hong Kong to make a little money and help support the children. She is a secretary in a private firm.

"When are you going to China?" she asks.

"End of the year."

'Better not go. They'll indoctrinate you."

"I'm already medically indoctrinated and not interested in politics. I hope the communists will give the people a fair deal."

"What about your daughter? Would you like to see her grow up a communist?"

"I don't want her to be a White Chinese, without a country," I say. "Nothing holds me to Hong Kong. Everything pulls me back to China, even my daughter."

We walk back through the night. The sky is thick with stars. Crossing the harbor by ferry I watch a heavy, lopsided moon plod over the night-tangled hills. A spangle of lights rides the island ahead of us, and now the quayside water is splintered into slivers of red and green, fragmented reflections of the neon signs on the buildings of the Praya.

Mei shakes me. "Do you think Mr. Elliott is in prison?" Nothing would please her better.

"He must be," I say. We drive back to the Hospital in a taxi, and my last thought before sleep is of Mark. I think, and I don't know why I think so: "That man needs a love affair."

# CHAPTER VIII

# *Unleashing Trouble*

*July 1949*

MOST PEOPLE DO NOT WISH TO REMEMBER SUFFERING. MY concern is not to forget it. It is not merciful to forget; to obliterate the live sore of remembrance with creeping, bloodless scar tissue. For me always the unabated rawness, the fresh profitable spur of pain. But alas, in vain I wish, for I too shall suffer healing. I must hurry before the verbiage of explanation usurps the live moment endured, now lost forever.

I remember so well the way Mark drove a car. His hands, which were to hold all my life given to him, were gentle with everything. People and things went quietly when he handled them. This was the sixth time we met, and it was two in the morning. He had come twice, since the incident on the Praya, to talk to me at the Hospital. We had stood facing each other in the entrance hall, the target of all eyes — myself awkward in my white coat, pocketing my hands and frowning at the polished floor; he quiet, standing easily, his eyes on me. We did not say very much; we were a little breathless when we saw each other. We wrote gay, absurd little notes to each other. "My schoolboy fluency has come back," wrote Mark. "What have you got which my paper has not got, and which makes me want to write and write to you, even when I have nothing to tell you?" "I put it down to sunspots," I replied, having just read *All Trivia*. His letters were like a song in my heart all day. My thoughts of him from the moment of waking, so joyful that I did not miss his physical presence. And so, because we had no pain, because we did not miss each other, we did not know. We may have been hypocrites, but we were convinced hypocrites.

It was very hot, and that night Mark suggested a midnight swim, but I was still busy at midnight, so he came at two, and drove us to Deep Water Bay, twenty minutes away from the Hospital.

A chipped opal moon dragged her tinfoil track across the bay. A few weary-looking stars hung wide apart in the sky. There was a slight mist on the sea. The water was heavy as oil, salty and lukewarm as we went in. Mark said:

"Since we've known each other over a month, do you think we could start calling each other by our names and leave off Dr. and Mr.?"

"All right. I'll call you Elliott and you call me Han."

"I mean, first names."

"All right."

We went back to the car after our brief plunge. It was cool now. My hair was sticky and damp, for I never wear a cap when I swim. There was a suspense, an unnaturalness forcing itself between us, and he did not turn the ignition key. As always we sat wide apart. "Will you give me a cigarette?" I said.

It would be easy to pretend innocence. I was guilty, for my request forced the moment. Half knowing, pretending not to know, deluding myself, not honest enough; knowing deep down, but not close enough to consciousness to call it knowledge. What many-layered beings we turn out to be!

Mark lit my cigarette, and when we had returned to darkness he took my right hand, and held it for a moment. I did not withdraw it, and so he bent towards me, and kissed my cheek, then he turned my face with his finger and kissed my closed mouth. He let me go, and we sat quite still. He started the car and drove off.

I said, as the engine purred smoothly, "There is a proverb: Don't wake a sleeping tiger."

He drove four hundred yards in silence, then he stopped the car. "When I kissed you," he said in his even, light voice, "I did not know

I was going to do so. It was a sudden compulsion. But I did take your hand first, and had you withdrawn it, I would not have kissed you."

"But it would have been rude to withdraw my hand," was all I could say. And we both laughed until the tears came into our eyes, and then I was in his arms, his mouth gentle and very sure, and my heart was pounding so loudly that I could hear it. "Oh," I whispered, stupid as any girl. "What shall I do with myself?"

"You taste of sea water," he replied.

Abruptly I hated him, a wildness leaping from sleep into wide-awake desire to destroy. My throat was tight and my jaws hurt and I pricked all over with goose flesh. I said: "May you be damned and burn in hell ten thousand years for doing this to me."

But I was still in his arms, close to his mouth, rigid as are the dead.

He withdrew his arm slowly and deliberately, started the car. We stopped a mile later, quietly as always, and he spoke reflectively:

"A while ago as we sat on the beach I was thinking that all my life it would be like this. I should be four yards away from you, for I said to myself, 'She is unapproachable.' And I kissed you, though I had no intention of doing so before I held your hand. You have given me so much already, so much happiness just to know you. Why should I want more?"

But I was not concerned with what he was trying to say. All that mattered to me was what was happening to me. And that was terrible.

"Look. You don't know about me. You think it is all right. You kiss a girl in a car, it does not mean anything to you. Just a kiss. But it is not so with me. I feel sick. I've got nausea, physically. I cannot tell you why it is so, because I do not know. It is like being on a boat that is capsizing. And it does mean something, because even in your world such things begin love affairs."

Mark was not angry. He drove on, then he said: "You asked me when we first met whether I told the truth. I do tell the truth. I think of you all the time. I cannot get away from the thought of you. I have never been so obsessed. I wish you were a psychiatrist, then perhaps you could tell me how to stop thinking about you."

"I think of you all the time, just as you do."

And Mark was very brave and as we stopped in front of the Hospital he said, coolly, evenly, his gentle hands resting on the wheel in front of him. "It seems to me that I am in love with you."

I replied: "No, I don't think so. I think it is just an infatuation. An island is like a ship, you know"—where had I heard this before?—"and things happen quickly on a ship. And Hong Kong is such a beautiful island. I think you need a love affair."

"Oh no," he said, detachedly. "Your diagnosis is wrong. I don't need a love affair. I've just had one. I came to Hong Kong with the idea of having a woman, just as so many men do. And I did. I don't want a love affair."

"Oh," I said, consumed with momentary curiosity. "What nationality?"

"English," he said briefly. And just refrained from saying: "Of course."

"I still think you need a love affair," I said, hugging my knees and feeling completely impersonal and medical for a moment. "There's something . . . unfused about you. Yet you are very strong, you have so much gentleness. But then perhaps, like practically everyone I meet in Hong Kong, you're at a loose end . . . perhaps you are on the brink of something. I know inside me that you are running away from something . . . and yet you are brave. . . . But now look what is happening." I seized upon myself again, much more interested in myself than in him. "You've put *me* in a turmoil. And I don't want to be in a turmoil. I never want to be in love with a man again. It's too complicated. I'm terrified. And now I want you to kiss me, and yet I have nausea at the same time. Damn you," I cried, my thoughts leaping forward to relentless conclusion, "what would I get out of all this but becoming a cheap Hong Kong Eurasian, and perhaps a bastard or two to show for it?"

He was really angry. "That's not true," he said. "Take that back."

"It is true, and I won't take it back. One starts these things, pretending that it does not matter. Later on one pretends it's love pushing one forward. Love," I said, spitting out the word derisively. "And in the name of love one makes a sordid mess of things. I won't have it. No one is going to mess up my life." And I repeated doggedly: "What I said is true and I won't take it back."

Since we were at the entrance to the Hospital I should now have got up and walked out; we would not have met again, and nothing would have happened. But of course I did not. I could not. I just sat on, shivering, choking, angry, blind and sick. Mark said quietly:

"I think you are very honest."

It was so untrue that I could not let him say it. "I am not. If I were, I would now get up and walk out. But I cannot. Because I want you to kiss me although I feel so sick. I have not been like this for years."

"I am *bouleversé* too," he replied equably. "Tell me, you were so sure the other day that we had no destiny together. Why are you so sure?"

Why? It was obvious to me, yet difficult to word clearly. "Because I am Chinese, and you are English; you are married, and I am a widow; you are a journalist, a front-row spectator, a looker-on not involved in the revolution of Asia; and I am a doctor, a technician, inevitably involved, with a duty towards my people: and you are going to Rome next year, though you hate the thought; and I am going to China next year because that is what I trained for; and we are both conventional people, and we do not want a love affair only; and we both have children . . . oh no, no," I cried, "there is no place, in time, or in space, for us, no place for us, nowhere, nowhere . . . we are doomed before we begin. Don't let us fool ourselves."

But Mark would not believe that Fate could not be dragged by the hair, that fortuitous encounters did not mean anything. "Let us not make easy things complicated and complicated things simple," he said. "Let us see what happens. There may be a place for us together in the world."

"I know what is going to happen if we go on seeing each other. I'm going to be your mistress. And I shall hate you and hate myself."

"Why?" His hands, so gentle, unmoving on the wheel. I had always been afraid of hands, men's hands. I was not afraid of his. Never.

"Because I'm not normal. I've hated even looking at men, and the thought of them was just frightening and impossible."

"I don't understand," said Mark.

"I'm all wrong inside. Inhuman, unfeeling, a barrier between me and everyone else . . . I wasn't born that way, but that is how I am now. You are the first man I want, for such a long time, and I want you and of course I hate you so much that I could faint."

He kept silent, and so, in the silence, I told him what had happened and what had been done to me.

Still he did not say anything. No exclamation of pity or distress. His face in the darkness unmoved. His hands I was watching stayed relaxed, quiet. If they had shown the slightest tremor of compassion, or surprise, if they had gripped the wheel, I would have despised him. But they did not.

When I had finished telling him, he said, looking through the glass in front of him, and his voice unmoved:

"Dear one, how long is it that you have been like this?"

"Five years or more. A long time. My family all think I am trying to become a monument of virtue. They think I'm keeping to myself because of the old-fashioned customs — a widow is not to marry again. But I wasn't born that way at all. It's not virtue, just repulsion. And now I would have an uncomplicated life, no upset, only work and work. It's so easy to work when you keep yourself dead inside. Do you understand?"

"I do."

"I could not imagine not being . . . neutral. The word sex a blank, as if it had never existed for me. The world of love closed to me. Not to be touched, not to be hurt, terrifying to others, so that I should not be terrified. Never, never to love again. Safely dead. No emotion moving me save anger and ambition. Until now. And now you have kissed me and instead of leaping back ten yards, as I should once have done, I cannot go away from you. What is going to happen to me? What shall I do with myself?"

There was nothing left of my privacy. This man had it all. I had given it all to him. Tomorrow I would curse myself. So I said bitterly:

"You'd better not take me on, you know. You'd better get away from me, while you can. I am inhuman and absolute. Take care."

He debated this with himself for about twenty minutes. From the third floor of the Hospital I heard the wail of a baby, a piteous animal whine of pain. Mark turned and looked at me, very steadily, for a long time, and then he said gently, so gently that it was frightening:

"I shall think about it, and I shall decide for you."

It was not what I had expected, but it was what I had been waiting for, all the time. All the time. A man who would have the courage to say this to me. So I replied, and for the first time since knowing him I was humble:

"Yes, you are stronger than I; you will decide for me."

It was four in the morning. The moon had gone and the sky was thick with cloud. Mark's plane was leaving at six for Formosa, where he was going for ten days. We left each other without saying good-by.

# CHAPTER IX

# The Goldfish

*July 1949*

Before I had met him I had heard a good deal about Ernest Watts. It was at a University party that his name was first mentioned to me. An earnestly gay party, with professors, lecturers, assistants and wives heartily deploying their comradeship. I had sauntered into this private enclosure, as I was to saunter into so many coteries, cliques and circles, by reason of my variegated past and my ambivalent accomplishments. I was here in the guise of an "intellectual," and being congratulated by one wife on my translation of a book of Chinese short stories. "I haven't read them of course," said she, "but I know they're wonderful."

Indignantly shaking his round head, one of the more eminent educationalists drew me into a corner to talk to me about Ernest Watts. Between sips at his cocktail he rumbled: "A disgrace to the Colony. Not at all the type to occupy a position of responsibility. Pity they couldn't keep him elsewhere. For your own sake don't go near him. He's an idealist." In those days I mistook bluffness for sincerity and I liked everybody in Hong Kong. I had never met so many friendly foreigners before.

From my friend and colleague John Tam I obtained a different Watts. John Tam said enthusiastically, in his clipped Malayan English: "He's a great guy. He doesn't suffer fools gladly, but he may like you. He's fierce, man, when he doesn't like somebody."

Tam was full of tales of Ernest Watts, a trait shared alike by the friends and the enemies of this man. Very few people remained indifferent to him, even among the Chinese; he was either loved or hated. John Tam's tales were not mild; they showed a sardonic wit, a quixotic defiance of ubiquitous hypocrisy, a deep honesty which left me stimulated, shaken and perplexed; certainly I must meet Ernest Watts.

In that month of July, surcharged with happenings, the Medical Service, temporarily without anaesthetists through illness and furlough, had asked John Tam and myself to help with anaesthetics. Tam specialized in pathology and I wanted to do surgery; we were far more frightened than our patients, who seemed none the worse for our ministrations of ether and curare. "I'm getting anxiety neurosis," said Tam, and droned gruesome ghost stories at me, a jumble of Chinese and Malayan goose-flesh raisers, while we sat at the heads of our patients, half asleep with the gentle fumes emanating from our machines. He was convinced that he believed in fox fairies, and dragged me for night rambles through the cemetery on the hill slopes opposite the Hospital, in the vain hope of encountering one of those malicious and beautiful creatures. Where live human beings were concerned, he was a fully developed pessimist. "I've never seen such a beautiful place as Hong Kong, and I've never known so many bloody-minded people."

I loved Tam. He was honest, enthusiastic and clever. He bred fish in his room at the Hospital for spiritual solace, and owned sixteen tanks full of fighting fish and angelfish; he also had several valuable lion-headed goldfish. The room coolie finally complained to the House Sister that he could not clean the floor of Dr. Tam's room because there was no floor left to clean. So Tam had to cut down the tanks to eight, and became even more pessimistic.

One evening as we were preparing two fighting fish, separating them so that they would fight when put in the same water, Tam said to me: "Watts has come back. Would you like to have dinner with him?"

"Oh, yes. I've heard so many awful things about him, he must be interesting." Already I knew that in Hong Kong hearsay was far more important than knowledge. Nobody bothered to find out what people were really like, rumor was sufficient; and Hong Kong is full of rumors all the time, for it is easier to appear knowledgeable than to become so. Servants are plentiful and cheap, women have little to do, and malice is a pleasant pastime.

Watts had returned to the Colony from wherever he had concealed himself for a time. This seemed to provoke some people, to elate others. "He must be stimulating," I said to Diana Kilton, who has been my English friend for six years. Diana was immensely valuable to me, for she kept me informed on English public opinion. She conceals a keen brain behind a perennially virginal face, a good game of tennis, the right clothes and conformist platitudes every time she opens her mouth in public.

"Stimulating?" said Diana. "He's a frightful crank. Nobody wants to know him."

"But you've never seen him, Diana."

"But I've been told such things. I'd hate to meet him."

I was half an hour late to meet Tam because an acute appendix had turned up. Tam was pale with anxiety. "We'll be late, man. Women have no sense of time. Watts hates people who are late. He isn't patient. We'd better hurry."

I was irritable myself. Bundled into the car without time to powder my nose, I was frightened and miserable by the time we landed, in sinister darkness, at the foot of a series of steps hewn in the hillside. These we ascended at running pace — "Watts hates waiting" — towards a Victorian mansion, its walls and pillars afflicted with leprous patches of fungus and damp. I was rushed into a little room full of small tables, upright chairs and book-lined walls. Around the table sat Watts, a small buxom woman with black eyes and a young man, her nephew. We drank sherry in small glasses whose rim hit my nose. Watts had blue eyes and was fair, verging on the reddish. He looked as if he might own a studio and never wear a hat. I found out later that he always wore a battered panama on his hikes, and had never owned a studio.

The small woman possessed a pair of startling black eyebrows, a determined chin and the mental agility of all dumpy people. There wasn't anything to say about the nephew.

We had Chinese food. I became involved in conversation with the nephew, while two pairs of eyes surveyed me leisurely. I was tired, irritable and ill at ease. Swiftly the talk turned to gossip in typical Hong Kong fashion. The nephew seemed to have acquired much accurate misinformation. He talked about the Palmer-Joneses. I already knew, through my Shanghai friends, Nora and Robert Hung, that the Palmer-Joneses were a power in business, or in the local expression, Big Shots. The nephew knew all about them.

"Palmer-Jones is so oily that he oozes. He bows and scrapes his heels and sprints fifty yards to greet the son of a famous Chinese official, or the concubine of a rich Malayan businessman. Once he knows you aren't important or well connected, he just uses you."

"That's very Chinese," I said laughingly. "I am to meet the Palmer-Joneses myself. He's quite famous in Hong Kong," I added, "and lots of people like him."

"Oh, he's got his finger in every pie. But she is worse. Trust Mrs. Palmer-Jones to be on every board or committee to run anything round here. Nothing goes on without her. She sits in judgment on everybody. She can never forget that she was a missionary once. Real pillars of society."

Watts did not say anything. He just sat, very quietly, and I was aware of him all the time. Mentally I sniffed round him, a reconnoitering puppy, and I liked him. But I was cross with the nephew.

The conversation then turned to Lucy Koo. It appeared that the buxom little woman and her nephew did not like Lucy Koo.

I now proceeded to lose my temper with them, for they were being scathing about Lucy, and Lucy had been more kind and helpful to me than anyone else in Hong Kong. I had a feeling of loyalty towards her. I said rudely: "You don't know what you're talking about. Without her I'd be terribly in debt." I proceeded to relate to them something of Church Guest House and the missionaries.

"Oh, she's probably been kind to you because she expects something of you," said the nephew's aunt.

"Don't be stupid," I retorted rudely. "I've never been in Hong Kong in my life before. I have no pull, no protection, no money; I'm on the fringe of everything and I belong nowhere. How can she expect something from me?"

Watts bent forwards. His voice was quiet, and I knew suddenly why I liked him. Because he was so much like Mark Elliott. "Did you discover, during your stay at Church Guest House, what those missionaries used as *livres de chevet*?"

I laughed. This was so much more entertaining than talk about people. "They were not addicted to any but detective fiction. I came in on them when they were being thrown out of China, shipwrecked voyagers, washed up by the sea upon this green rock of our exile, Hong Kong."

"You come in on the tail end of a dying world," he said. "Charming to know that the dead and the dying sat up in bed and read murder stories to lull themselves to sleep."

Yes, I liked Watts very much. But I had marred myself with the others, and awkwardly, after a few enforced courtesies, we parted. I remembered him. His face had a theatrical streak, but his hands were sincere. I thought: "I must tell Mark about him. And get Watts to have dinner with Mark. It will be such fun. I'm sure they will like each other."

"I liked Watts," I told Tam as we were cleaning his fish tanks a day later. "But I was bad-tempered and I don't think they liked me."

Tam uses no pretense towards me. He is hot-tempered too.

"I don't think you got on well with his friends. You're both rather fierce women, and she says you are too outspoken. You weren't a very good diplomat, man."

We cleaned in silence. I poured the sand and pebbles back at the bottom of the glass tank. We inspected the water plants, then we filled the tank half full of the old water, and added fresh rain water collected from a nullah on the hillside. We put in a drop of mercurochrome to kill the parasites. Then very carefully John Tam lifted the glass bowl with his latest acquisition, two sooty black goldfish, and lowered it into the tank. At first the goldfish did not move out of the bowl. Then they tasted the water, and liking it, shot out with a flick of their bodies. We sighed with pleasure to see them arrowing across the tank towards the light bulb kept at one end, and suddenly spreading out their gossamer tails, wide, wide tails, five times as long as their bodies, so transparent that the weeds could be seen through their flesh. The small hard body, solid with its hints of gold among the black scales, an offshoot of the enormous blossom tail, supported at its other end the arborescent eyes, symmetrical tortured growths massive on their frail stalks, swaying gently on either side of their squat faces. "One hundred and sixty dollars the pair, man," said Tam, "you couldn't find a better couple anywhere."

I was upset by the beauty of the fish and could not speak. We sat in companionate pleasure, gazing at them through the glass walls of the tank.

"I always see people as fish," said Tam, half to himself. "Fish become odd, you know, swimming in their tanks, separated from the rest of the world. There are all sorts of fish — the gregarious type that flock together, like the angelfish, the fighting ones, fierce as tigers, and as stupid; and then a few like these, rare and beautiful, with enormous chrysanthemum eyes and a tail like a mantle of mist. Some people are like these goldfish. They isolate themselves, and gradually become inaccessible to the legions of the mediocre and the hordes of the stupid. Safe from the loppings of curiosity and the assaults of malice, they develop in their solitude their own excrescent burgeons, they sprout strange mental blossoms, and slowly unfit themselves to dwell with their more utilitarian brethren. To me Ernest Watts is a goldfish of a beautiful, rare kind. He is not like the others."

I nodded. I was aware only of one thought. "When Mark comes back from Formosa, I must show him the goldfish. For they are beautiful, and I want his eyes to see all the beauty there is in the world."

# CHAPTER X

# Suzanne

July 1949

IT WAS WEDNESDAY AGAIN, MY AFTERNOON OFF. I WAS strolling through the Gloucester Arcade, the passageways lined with shops which lie between the Gloucester and Hong Kong Hotels. In front of the Cake Shop, a woman with yellow hair and a red dress with white spots turned to look at me. From the back a complete European, there was Chinese in her face behind the foreign way of making up and of moving her eyes and her mouth. She walked towards me.

"Excuse me. Are you not . . . Suyin?"

I looked at her. From underneath the powder and the unknown features, gradually familiar, another face emerged as a fish coming up out of layer upon layer of water; a face known long ago. "I know you. We went to the Catholic Convent together. You are Suzanne. . . ."

She was delighted. Her eyes shone, lustrous, dark, incongruous with her golden hair. "You've dyed your hair."

"Yes. Now I see that you remember me. After all these years, nearly twenty. We spent two years in Convent together." She was overjoyed and shook both my hands. For a moment we stood, looking at each other, then moved towards the Hong Kong Hotel lobby and managed to find a small table at which we sat.

The lobby was as usual crowded with exuberant Chinese in groups, in families, never alone. Women in sleek dresses and earrings, with the new fashionable high busts and rounded croups; sharkskin-clad men, vociferous about business and money — all eating cakes and drinking orangeade. There were no English about; crowded out by the less inhibited, more numerous race, they had retired with quiet dignity to the first floor, abandoning the lobby with a skillful indifference which transformed their retreat into a tactical victory.

Suzanne said to me: "What has happened to you during the last twenty years?"

"I went to a Chinese university. I toured Europe. I came back to China. I married and I was inland, in Chungking, during the war. We went to England, my husband and I. He was killed in battle by the communists when he returned to China to fight the civil war. I finished medicine in England. I have a child." My life compacted of many fragmentary lives, each one a separate, private identity — undergoing many changes, yet always mine. "But I'm not interesting, tell me about you." I was avid for her story, the life of a Eurasian like myself, co-inmate of that expensive Convent where, to please my mother, I had spent two years of my life learning French, useless manners, and to hate Europeans. A world of myself when very young which I had left so completely. She was still linked to it; all of it, in her mind, a pleasurable memory. Because of those Convent days our lives had now crossed and would influence each other. "Tell me," I repeated. "We made our first Communion together. It was cold, I remember, that day in spring, and someone fainted. . . ."

"Yes, yes. Bettina, her mother was Japanese and her father English. She ate blotting paper, hiding behind the lifted top of her desk. Mother Angela (very fat, she died of a stroke, don't you remember her?) used to shake and shake her to make her throw it up. Bettina fainted at the Elevation, slipped down and banged her forehead on the floor. They gave her vinegar and water to revive her. She couldn't communicate, and had to do it alone the Sunday after. She married a German and died of a baby."

Suzanne changed her mind too often to marry. Her hands rose and fell, fingers curling outwards, her laughing mouth exonerating the mutability of her affections. "My life seems to have been a succession of love affairs." And again ripples of laughter ran through her.

I was rapt with envy. It sounded such an insubstantial occurrence in her laughing voice: a thing of no importance, a pleasant pastime. Why was it not so with me? Why did I have to be the way I was? "Tell me," I said. "How many?"

Her hands covered her eyes in a mock gesture of horror. Between the parted palms her mouth was smiling. "I was trying to count them the other evening." Again the sparkling ginger ale laughter. "I made it, yes, I think I made it ten or so. Is that a lot?"

I swallowed. "I don't know."

Suzanne's mobile face became solemn. "But I've never missed mass, never. I still say my prayers every night, just as we were taught in the Convent."

I gazed at her, a rabbit in a trance before an outsize cobra.

Suzanne's father was English, which made her English, but she was French by choice of education. "The English are so sentimental," she said. "Yet they have no imagination in love. They take it so seriously; they're either hopelessly fond of you, or else you don't mean anything to them, and they let you know it all the time." Frenchmen were Suzanne's choice, the safely married ones, looking for the sentimental episode in a satisfactorily unsentimental existence. "So many men become sentimental *after* they are married," said Suzanne.

"Did you never, well, have a Chinese?"

"No," said Suzanne promptly. "They don't appeal to me."

How odd, I thought, that there should be this feeling about race. I could not have dreamt of being touched by a foreigner. Until Mark. . . .

But Suzanne was opening new vistas to me.

"I very nearly did get married once," she was saying. "On a boat. You know how quickly things happen on a boat. In three days we were madly in love. He wanted to divorce his wife and marry me. But I couldn't do that. I want to be married decently, in church. He wanted me to live with him while he got his divorce. I said to him: 'But what about my reputation?'"

She launched into the heart of the matter. "I've seen so many marriages go on the rocks just because of that, you know. It's when they have difficulties with their wives, and look for something to suit them better. That's why I have to find out first, you see, what they are *really* like. And there's only one way to find out. I can see you don't know much about it. I expect you were married a long time. Were you ever in love?"

I felt my shell tighten around me. "Yes," I said, inadequate and inept. "Of course, with my husband."

"I can see you've had a sheltered life. And the longer you're married, the less you know about it. It must get rather dull," she added thoughtfully. "You'd be surprised the things men think up, so you've got to find out about them before you get yourself all tied up and realize you don't like them. When you do it with a man, you know all about him. He can talk to you for months about himself, take you out day after day, and still you don't know. Until. There were some men I was mad keen about, and then, after that, finished. Ah my dear, I said to them, if that's the kind of man you are, someone else can have a try."

I had a steel trap round my throat. I said in a strange, hoarse voice: "But isn't it a sin?" And was surprised when I had said it.

For a moment Suzanne was sad, then sighed in comical regret, while tears of merriment glistened in her eyes. "I know. But that's how it is for me. I don't feel sinful the first few days, when I hover between heaven and earth, levitated with love. But afterwards I come down with a bang, and I know I've sinned. I know it especially on Sunday mornings."

But her oval face was unlined and she shone with happiness.

"What about you," she said. "You are no longer a Catholic. You left the religion, didn't you, after you kicked Mother Superior on the shin? Your mother was devout, though."

"Yes." I did not tell her why I had walked out. The Mother Superior had nothing to do with it. I had wanted to be all Chinese, not a counterfeit semi-European, one of those gay, generous people who lived on the brink of the small European circles of Shanghai or Peking, in that curious half-world of concessions and color bars, a world now dead, like the missions, and the superiority of the whites, and many other things.

"I gave it up, for many reasons, and now these reasons no longer exist. I am just myself and I don't need a religion."

"Perhaps you're born a puritan. You could never accept things as they are, could you? It's more difficult for people with puritan souls. They're inhuman. I knew one, he gave himself hell all the time. Religion is for human beings, human beings are imperfect and must accept it without too much anxiety. You will go back to the Faith, I think. When you fall in love again, you will go back to the Church."

"Oh never," I said, "never. I haven't got a Christian soul. I'm too unfeeling and inquisitive to worship anything. I won't go back. I won't fall in love again. . . . Never."

"You say the word love as if it were such a big thing," said Suzanne. "Love isn't all that big. Very little can put you off. You can go to bed full of it, and wake up to find that it has vanished. I remember a man I was in love with. We arranged a rendezvous in his hotel. And when I entered his room, there he was, waiting for me, already in his undershirt. So tactless, don't you think? 'Really,' I said, 'you are very much in a hurry. You could have waited a little.' And after that, he did not mean anything to me."

We had finished our orangeades. "Where are you working?" I asked Suzanne.

"I'm working for Humphrey Palmer-Jones," said she. "I'm his secretary."

I was delighted. "I've heard so much about him from so many people. I may meet him soon. Some friends of mine in England have given me a letter to him."

"He's very nice," said Suzanne. "His wife . . ." She puckered her face. "She's . . . well, she's rather terrifying. . . ."

Suzanne did not like Mrs. Palmer-Jones. But she was full of praise for Humphrey. "You'll get on if you know him. He's got a lot of influence. He's a good fixer. And he's really kind."

We rose, exchanged telephone numbers. Lightly, tripping a little on high heels, crowned with youth and her dyed golden hair, she disappeared down the Arcade.

And as she went, I felt withered, unused, avaricious of myself. I went back to the Hospital and stretched on the bed. One name hammered at me with each heartbeat of my heart. I stripped and looked at myself in the mirror a long long time. I was unhappy for nearly an hour.

# CHAPTER XI

# Treasure Hunt

*July 1949*

AT LAST I WAS TO MEET THE PALMER-JONESES. "COCKTAILS and dinner," the card they sent me read, at their residence high up in the hills of Hong Kong.

Five minutes before I left the Hospital, the telephone rang. It was Mark, back from Formosa. Above the pandemonium of the residents' common room, I managed to shout: "I am going to a party. Now. Come at eleven."

And, unlucid with the thought of Mark's return, I went to the Palmer-Joneses.

I had heard much about them. Suzanne was Humphrey's secretary. Robert and Nora Hung knew them socially; Robert had business dealings with him. Humphrey's financial ability was well known and highly thought of. Rumor found him charming, conceded both a good deal of influence and a finger in every pie.

Adeline Palmer-Jones bore down on me with benevolent majesty as I entered her packed drawing room. "Now aren't people silly," I thought, as she piloted me through the close-pressed multitudes. "She's not a bit frightening. Regal, yes, unctuous too, but then she's fat. True, her nose is rather high, her eyes are on the small side, her lips are thin. But she can't help the way she looks."

I got wedged between two Englishwomen and a wall with an oil painting of Adeline wearing a blue hat. A small stodgy man materialized close to me and confided gloomily that the cocktails were on the weak side. The women, over my head, batted an acidulous conversational ball back and forth, "Isn't she a bitch?" said the more freckled and bony one. "Isn't she just," replied the blonde with the fine down on her upper lip. They went on briskly and I twisted my neck right and left but they did not notice me. Our hostess now advanced towards us and Freckles greeted her enthusiastically. "I was telling Mary what wonderful parties you do give, Adeline dear. I've met everyone I know."

Adeline smiled down at me. "I feel I've known you for a long time, Dr. Han. Lady Brimbles wrote to me all about you. She's such a great artist, isn't she. Understands so well the peoples of the East, the culture of the Orient . . . your five-thousand-year-old civilization. . . ." She looked benignantly at me, representative of those five thousand years. Our talk veered to the modern, and her sentences became studded with the names of Important People, none of whom I had met. Her friend had certainly written in unrealistic terms about me. I had to produce a few good old stand-bys of the Nationalist government and her smile expanded. I was all right.

"Humphrey and I know all the nice people in China. We had so many friends there. The wonderful things they used to give us; embroideries, carpets, vases, pictures . . . those dear old generals used to send me presents all the time. Humphrey, you know, had to deal with so many people. We love the Chinese. Dreadful to think that all this is now over."

She sighed.

"I'm so glad you like Hong Kong. It's all right if you have a car. Do you drive, or have you got a chauffeur?"

"I haven't got a car. I can't afford it."

A shadow cast itself upon the smile broadsided on me. I explained that I had to support myself. Had, in fact, come down in the world. The shadow deepened.

"Well," said Adeline. "We all have our ups and downs. You'll be staying here of course. Private practice is of great service to the community. Very great service."

"I was thinking of going back to China."

The shadow was now definitely puce. "But all the *nicest* people are getting out of China," she said stiffly. "You young ones get so carried away by ideals. Are you in favor of the Reds?"

"No. I'm not political-minded. But it's my country, and it needs all its doctors. . . ."

"Of course," said Adeline, pursuing her own thoughts. "My husband has to deal with them, you know. It's such a responsibility, but trade must go on; we've got to stick it. Somehow I can't help feeling, though, that twenty-five years ago we'd have coped more efficiently with this sort of thing — sent some gunboats up river and restored peace and order. We've always protected trade, everywhere."

I felt a little heat floating up my neck beneath my Chinese collar (many Chinese feel a little warm when Europeans talk glibly of sending their gunboats up Chinese rivers), but was saved from a reply by Adeline's leaving me with surprising agility. A tall handsome man with rugged features and graying hair had entered the room and was surrounded by a bevy of ladies, who, heads together and ears stretched out, listened raptly to his remarks. Gay laughter floated from them in wisps.

"That's Humphrey," said James Manton, who appeared and shook hands with me. "How are you? We have not seen much of you lately. Fiona will soon be back, and you must come and stay with us for a while before you go to Peking. Tattybogle sent Fiona a telegram for her birthday. He's her dog, you know, not mine."

Evelyn Walsingham was talking with a tall handsome Jesuit who held an orangeade with both hands. James and I joined them. Father Low spoke eight European languages and two Chinese dialects most beautifully. "Isn't this a well-crowded party," he said amiably. "I don't know why I am here. Representing the temporal power of the Church, I suspect."

"I think Mrs. Palmer-Jones is an outstanding person. So energetic, public-spirited, and kind," said Evelyn.

"Glazed over with kindliness like something in aspic," muttered the small stodgy man who seemed to follow me everywhere. Nobody knew who he was or how he got there. "However, one must not say these things on two watery drinks," he added sadly.

Father Low and I discovered our affinity through our love of Chinese poetry, and were just quoting to each other the song poems of Nah Lan when Humphrey came to our group. He was charming. He bent down to shake my hand, and I felt petite and beautiful. "We've heard so much about you," he said, and I felt intelligent and popular. He turned to James. "Sorry I am late. Held up by that meeting on hawkers' licenses. I opposed the motion absolutely. We can't have those people cluttering up our streets. It's too messy." When he had gone, James explained to me that the fish industry was one of Humphrey's smaller interests. He sat on some board or other about it, and had definite ideas on the subject. Fish and rice are very nearly the sole diet of the native population, since the Colony imports all its meat. Before the war the fishermen, numbering sixty thousand, used to give their catch to a species of rich moneylenders, who made loans to them at high rates of interest, and to whom they were in debt from generation to generation. The government of the Colony had broken the power of the moneylenders by establishing markets where fishermen brought their catch and sold it at fair prices, by giving loans at very low rates of interest, establishing co-operatives and social services. But on the other hand rings of middlemen had now formed. These cornered the sale of fish to the people, and raised the price to many times what had been paid to the fishermen. The Colony had no freezing plants to store the fish, and a shortage was easily produced. The consumers now suffered, and the poor could not afford fresh fish. Year in year out they ate rice, and a few salted vegetables, and salted shreds of a local sardine. One way to bring down the price would be to grant more licenses, to street hawkers for instance, instead of confining them to such dealers as had stalls, and who were organized to co-operate with the middlemen. The erstwhile moneylenders had now invested their wealth in these middlemen rings and throve as well as ever. "But Humphrey says that no good would be done by altering the established order. He's a loyal person, you know; he's got business friends among the middlemen. He sticks by them."

"But that means many poor people haven't got anything to eat but rice," I protested grandiloquently. "It creates disease, malnutrition, the world's scourge. . . ."

"Well, it's very difficult," said James, reasonable as always. "The government has done a lot for the fishing population. There are so many interests involved in this sale of fish . . . we've got to go slow."

Evelyn Walsingham was being frank about Chinese students and their country. Evelyn's heart would always be in her little house in Kent, where amid a few choice belongings her tidy mind moved with pleasure and dignity. "I find nothing admirable in Chinese philosophy. I think your attitude towards life is rather cruel. Your students do not seem to have much gratitude for what has been done for them. Look at the denunciations and confessions in the communist newspapers by former recipients of British and American scholarships. And so many of the Chinese who come to Hong Kong to find safety won't do a thing for the social services of the Colony. They are not interested in contributing to the welfare of Hong Kong, though quite happy to benefit from its stability."

"They've ruined the Colony," said a stiff, military-looking man with a brushy mustache and a spotless pink shine on his head. "Those rich people from China have ruined us."

"I should say," muttered my small stodgy man, obviously bound to me for life, "that the Colony has skimmed the cream of their savings and ruined them."

"This is Mrs. Palmer-Jones's big annual cocktail party," said James to me. "Will you come back and take potluck with us, or are you among the elect who stay to dinner?"

I confessed I was an elect. Mention of dinner made me look round for a clock. On the wall opposite to Mrs. Jones's portrait a Swiss cuckoo clock perched, and it upset me, for it was nearly ten o'clock. Ten o'clock. In an hour's time Mark would be waiting in front of the Hospital, waiting for me. I would be late, and perhaps he would go away and I would never see him again.

Someone touched my arm, and it was Helen Parrish from Church Guest House with her husband Alf beside her.

"You naughty girl, you haven't been to see us since you moved to the Hospital."

"I haven't had time, Mrs. Parrish. How's everything?"

"Not bad; quite good. We've been lucky. Alf is now a junior sales manager in the Palmer-Jones firm."

She lowered her voice. "Humphrey and Adeline are the sweetest people. They were missionaries like us once upon a time, a long time ago, but they've come a good way since then. We're awfully, awfully grateful to them."

Mrs. Parrish was very pleased to be at such a large cocktail party. "Our Mission has just sent some new missionaries out from the States to go to China. They've been applying for entrance permits. They're in Church Guest House, waiting to go into China. Isn't it funny? They'll never get in now, of course."

The bluff man who had talked with great indignation about Ernest Watts now hovered into our group. His name, I learned again, was William Monk. "Fancy you forgetting my name," he teased me, turning on the charm full blast. A thin intense woman cast a look at me, then at Evelyn, retrieved William Monk with a minimum of words and fled down a corridor of people. Evelyn sighed. "Dear Mr. Monk, he's sweet in spite of his manner, don't you think? Martha is a bit difficult, she thinks every woman is after her husband. He gets gastric ulcers when she's specially difficult."

A blond small woman near whom I found myself told me that her husband was in "The Concern." The group she was with all belonged to "The Concern."

"I never get much out of our circle, it's such a thrill meeting you," said she charmingly. "In Hong Kong, you know, one sticks to one's own circle of friends. You don't get to know many people outside. I've only been here three years. I don't know a word of Chinese, of course.

We're so busy, you see, entertaining in our own circle of "The Concern." We've scarcely finished one round of parties than it's time to start all over again."

"I think it's so intrepid of Adeline," said another, "giving this annual mixed affair. I'd be terrified. One never knows what social *faux pas* one might commit. I never meet any Chinese at all, except occasionally," she added hurriedly. "So brave of Adeline."

It was indeed intrepid of Adeline. My liking for her increased. She certainly had courage. In six months in Hong Kong, going from one circle to another, from one race to the other, I had sometimes wondered why people did not mix more. All the ingredients were here, ready for the mixing. The melting pot of the Orient, they called Hong Kong. Indeed no. The place where everyone met and many stayed apart, divided by hedges of prejudice and hearsay. However much one shook the mixture, it stratified into immiscible layers again.

A mild stampede began. Apparently it was the end of the cocktail party. An obedient army, the nonelect trooped out. I looked sadly at their departing backs, wishing mine had been among them. Then I gazed round the room, empty save for the elect. On lacquered shelves silver Manchurian carts and Tibetan turquoise-encrusted bowls neighbored Dresden shepherdesses. Large Japanese dolls were flanked by Ming vases. Two Chinese paintings of plum blossoms, magnificently done, framed the Swiss clock. A lithograph of Van Gogh's sunflowers companioned Mrs. Palmer-Jones's likeness on the wall. The chair backs were carved with solid clusters of grapes. Two Chinese rosewood altar tables supported books and magazines. The sofas were heavy and covered with bright patterned material. The Tientsin carpets were deep of pile and beautiful in design. There were many little tables about. I could now see the whole of Adeline at once, and was impressed by the large number of silver sequins scattered in places on her pale blue gown.

It was eleven before we sat at the well-appointed table gleaming with Royal Worcester and silver, served by silent-footed boys respectful of countenance in their long white robes. Between spoonfuls of tomato soup a very thin woman with discouraged hair waxed enthusiastic over Hong Kong. It was her first visit to the Orient. "I think it's perfectly wonderful to have so many servants, all the leisure you want. You can devote your time here to really creative work. No housework to struggle with, so different from England."

"But we don't have time," protested Freckles, who was also among the elect. "So much going on in one's own circle, you know. Quite killing. I'm often completely exhausted. I had to stay in bed a whole day last week."

The pink-headed military man talked about the new tank roads built along the border with China which were to protect the Colony from invasion.

"Hong Kong is quite impregnable, quite impregnable. Our tanks can get anywhere they're required. I'd just like to see anyone try to invade us."

"It's the police force we ought to strengthen," said William Monk. "We want a network of new police stations all over the Colony. We're undermined from the inside. The natives are already organized against us. Subversive activities going on everywhere. Even in our academic institutions."

"Hong Kong would be a wonderful place if there were not so many Chinese about," assented Martha Monk, helping herself to more fish.

Adeline rushed into the small silence which followed this remark with a tactful glance towards me which reassured me as to my visibility. "The only remedy," she said, "is contraception. Far too many babies being born. Far too many people in the world. We shall all starve in fifty years. It's a thing I feel one ought to take up. A really big campaign in the Colony, among the Chinese. . . ."

"Adeline, dear, you're such a genius," said Freckles. "Your wonderful energy . . . I'd be dead. . . ."

The thin woman from England was still lyrical about life with servants. "Amazing to find a spot on earth where people can still live the life beautiful."

"Mind you," said the military man, "Hong Kong isn't what it used to be. Why, in the old days. . . ."

Everyone except myself joined in a gold rush of reminiscence.

Japanese camp experiences, a famous authoress who lived here and wrote a book about it, and the good old days, are the staple topics of English dinner talk in the Colony.

"I was in Kakoo Oil twenty-five years ago. We had a jolly good bonus at Christmas from selling munitions to all the warlords in China."

"We'd have broken them with cavalry charges, if those coolies had dared to strike."

Half past eleven. Insidiously, ferocity blossomed on all those faces. Freckles was no longer a woman, but a strange spotted carnivorous beast, and the sagging neck muscles of Mrs. Monk an intricate machinery for torture. The military man paralyzed me with fear as he laughed, revealing some carious teeth and the pink plate of his palate. I had not noticed before that William Monk's hands were so brutal. More frightened every minute, again invaded by the shadows of terror which Mark alone could take away, lost in the champing of their jaws, the clatter of their words, I called upon him, I whispered his name, a talisman to comfort me, but I was still afraid.

And then suddenly it was all gone; they were people like myself, stupid people saying trivial, cruel and stupid things around a dinner table. Overfed people talking of their way of life in a world mainly ruled by hunger. It was very late and all I wanted was to go away. Adeline and Martha Monk were conversing earnestly:

"Yes, I had to ask her to dinner. One's responsibilities . . . but how could I keep her from *talking?* She's such a socialist . . . I organized games. We played Treasure Hunt. It was a bit difficult during dinner because there's no game one can play while one's eating. . . ."

Martha did not like the Labor government. "Giving our Empire away. . . . Look at India now . . . natives could never rule themselves. . . ."

Humphrey explained trade with China.

"Live and let live. So long as they behave decently and will trade with us. We've never yet refused to trade with anyone."

"Kennaway is still in Shanghai, hanging on to the bitter end," said William Monk.

"There would be no Shanghai without Kennaway. Of course we'll recognize them; every country ought to have the government it wants. So long as they'll trade."

Midnight. We retired to powder our noses, leaving the men to their port. We came back and sat in the drawing room. We sipped coffee and were offered liqueurs.

Mrs. Palmer-Jones addressed me once. Had I really got a child? How nice for me, such a companion. Our conversation died spontaneously. She and Martha Monk and Freckles and the thin newcomer chatted. Committees, balls, charity concerts, meetings, rolled off Adeline's tongue smoothly, effortlessly. "I didn't think she had the right ideas. I'm glad to say she didn't become a member."

The men joined us. Nearly one o'clock. I knew what was going to happen. And it did. The little door at the summit of the cuckoo clock sprang open. The little red and white bird snapped out and backed in again. One o'clock. The ladies discussed personalities in slightly lowered tones. William Monk was off on a story:

"Girl coming out here for a post. Must be careful with those youngsters from home.

" 'What's your politics?' I asked her. 'I read the *Economist*,' she said to me. 'Well,' I told her, 'don't. Out here in Hong Kong we haven't got politics and votes, but we've got golf and swimming instead.' "

Past one o'clock. The Monks were going. I accepted a lift in their car, although Mrs. Monk's face pinched slightly as her husband offered it. I shook hands with Mrs. Palmer-Jones, regretfully, knowing that I would not again find myself among the elect. Perhaps not even one of the Cocktail Annual. I still liked her.

I sat in the back of the car, for Mrs. Monk told me how carsick she became unless she sat with her husband in front. I did not get upset, although William Monk drove so slowly. I was two and a half hours' late. There would be no green Morris waiting outside the Hospital, waiting with muted lights. Abject with self-pity and ready to weep, I prayed. "Please, please, Heaven, if there be a Heaven, let him not be angry with me. Let him not go away before I have seen him, for I do so want to see him again. Please . . ." Loud was my prayer to Heaven, tumbling childish words in the silence, and Heaven must have heard, for we rounded the drive, and I saw in the darkness the shadow that was his car. Dark, no lights on. But I knew.

Leaping out, thanking the Monks cheerfully, I rushed into the hall, and when the red taillight had disappeared down the drive I was out again.

He sat in the darkness, silent, and he turned his head very slightly, a movement within the darkness itself, as I opened the door of the car and sat down.

"I am sorry. The party just went on and on. . . ."

"It does not matter." His voice was so quiet, so calm, as if he had not waited at all. And suddenly it was as if time had disappeared, rubbed out by the whispered words; and the futility, the smallness, the meaningless irritations of the evening, they were no more. "Oh, how good it is," I whispered, "how good to know a man who does not live strapped to the watch at his wrist, measuring time by the minute and the hour. I do like it so much."

"I believed that you would come. I sat, and I did not know that I was waiting."

We did not look at each other, draw near, or touch. Only to be like this. Not to want anything. To sit, a little tired, a little muddled with weariness. Happy to know that in the world he was alive, and I was alive, on the same spot on this earth, at the same moment, aware of each other. Knowing each other well, strangers come from afar to meet. And such a little thing, an accident, putting us together. We sat, frightened and grateful.

Frightened because so easily we might have missed each other; grateful and asking no more than what we had already, because even what we had was too big for us to encompass.

And as we sat with darkness gentle and quiet around us, and silence holding us safe, there flowed into us from the throat to the knees and back again, melting us from within, a great, a terrible sweetness.

After a while Mark said: "You must rest, for it is late. Good night, my dear one." I opened the door of the car and left him. He sat on alone.

# The Nets of Fate

*July 1949*

I DID NOT KNOW THAT MARK WAS BEAUTIFUL UNTIL THE swimming party on a Sunday at Repulse Bay. Robert and Nora Hung, my Shanghai friends, had taken a house at the Bay for the summer months. My daughter, Mei, and Maya Wong and her children, who had come from Shanghai for the holidays, were staying with them. Robert and Nora had known Mark Elliott in Shanghai, and had asked him to come for a swim.

Robert was listening to Radio Hong Kong when I arrived from the Hospital. The night before, in China, the *Amethyst* had slipped her cable and in darkness made her getaway from the Yangtse River. She had been shelled, had sustained casualties, escaped, and was steaming towards Hong Kong. "They've chartered the *Belfast* for correspondents to go and meet the *Amethyst*," said Robert to me. "I don't expect Elliott will be coming here today."

Ten minutes later, cool, leisurely, Mark sauntered in, wearing his white drill suit. I looked at him, and I swallowed and my knees were weak under me. I turned away and stared at the smudged horizon, a hot vagueness of sea and sky between the pine trees at the end of the lawn.

"I didn't think it very intelligent to get myself shut up with a host of my colleagues, away from any means of communication for two days," Mark was saying to Robert and Nora. "Besides, it's a beautiful day, and I adore swimming," he added flippantly.

Nora smiled at him, well pleased that he should have come, for she hated last-minute changes in the composition of her parties. Maya stood in front of me teasingly.

"He is nice," she whispered.

My cheeks burnt and I glared at her. "Go away," I said.

When Mark came out of the bathroom in his brief red bathing trunks, my eyes flicked over him and again I had to look away. It always upsets me physically when I see a beautiful thing. Slim-hipped and waisted, the body of a young man, not thick-chested, and only a little fine blond hair in his armpits, otherwise smooth-skinned as any Chinese would be. I saw the narrow feet, the brown legs, the small ears, the beautiful set of the head. It was like being kicked again and again in the belly, an experience I had endured years ago, when the secret police of the Kuomintang made a slight mistake in my identity.

I knew, looking at him, what the poets of my country and the Jews of the Bible meant when they spoke about the melting within the belly that is emotion. A soft hot flame inside, warm and throbbing, daggered sweet fire kindled at the back, licking into the loins and leaping up below the navel, running down my legs and up into my arms. And the immediate knowledge of the stuff of things, awareness of the sea, the rocks, the bark of the pine trees at the edge of the lawn, the grass under my bare feet, the small pebble between my toes. Everything painfully alive, shouting with the exultation of life. Everything I saw and heard and touched was Mark.

So I said insolently, "You are brown, you've been in the sun."

"Yes. I played a lot of tennis in Formosa, and here I swim every day."

Robert and Nora proffered drinks, and I swallowed a brandy and ginger ale, but it did not work. I went to the bathroom and locked the door and was sick, quietly, definitely. I sat on the red tiles of the bathroom floor and tried to think.

"Don't lie to yourself. You want this man. You want him to make love to you. But you don't know whether you won't hate it afterwards. You're now like a sick cat, it's shameful. He's a foreigner, and you

are going to China. It will mean disaster, and sorrow. He is married.
Don't lose your head now. You cannot afford it. This is not love. It's
hunger. Why should you be so upset by this man? Remember, he's a
foreigner, and you are going to China."

I could find no answer, so I cleaned up the place and came out again.
They had all gone down to the beach, except Mark, who was waiting
for me, sitting cross-legged on the lawn. He rose and smiled, and we
looked at each other.

"Walk in front of me," I said roughly as we went towards the steps
carved in the cliff wall leading down to the beach. For I could not bear
his eyes upon me.

Mei and Maya's three children were running about happily, brown-
skinned Chinese children, who do not need a hat in the sun. Mei came
to stare at Mark. "You're not as brown as I am," she cried, and rushed
off again. Robert had made a net out of an old shirt, and was trying
to catch small fish for the children. We sat apart, four yards from each
other, turned facing opposite ways, he looking at the sea and I at the
house, so that we did not meet each other's eyes. Always thus we were
to sit, whenever we talked of distressing things. Until nothing could
distress us any longer.

"I do not know what God intends for you and for me," said Mark.
"But I do not want only a love affair with you. You persist in calling
my day-and-night fixation on you an infatuation, don't you?"

"You English call anything love," I replied. "You say 'fall in
love' so easily, so easily. In China we say we love with, or towards,
or upwards. What I hold for you now I do not dignify by the name of
love. Love is so . . . immense."

"Loving upwards or towards," said Mark, "describes the general
direction of my feelings towards you. I wanted to ask you a question.
Do you think I am superficial?"

"No. Why?"

"I have been found superficial, shallow — in fact, emotionally sub-
normal. I do not seem to fit into the accepted patterns of emotion, the
conventions of affection that others have. At first it bothered me, then

I accepted it that I was cold, emotionally neutral as you have been physically neutral, incapable of deep feeling. I thought that I must find my outlets in other directions. And so . . ."

"And so," I finished for him, "you have been feverishly active, reporting wars and troubles, climbing mountains, and throwing yourself into danger."

He did not reply, but half rose, as if he wanted to go away.

"Don't run away now," I said. "Let's talk about me. I have always been hard and unfeeling. "Heartless," said my mother. "Suyin never weeps except with rage."

He smiled. "You, my dear, are an Elizabethan, with a power of passion that is frightening to many people. With you, it is all or nothing. . . . You are so alive that it spills out of you. And when I see you I, too, become alive . . . and that is why I cannot let you go."

"You bite your nails," I remarked.

"Yes. I do." He was not on the defensive. He bit his nails.

"You will stop biting them one day."

He smiled. "When I do," he said lightly, "I shall know that you really have a hold on me which no one else has ever had."

"I want no hold on you. No burden of feeling between us. Love is not feeling or emotion. Love is a stripping for battle, a blankness leaving nothing behind. Love is not sentimentality and childish greed, not the mockery of possession, not the blackmail of tears. Most people don't know what love is. And I did not know, until this moment, until because of you, I say this. Love is growing up."

Mark said: "I want to be with you all the time. I spend my life nowadays waiting for the next time I see you."

"I too cannot let go the thought of you. But I do not call this love. Not yet."

"It is a bit different," said Mark. "You want me physically more than anything else. It is the male in me you want. But for me it is not so. It is not the most important thing to me that we should become lovers. I want something else. . . . I want," he said very low, "one steady, passionate flame. . . ."

"You," I said, "speak as a monk without a God."

We both rose, for I had said too much, and Mark shut himself up completely. But I did not care. "The day will come when you will face the emptiness within you, as I shall, as all of us must, for we are all the same. All of us run away into the agitation of work or pleasure. One day you will no longer be able or willing to buy a ticket for Sinkiang or for Timbuctoo. You will not run away to bravery and to prowess and to wars. And I shall not run away either."

Mark did not reply. He talked about shells. For he refused that anyone should attempt the self within him. To the assault of possessiveness he opposed an implacable blandness, a fortress-wall charm which made him impregnable. He leapt out of the encirclement of emotion by quoting comic verse. Amusing was his favorite adjective, and boring his utter condemnation. At thirty-six he was a boy in his infinite capacity for recoil from emotional upset.

Talking about shells, then, we swam side by side for a while in the smooth water, then I pushed on, leaving him. I swam to Middle Bay and back, three quarters of a mile each way. Bereft of emotion by the cool sea water which washed me clean, lucid, and steadied my thoughts, I swam. And when I landed again, I knew that I would tackle him, although it meant disaster in the end. I would not refuse what had been sent to me.

A verse from Mark's favorite poet, A. E. Housman, came to me:

> The King with half the East at heel is marched
>     from lands of morning;
> Their fighters drink the rivers up, their shafts
>     benight the air.
> And he that stands will die for nought, and home
>     there's no returning.
> The Spartans on the sea-wet rock sat down and
>     combed their hair.

Mark drove me back at night. Mei was staying with the Hungs at Repulse Bay for the summer holidays. Basketfuls of stars littered the sky. There was no moon. We passed Deep Water Bay on our way to the Hospital, and he stopped.

Across the dark water, in the distance, loomed the lights of the fishing fleet. Bright-light fishing. Two junks with a net suspended between them sailed slowly, away from one another, describing an arc to open the hanging net in a wide sweep. Towards the gap left between the junks, from the opposite direction, came a sampan carrying large kerosene lamps and flares. It went into the gap and over the hidden underwater net. Attracted by the lights, the fish followed the sampan and swam straight into the outspread net. They were unable to escape when they reached the meshes, for the sampan with its lights was still in front of them and towards it they strove. The junks then hauled up the net with its catch.

Mark put his hand lightly on my shoulder. "I do not want to complicate your life. And I suppose I ought to think of my family first of all. I do think of them, all the time, and yet, somehow, I cannot let you go."

We were doomed before we began, for everything was against us. The Spartans on the sea-wet rock . . . "Let us accomplish our destiny," said I, "for good or ill. But you must decide, for you are stronger than I am."

"I think you are stronger."

"I am not, for I am always on the defensive. And you are gentle, you carry no armor. There is nothing stronger in the world than gentleness. I will follow you."

And though we waited another three weeks, the end was sure, and we did what we had to do. Fate had spread her nets and lighted her lamps, and into her snare we went, our eyes wide open, like the fish of Deep Water Bay.

# CHAPTER XIII

# Decision

*August 1949*

I WAITED FOR HIM OUTSIDE THE HOSPITAL, PROPPED AGAINST
the low wall in front of it. Below me ran the road of Pokfulum, trav-
ersed by an occasional red bus or a car. The quiet sea lay in front,
sheened with silver after the heat of the day. The fishing fleet had
already sailed out, the junks like a spill of silver leaves on the smooth
horizon. The seaborn mountain islands rode the sea's rim below an
apricot evening sky: Cheungchau or Dumbbell Island with its twin
humps, Lantao and its cloud-topped peaks casting thin mauve shadows,
and Lamma a blue man on a blue horse. In the camel-foot trees ranged
along the Hospital drive magpie robins held converse, and black-
crested bulbuls shook the boughs in clumsy saunter through the foliage.
A golden haze of dragonflies went skimming over my head. I saw his
car rounding the drive. It stopped near me, I stepped in and we drove
away.

"I brought some sandwiches and a small bottle of brandy. I thought
we might be hungry at some time or other."

We drove on, past Deep Water Bay, past Repulse Bay with its tow-
ered Lido, past the house of Nora and Robert Hung, where Mei my
daughter must have been eating her supper. The brusque night came
as we parked under some trees on the side of the road. A few secretive
stars smudged the sky over the hill, a sliver of moon peered above its
shoulder. "We'll have to go down some steps to the sea," he said.

"Would you prefer to change here or on the beach? I'll change here."

"I'll change on the beach," I replied.

He carried my Hong Kong basket with my swim-suit and a towel in it, and a bundle of his own things. He walked in front of me, and I followed him as he led the way down the stone steps from the road to the beach. The stones of the path were uneven and shone faintly, like dry bone. I put my feet where his bare feet had been, and the steps twisted and turned as we went down, through stunted, untrimmed bamboo, wild banana, orange and persimmon, to the small crescent cove encased on either side by crumbling rock. "We are now on sand," he said.

It was low tide. The water's edge fretted the sand softly, like a hand sifting through grain. One small black junk was moored to the left, its bottom clapped the water without stop. He unfolded and spread on the sand a striped blue and white blanket. "This is my good-luck blanket. It goes everywhere with me. I believe that when I wrap it round me nothing will ever harm me. We'll lie on it."

We sat on the blanket. "Let's have a ham sandwich and some brandy," he said. "We'll drink it out of the bottle. I didn't bring glasses."

The brandy was raw and burnt steadily as it went down our throats. He coughed and spluttered. "Oh, it isn't at all good. More like the stuff they make in Indonesia, a kind of local whisky. I think they must have emptied out the Courvoisier and replaced it with some of their own Hong Kong brew."

I smiled at him. At that moment I had no hunger for him, only the willingness to let him take my life in his gentle hands and rule me. And so I put my forehead against his shoulder, that he might know without words.

"Will you undress while I walk around," he said, and rose and walked away. And that was as it should be. So I undressed, and I was just pulling up the straps of my swim-suit when he returned, walking without noise across the sand. It was dark, and I only saw him when he sat beside me, and then he put out his hand on my upraised arm, stopping me with his quiet, unemphatic gesture. I looked at him, and I was not afraid.

All his movements were quiet, unstrenuous, springing from unconscious sureness. Each deliberate thing he did flowed into the next thing without any self-will about it. What we had to do had to be, not because of our articulate wills, for now we had no more say in the matter, but because it already was. Deep and dark in us beyond hunger or knowledge, beyond word or pleasure. And so he turned me sideways to him with his finger on my shoulder: "Dearest," he said, "forgive me if I blunder. For I am not very *expérimenté*."

"Neither am I. Forgive me. Our bodies have to learn each other, too."

And so he took possession of me, and because I had unknown so much during the years, I obeyed him in everything, blank and submissive and content to be no more. I had not been used for so long that he hurt me a little, but it was not his fault. All the way he led me and I followed him all the way. For of that I was sure, that he was stronger than I, and that I wanted to follow him.

Then we came apart silently, and he did not burden me with word or emotion, but drew the towel over me, and I turned on my face and fell asleep immediately.

When I woke he was sitting a foot away, looking at the dark sea as if he had not moved at all. An errant low cloud lagged above us, and a few large drops of rain fell clicking like coin on the sand. We picked ourselves up and went to shelter under some rocks.

"Wouldn't it be funny," I asked him, "if God, dressed as an old gentleman with a white beard, were suddenly to come round the rocks and upon us?"

"You would say how do you do, politely," he replied, "and we would offer him some of our terrible brandy."

After standing for some minutes sheltered, as we thought, under the rock, we looked up to find the sky above us, and the rain falling unhampered on us. Laughing like children, hand in hand, we walked back to the blanket on the sand. I strode into the water. The water shimmered as I moved, shattered into a thousand splinters of light, like broken diamonds, when I shook my hand in it.

"Oh, look, look," I cried. "How lovely. I want to swim." So I swam, way out, and back again. And when I came back I sat near him and dried myself.

We went up the steps to the car and I shook the wet sand out of my hair, unpinning it so that it fell round my shoulders, and I combed it out.

"I did not know that your hair was so long," he said. "How nice you are, full of surprises."

We looked at each other, and then away, stirred by a new awareness of ourselves, and also a new deep sadness. We had begun something of which we could not know the end. We might glean a little joy, and certainly would gather sorrow, but the rest was beyond us to fathom. But Mark did not wish to look forward to trouble, for he maintained that it helped trouble to come. We drove back without a word along the road between the crouched hills slumped like sleeping dogs around us. When we got to the Hospital, he switched on the lights of the car, so that I should not stumble on the white daisies ranged in pots round the entrance as I went in.

# CHAPTER XIV

# Macao Week End

*August 1949*

Maya Wong and Diana Kilton and I went to Macao together one Saturday afternoon. Maya was visiting a Shanghai relative now living in Macao, Diana was visiting English friends; and I was going to see Mark. Diana had taken a great fancy to Maya, because she could span her waist in her two fairly large English hands. Maya was gentle, good-natured and beautiful; so slender no one believed she had borne three children, with a skin like pink ivory, enormous dark eyes, and the most delicate nose one could imagine. "You must be a Yangchow lady," I used to tease her. Yangchow people are lovely, with small bones, fine features, large eyes fringed with long lashes, and tall noses. Marco Polo was a magistrate of Yangchow many centuries ago, and so we tease people with aquiline features as coming from Yangchow.

It was a hot late afternoon when we arrived in Macao, after a three-hour crossing from Hong Kong. Maya's relative pounced on her at the quay, and she waved us good-by. Diana Kilton and I wandered a little up and down the waterfront. Diana got prickly heat round the waist, and swore very competently.

"I'm going to get a taxi and leave you now," she said. "Will you be in your cabin on the boat tonight?"

"I don't know," I replied truthfully. "I'll see what Mark says."

"All right," said Diana. She hailed a taxi and departed. I was alone.

I ambled up the cobbled small streets in the swiftly gathering dusk, delaying the moment when I would see Mark. I was apprehensive. Here I was, going to fetch my lover at his hotel. . . . Just like Suzanne, I thought, and felt my cracking shell reforming a little round me. So I loitered, walking up one street and down another, looking at the leather goods, the plaster saints, the churches. I stopped to stare at the front-age of St. Paul's Church, divested of any inside or any walls behind it, an abandoned stage prop, high on a hill, framing the evening sky in its doors and windows.

As I turned round I nearly collided with two men. We looked at each other's faces. They were familiar to me. "Ah," they said, "you are . . ." and called me by my married name, and then I knew them. Two Kuomintang officials, known in Chungking long ago, many, many years ago, when I myself was the young bride of a promising Kuomintang officer; when we believed in what we fought for, and the world was very simple. And here we were, all three, out of the past. We laughed.

"One meets everyone either in Hong Kong or Macao," I said. "I have met so many people I knew that I am bewildered."

"So have we," they replied. "The Old Man is backing off the stage, the scenery is collapsing round us, and we are out-of-work actors look-ing for new roles."

"Are you here to buy a passport, too?" said the other.

"No," I said, "why?"

"Passports are cheaper here than in Hong Kong, Bangkok, Manila, or anywhere else," said he.

"You ought to try," said the other. "In case anything happens to Hong Kong."

"But I'm going back to China," I said. "I'm a doctor now, you see."

"Of course if you are a doctor, you must go back. The people need you and politics don't matter."

"We might be going back, too," said the other. "After all, we are Chinese, and there is no world without China. We're waiting for the dust to settle. The new rulers may use us yet."

"Yes," said the other. "And China is China. Who cares about politics, so long as the people have a government who cares for them?"

"But just in case, in case things don't turn out well," said the first one, "we're buying passports. I advise you to do so too."

"I'll think about it," I replied courteously. And then we talked of friends we had known; some were in the new government in Peking, and others were in Formosa, and others in America . . . each one fulfilling his destiny.

It was evening, and Mark would be waiting. I walked towards the Havana Hotel, a tall imposing building on the largest thoroughfare. There were two receptionists behind the desk where I asked for his room number. One was a Portuguese with a magnificent bosom in a lace blouse, the other a Chinese girl with a skin like smooth honey. They laughed gently, and I heard one say to the other in Cantonese, "The beautiful Englishman," and felt as if I had been stripped of all my clothes right there in the lobby. But they were not condemning me as they handed me his room key, for Macao is a very human place.

Mark lay on the settee beside the wide open windows. Out of the window, Macao glittered as Hong Kong did, and the lights of a fishing fleet were in the harbor. Mark was fanning himself with his black fan, eating watermelon and spitting the seeds into the brass spittoon with which each room was provided. He rose immediately as I came in and smiled his enchanting smile. "Come and have some melon," he said. "I've just bought it, it's very good."

I looked at him, the thick auburn hair, the deep blue eyes, my beautiful Englishman, and I had that funny sick feeling again. And Mark knew what I felt, for I must have been staring at him. He took my hand and led me out saying: "Let's go and play fan-tan, and win large sums," and so he freed me from myself, and we went to the fan-tan rooms on the top floor of the hotel.

Such an extraordinary collection of people gather round the fan-tan tables of Macao. Peasant girls, amahs in white tops and neat black trousers, their long pigtails dangling on their backs like limp snakes. Coolies with odd soft hats on their heads and slippers on their bare feet. Rich young men with flashy ties and glistening spectacles, gleaming hair and teeth. Clerks and thieves, bankers and pimps, concubines and servants, officials and stool pigeons, pirates from off the junks and policemen on leave. We were hilarious, seized with the irrepressible gaiety which was ours when together. We put small sums on one or other side of the squares drawn on the tables. The man in charge of the table had a pile of white plastic buttons in front of him, and removed a few at a time with a white stick until only a few were left, and that number was the winning one.

The manager of the hotel came up to Mark as we stood there, and beamed, and shook hands. He was half Portuguese, and was smoking a big cigar. He had a large gold pin stuck in a tie which sported a design of wide-eyed marigolds two inches across. When he heard I was a doctor he shook hands with me again.

"Business good?" he asked me.

"Oh, I'm not in private practice."

"Bad, bad. Ought to make money now. Woman doctor, make your fortune in no time. Men don't like their wives to be seen by men doctors. Come to Macao. I'll lend you some money. How many thousand you want, forty, fifty?"

I started to say something, but he drove on.

"Macao full of rich people, all people with money here, safe, peaceful. And all rich people have lots of babies. Even poor people like me have them. Look at my wife."

The manager was shaken with spurts of laughter which made his tie jump away from his shirt.

We then noticed the manager's wife, a small, enormously pregnant woman, who kept hitching her protuberance on the edge of the fan-tan table to rest herself. She smiled at me. "It kicks so nowadays I have to slap it to keep it quiet," she confided in her rich Portuguese voice to all of us.

The manager had taken a great fancy to Mark, for there was always such gentleness about him that people loved him at sight. We escaped him with difficulty, and had supper in the Chinese restaurant of the Hotel, which was on the ground floor. I saw my two Kuomintang officials at a table but this time they did not recognize me, for that would have been rude. Mark perceived some people he knew, foreigners, having "Chinese chow" as part of their tourist education, and nearly hailed them. "I do so want to be seen with you," he said, "I want all my friends to go round saying: 'But who is this beautiful Chinese girl that Mark Elliott is taking out?'"

"Eurasian," I corrected.

"You look all Chinese to me, and I've been fifteen years out here. I didn't think you were Eurasian until you told me."

"Even you," I said bitterly, "have a prejudice against the mixed bloods."

"Dear one, it is not so," he replied with some warmth. "You must not carry a chip on your shoulder as so many Eurasians do. You want to be Chinese, and you have trained yourself to have both East and West. You have a dual mind, and I envy you the way in which you become different worlds, different beings. There is more richness to your life than we poor one-world people possess."

"But it is awful to be two or more people all the time. It's schizophrenia," I replied.

"How I wish I were you," he said. "And how I pity all the men who do not have the pleasure to know and to love you."

I could not understand either his wish to be me, or the eagerness with which he said that he wanted to be seen with me. But I asked no more, for this had its roots in that part of him which I must never question and must pretend not to know.

After supper we went for a walk out of the hotel, pacing the bustling streets full of gay people. We sat by the fountain on the Praya Grande, and Mark was very gay and loquacious. He talked charming comical nonsense holding my hand and fanning us both with his black Chinese fan.

Suddenly he rose and said: "Come, my darling, let us go, *car tu me fais drôle*."

"*Tu me fais drôle aussi,*" I replied.

Hand in hand we walked, reading the shop signs painted in large black letters and in Chinese characters across the front and the pillars of the entrances. "Quinquilharia," said Mark, "how wonderful to be the owner of a quinquilharia, so much more interesting than a mere grocer." We bought some cigarettes from an edentulous old Cantonese woman; her face was creased and tucked and puckered with the years, her eyes held the bright sparrow look of old people who sleep badly.

It was slightly cooler, and the stars had disintegrated into fine dust powdering the sky. The cocks were crowing drowsily, waking each other up, then going to sleep again. We went up to Mark's room in the lift. "Have your bath first," said I. "I'll have one after you."

He was in the bathroom for a little while, with the door open and no water running. "What are you doing," I called. "Come and see," he said, and his voice sounded far away. There he was, loofah in hand, watching the bathtub. "There are ants in the tub," said Mark, "and I cannot bring myself to drown them, so I'm trapping them in my loofah and putting them on the floor. It's very difficult to pick up an ant with one's fingers without damaging it."

We both crouched over the tub and trapped ants, and saved the lives of as many as we could.

Wrapped in the sarongs he had brought, we lay on the bed. My sarong had a butterfly design and I looked at myself in the mirror and said to him: "I look quite pretty in a sarong." He let down my straight long hair, weighing it with his hand, running his fingers through it. "I've always dreamt of a woman with long black hair," he said. I tried putting my arms round his neck, but I was again gripped by fear, by that terror which had kept me untouchable for so long, through no conscious restraint of mine. And of course he knew, though I pretended to be gay. For Mark always knew me much better than I did myself, and there never was any misunderstanding between us. And so he held me gently in his arms and quoted passages from Boswell's *John-son,* and got up to fetch his Housman and read out his favorites, and told me funny journalistic anecdotes, and made me laugh till I nearly choked and buried my face on his shoulder and went off to sleep suddenly, as a child does.

I woke to see the delicate morning, fresh and clear and pink, soaring from the harbor, crossing the sky towards us. Mark opened his eyes a moment after, and we looked at each other. "Oh, dear one, I've dreamed, so often I have dreamed of your head next to mine, sharing the same pillow," said he. "You've cribbed that from a Chinese poem, and I don't use a pillow," I replied. And now my fear was gone, having lain in his arms to sleep, and I wanted him very much, so I said: "Please will you take me now if you so wish, for I want you." "Are you quite sure?" he asked me. "You must never do anything only to please me. "Oh, I am quite sure," I said. "I do want you so much." And so his hands flattered me, and his mouth was on mine, gentle and then deliberate and relentless, until I moaned with want of him, and he undid my sarong and we were together, and this time it was the greatest pleasure in the world, and something I had never known before, never before, never like this.

All the way to the firecracker factory with Diana Kilton and Maya, and to the Grotto of Camoens, and round the harbor, and down the main street to buy Aqua Vita and Bols, and onto the boat which was taking us back to Hong Kong, I was in the arms of Mark, entranced and dreaming, every cell of my body quivering with remembered delight.

From that day I must have begun to wear that abstracted, unearthly look, my lips half parted, my eyes unable to focus, which may be described as stupid, or beatific, or both together. As the water churned behind our boat, and Macao receded in the distance, I saw myself again, stretched near Mark, limp with the happy spending of passion. Opening my eyes I had found him watching my face in the morning light, learning from my unguarded face, all given to him, what he could do to me. His eyes watchful and his hands capable and tender. "Oh," I had said. "What a wonderful lover you are. I am such a lucky woman."

He had laughed a little, and the pleased note in his voice was good to hear as he said: "Darling, I don't think you can really judge."

I replied with dignity, for I was ashamed of appearing ignorant, and afraid he might dislike it. "A person with awareness can know many things without having to incur them. Not to go out of the house is to know the world of men. . . . I know you're wonderful."

"Taoist," said Mark, rubbing his finger along my nose. "What a sententious person you are. So many things I want to say to you," he added, "so many thoughts, plans. . . . They go round and round in my head. . . ."

"I don't want to hear them," abruptly I turned my head away, suddenly remote from him. For I knew what he wanted to say, but it was too early for me to hear it.

On the boat Maya looked at me and put her arms round my shoulders as we watched Macao dwindle in the distance. "You are in love," she said definitely. And went away.

I sought Diana, who was reading *The Home Companion*. She was English and she would know about an Englishman's way of thinking, and tell me whether I had guessed right or wrong.

"Diana," I said. "I think Mark wants to ask me to marry him."

"I doubt it," she said. "Has he told you so?"

"No, but I have a kind of feeling."

"Feelings are misleading," she replied, still reading her magazine.

"He's got a funny mysterious look about him, like a little boy with a big secret. Didn't you notice this morning, when he came to see us just before our boat left?"

"Only that you couldn't take your eyes off each other. You went into a kind of trance. I don't believe you were in your cabin last night, however early you woke me up this morning to go and visit the firecracker factory. But Mark can't marry you just like that. He's married already. . . ."

"I know, but you see, neither of us want a love affair — it's not what we want. And now, what are we going to do? What is going to happen to us next?"

# CHAPTER XV

# The Proposal

*September 1949*

"How would it be," mark said, sitting on the camp bed in my Hospital room and crossing his knees, "if I went away, and got my affairs arranged, and came back and married you?"

That was three days after Macao.

"How can I marry you and go to China?" I replied.

"But I want to go to China, too. In fact, as soon as the Nationalist government has finished crumbling. Other correspondents seem to think that the Nationalists will be able to hold the South. It is my guess that they will not hold anything Then we shall establish relations with the new government. Trade can't be at a standstill forever, and everyone in the business world here is in favor of trade relations. Then I shall go to Peking for my newspaper. I don't really want to go anywhere else."

I was shaken. It sounded so easy.

"There may be a little difficulty at first, there always is when one has to make other people accept a situation. But I haven't been a satisfactory husband, and I don't think it will be too difficult."

I said: "I hate to think that through knowing me you've taken new decisions."

"I don't think so. You've acted as a catalyst, perhaps, fused the amorphous unrest in me into a definite want. But that is all. I have been empty for a long time, and now you are the person inside me."

I stared at him for a while. "I'll have to think about it. It may not work. It sounds too easy. I don't think somehow I can be married to you and work in China. And then, you must realize that I am not English. I shall never be a European in my feelings. So I may not be satisfactory to you. It might hurt your career, marrying me."

"I don't think it will. I'll be so proud to have all my friends know you. I always want to show you off. And I never want you to be anything but yourself."

I was cross. "You think you can show me off to your friends as your Chinese scoop, yes?"

Mark grinned: "I know that in your eyes, my dear, I am only a foreigner and a reporter. What a superiority complex you Chinese have! Worse than we have. Yes, I would like to show you off."

So what could I say but: "Well, I can't promise anything. But if you think we can be together in China, and work, then I will marry you."

"I'll just go ahead then," he said. "You need not promise anything."

"And you must not either. No promises between us. Because you might change your mind, and think better of it, and I'd hate it if you felt you had to stick by a promise."

"Yes, it is possible," said Mark, meaning that it was impossible for him to change his mind now.

"You must never do something in order to spare me. I hate kindness. Kindness is a horrible vice. It creates so many obligations. Don't be kind to me."

"I won't ever be kind. Tell me," he said with the hint of a swagger in his voice, "did you know before I spoke that I meant to ask you? I've been thinking about it a little while now. Ever since that day the puppy crossed in front of our car on the Praya, and you were so calm."

I said as crossly as I could, to hide the tenderness choking me: "Of course I knew. Englishmen are predictable."

"Actually I'm part Scots," he replied, and rubbed his finger on my nose, and was gone.

# CHAPTER XVI

# The House of Wisdom

*September 1949*

"WHAT IS HAPPENING TO ME?" ASKED MARK. "I QUIVER so easily. I oscillate within as if I were on board a moving ship. Everything has become so vivid. A bar of music, a line of poetry, voices, the color of flowers, the infinite variety of the sea. I weep and laugh all at once. I was reading the sonnet 'They that have power to hurt and will do none' in the bus coming to see you, and the tears went coursing down my cheeks. A Chinese lady sitting opposite kindly patted my hand. When I have been with you I am satiated with contentment, surfeited with happiness. Everything is simpler, yet I have so much more to say. I remember coming back from the events in Indo-China (and they were pretty terrible), and from the communal troubles in India (also rather horrifying), and being asked what had happened. 'Oh, nothing much,' I replied. People got very irritated with me but I really had nothing much to say. Now I spend a few hours away from you, and I have so much to relate that I write a letter to you an hour before I come to see you, and bring it with me. I did not know one could be like this, so alive."

"What is happening to me?" I asked. "I am like a seed split wide open with roots pushing out, stalk sprouting up, clutching at life, every moment of it so good that I hurt all the time. I see a wagtail jerk across the road and the way it beats the earth with its tail gives me a pain in the chest. I hear and smell the sun, and as for the moon to whose presence I ever was sensitive, the joy of her is unbearable. I did not know one could thus ache with life."

We were sitting on a large flat stone in the lane above the mortuary. It was the only place in Hong Kong where we could meet to learn each other's minds in peace, to learn what love is, to learn to love. For love is not accomplished the day it is. Love is a slow growing tree, a live thing, and there is no immobility in life. And so we let love grow quietly, a strong-rooted tree, as every day we learned to love a little better.

And the white stone set in the middle of the lane above the mortuary was to be the only home that we ever had.

In those early days, still ignorant of ourselves, beginners in love, amateurs of suffering, believers in happiness, and foolish enough to talk of the future, we were occasionally worried and gloomy. I could never forgo altogether that foreboding of destined failure, the conviction of our inevitable doom, though ignorant of the form it would take, and unlucid enough with passion to doubt my own distrust. Mark was discouraged for less nebulous reasons.

"There are so many difficulties of the practical, tangible kind in the way of our love, let alone the many obstacles to any plans I may have for spending our lives together, that above all our relationship is supremely comical. We are denied even a few minutes' meeting every day. I dislike coming to your room, for it makes you conspicuous. You cannot leave the jail-like structure in which you live and work. On your fortnightly Sundays and your Wednesdays I see you among one or another of your various circles of friends, often with your daughter. And though I am content only to see you, yet I want to hold your little finger, and talk to you all the time. How right you were when you said that there was no place for us in Hong Kong."

We had been standing in front of the Hospital while he spoke, after one of his frustrating visits to me. He had sat for an hour in the Residents' Quarters common room, waiting for me among the other residents. Some sprawled in their striped pajamas on the chairs, reading the comics. Some rushed by with tubes in their hands. Others shouted amicably, for the Malayan Chinese always talk, as do most Southern Chinese, as if they were quarreling with each other. Mark knew that on the whole the Chinese are even more exclusive and snobbish than the English are, and that his presence there, although not resented, aroused some comment.

"I know," he said, "that when I, a foreigner, take you out, a Chinese girl, and we are nearly always the only mixed couple, and everyone looks at you because you are beautiful, it is not good for your career."

"But it's you everyone looks at, and I'm not worried about my career. I am so proud of you that I want to stand on the roof of the Hong Kong and Shanghai Bank and shout: 'Look at me. I am the woman that Mark Elliott professes to love.'"

We laughed with that easy exuberance which came from the joy of being together.

A car, an enormous, gleaming, latest-model monster of a car, swept past us, and in it I recognized the aquiline features of Mrs. Palmer-Jones, who threw us a keen, unsmiling glance. On the tiered verandas of the Hospital, leaning their elbows on the railings, the patients sunned and spat, like swallows perched on telephone wires. A few nurses strolled by inquisitively. Everything looked at us, even the islands of the sea. We were unable to tear away from each other. I had an inspiration. "We can meet at the mortuary. It's the only place where we can meet."

The mortuary, a small concrete structure shaded by bamboo and sheltered from Pokfulum Road below it by a hibiscus hedge, lay two hundred yards away from the Hospital, along a cement path. It was on a lower level of the slope, and fifteen steps went from the path to its door; another twenty descended from it to the road. Along these latter steps the relatives of the dead sat in the sunlight to wait for the body, after my friend John Tam, who was now back in pathology, had dealt with it behind the closed door. The relatives would burn incense sticks and paper, and wail appropriately, while a bronze-clad monk clashed cymbals or blew a flute. At last the doors would open and the corpse, decently clothed again, be delivered to them in its open coffin.

From the mortuary the path continued above it into a lane paved with wide stones. It was called Lovers' Lane, and I wonder why, for apart from birds and butterflies who frequented it in assiduous couples, we seemed the only human lovers to use it. Lovers' Lane continues, pitched midway up the hill slopes, for about two miles until it reaches the water reservoirs at the end of Conduit Road and just above the University. It was at the beginning of this lane above the mortuary that we found our stone. Mark felt it with his hand and sat on it. And thus it was ours.

And now at night Mark walked up the steps from Pokfulum Road, I ran down the steps from the Hospital. We would go to Lovers' Lane and sit on our stone.

The weather was fine, and we could meet, in brief minutes snatched from the night and from sleep, somnambulist moments between midnight and three in the morning. We could talk, hold hands, look at the galaxies of the fishing fleets toiling the sea, and the River of Heaven rolling its innumerable sails above our heads. The moon was often with us, an affable companion, casting her pale blue glow on our faces and on the stones of the Chinese cemetery opposite the Hospital. At least for a few minutes, nearly every night, we could see each other, Mark could hold the little finger of my right hand. The mortuary was a good place to meet.

The House of Wisdom, we called it, after our extrovert friend John Tam. Mark and John Tam had now met over the goldfish. Mark had duly peered at them through the glass sides of their tank, and smiled his lovely smile, as he watched them, suspended in the water among the weeds, fragile and sumptuous, elaborate and living flowers. In a moment between Mark and John Tam had sprung that delicate and sure feeling which I, a mere woman, feel and delight to find in men. John Tam, though young, knew people by instinct, and did not give his friendship to everyone. He came to see me several times in the days that followed, catapulting through the ever-open French windows which made all our rooms communicate along a common veranda, so that we had no privacy at all.

"Nice fella, Elliott," he said. "That guy's a real man, you know. He's no stuffed shirt, although he does live in Singapore." (For Tam, from Malaya, disliked the white men he met there on unequal footing, and thought the English in the colonies generally unpleasant.) "This guy's different, he's civilized. Of course he has to live in Singapore because of his work, poor fella, rushing round all the time. They do say that in England the folks are better educated than the types they send to their colonies. Elliott feels okay to me. I can respect a man like that. Do you think he'd like to see my color photographs of cirrhotic livers, and my specimens? I've got some pickled Siamese twins, man, real beauties, I tell you."

"John calls it the House of Wisdom," I said to Mark, "because death really does not lie. In the insignificant structure below us the obscure is brought to light, truth made plain, and our most arrogant diagnosticians strike their breasts and bite the cement floor."

"How perfectly horrible it all sounds," replied Mark.

No one disturbed us. The Chinese whose staff quarters were near the mortuary kept away from it; their servants were afraid of ghosts; the European quarters were far from it. From our stone at night, we would occasionally watch the advent of another corpse borne away from the Hospital to freeze in peace until the next morning and John Tam's knife. Carried by three coolies on a stretcher covered over with thick white canvas, a little nurse coifed in white, like a dove with outspread wings, hurrying behind, the dead proceeded briskly towards us, for the bearers always ran at night. Perhaps they were really afraid, perhaps they only told themselves they were. We could hear the panting down the steps, the click of keys turning in the locks, the clang of the freezing-room doors as they rolled back on their grooves, the dull thud of the body joining its ice-cold companions on the shelves, the loud expostulations of relief, the padding back. Then all noise ceased save for the soft churn of the freezing plant, and the burbling toads, and the night crickets. No one disturbed us.

Thus it was near the peaceable dead of the House of Wisdom, the dead no longer worried by the business of living, that Mark and I came to life. It was on that stone that the shadows which frightened me left me forever. Sitting near him, filled with tenderness, melted from within, I felt my fear slip away, dissolve in the moonlight, evanesce in the night. My shriveled spirit, like those little paper pills that children throw in a basin of water and which open and unfold into multicolored blossoms, my shriveled spirit breathed and blossomed and rejoiced. Mark made me alive.

And Mark said: "Who, having once known what it is to be alive, will go back to the dead?" And I kissed his hand, humble, gentle because I was no longer terrified, peaceful because I had accepted myself. And there was no more time, no more space. Only the sky above us, the slight movement of the breeze, the moonlight, and our stone upon the earth. We needed no more. We were full to the brim. We neither slept nor kept watch. We were alive.

PART TWO

# Progress

# CHAPTER I

# Return to Chungking

*September 1949*

Our feelings are very much governed by commonplace associations, and often influenced by that sort of short term logic which renders steady thinking superfluous.

For many months now, practically ever since my arrival in Hong Kong, my sister Suchen had been writing to me—distraught, disconnected notes, about her child's illness, and the communist advance, and her terror. Then she wrote about our Chinese family's many unkindnesses to her. I received a note saying that she was coming to Hong Kong, and that I must put her up and find her a job; she added accusations against Our Family which irritated me a good deal. I could not understand that people whom I loved and who had been kind and generous to me should have been unkind to her. I put it down to the exaggerations of a highly strung temperament; she misinterpreted their motives. And so I wrote back a short letter to tell her to stay where she was. "You are safer in Chungking, surely, with Third Uncle and The Family, than you would be here in Hong Kong, without a job. I cannot support you, nor your child. Hong Kong is overcrowded. Third Uncle and Third Aunt are kind and good. Third Uncle is our father's brother. I do not believe he can have done the things of which you accuse him."

Scarcely had the letter been posted than I knew something was wrong. I became uneasy. Something was very wrong. It was not what my sister had said in her notes which caused this uneasiness. I remembered that my uncle, in his long, beautiful literary letters to me, had never once mentioned her, or her child. Knowing my Chinese family as I did, with that wordless instinctive knowledge more reliable than any reasoning, I should have used less haste in getting rid of my irritation.

The more I thought of it, the more I realized that something had to be done about it. And there was also another question which I might attempt to answer at the same time: the question of my relationship with Mark.

And so I decided to go back to China to see what I could see, for at a distance, in Hong Kong, I could not judge and act in a fitting manner. I went to the Head of the Department and obtained leave. I borrowed money from Nora and Robert Hung to pay for my plane passage to Chungking and back. I sent two telegrams, one to Suchen, one to Third Uncle, announcing my arrival by plane the following week.

It was still dark when I reached Kaitak Airport to emplane for Chungking. The sea and the hills were smothered in the ubiquitous soot of night. My omniscient taxi driver went by smell, for his lights did not work. The back of his neck was the only thing that I felt I could trust in the blackness spread around us. Suddenly there was a glare of neon light, raucous, solid in its intensity; smells of gasoline and steel told of prostrate engines in their hangars. The passage from tactile apprehension to visual information as I entered the airport waiting room gave me a sensation of astonishment. Not because the light revealed so much more, but because it instantly limited one's mind to so much less. In the darkness I could feel myself a phantom wrapped in eerie cloud, dissolving and reforming; I heard an ebony sea scudding all around me, pleasantly terrifying; I butted the nose of my imagination against sharp-crested hills suddenly erect in front of me; and now, in the light, I saw a counter with rows of Coca Cola and orange squash bottles safe behind shining glass, table tops with wet rings on their smooth surface, groups of airmen in blue-gray, their legs strangely entangled with table legs, and the whole hemmed in by papery white walls, pressed down upon by a dead white ceiling. And Mark alone, at a side table, his head bent over a book, for he had come to see me off.

"I am so frightened of planes," he said, "that I want to have a look at the machine which is taking you away."

"Up to the last moment, not relinquishing your hold on your victim," I replied.

"In your province of Szechuan," said Mark, "the Chinese you will dominate, to the exclusion of all the other yous I know. You will look at me from over there with purely Chinese eyes, and wonder whether to keep me or not."

"That I shall do. I want to see you from there; see what you are like. For we must live together, the Chinese me and the English you as well as all the other us."

Airplane travel more than any other means of transport employed by man alters the relationship of space with time, and incites a fission of personality. One is always different in a different place, and transformation occurs quickest by plane.

I left Hong Kong and my English lover at eight on that late September morning. Autumn's subtleties were about us already: the first hint of coolness, a pensive calm informing the air, a slight withering of the early heat. The airplane engines coughed, roared, sputtered and stopped, like old men clearing their throats in the morning. Mark and I ate a large breakfast, three eggs each, with toast and cups of coffee. "For we forgot all about dinner last night," he said, a little surprised at his own hunger. We watched the day move in and the planes wheel out on the spick-and-span airfield, one by one, smoothly, effortlessly, winging up into the blue sky; until my turn came and I left Mark standing in the sun which streaked his hair with gold.

I left Hong Kong and my English lover at eight on that beautiful September morning to arrive at Pei Shih Yi, the airfield of Chungking, in the heart of the Szechuan plain, three hours later. The same plane stumbled drunkenly across the plowed airfield, reeling from stone to stone and mud heap across that furrowed, wrinkled, sun-caked and mud-churned patch of ground, leaving a comet trail of yellow dust behind it; I came out from the machine under a bleached sky, and felt the immediate parching of my nose and throat in the dryness of the Chungking climate; I trailed wearily in the heat; saw, with dumb surprise, the dirty rags instead of the clean black silk of the airfield coolies; watched the faces creased with poverty, like beds that had been slept in; heard the brutal voices of officialdom, instead of the affable tones of the well-fed Hong Kong government servants; watched the open smuggling, under the coarse mat shed where a bogus Customs inspection was held; and remembered Hong Kong, so clean in comparison, the Hong Kong of the rich who can afford to travel by plane. My heart tightened, for here all was decrepitude and inefficiency. "How can they carry on like that?" I thought. "No wonder the communists win without spilling a drop of blood."

I heard the Szechuan voices and the Szechuan accent. The tea we drank, sitting at rough tables of unpolished wood under the mat shed, was lemon-yellow Chinese tea, not Indian brown; at the bottom of each cup there was a little heap of dust, as there always was in Chungking. The water tasted different.

And then the transformation occurred, and the Hong Kong me was gone, it had vanished, dissolved like a cloud in one's hand, and I had never left this place at all. I knew this airfield better than my room at the Hospital; my tongue started rolling the syllables, my voice altered as I asked for my bill; I had already forgotten my acquired Cantonese. These hills were the only hills I ever knew — fuzzy, the trees like gracious small herbs growing along their crests, not bare like the Kowloon hills I had left this morning. And that deep mud rut which called itself a road, ploughing between the slopes up and down to the city seventeen miles away — that was the only way I could think of a road now.

At Kaitak Airport it took twenty minutes to clear the Customs, check the papers, get into a bus and drive to the air terminus at the

Peninsular Hotel. It took us seven hours to get from the airfield to the air terminus in Chungking. Enough time to go to Hong Kong and back and with an hour to spare for lunch. The thought amused me very much. Yet we had no breakdowns or spills on the road, although the structure which conveyed us over the seventeen miles of road to the city was so appalling that even the hardened Szechuanese traveling with me said: "It is not possible that this vehicle can still walk."

The bus had not been painted since the end of the war. Not only had the paint peeled off, but the wooden body was shredding away as well. It had parted with window panes, doors and seats and half the driving wheel, as also with the hood, the headlights, and the fenders. We all looked round for something else, for none of us believed that this derelict was to be our transport. But it was the only conveyance of its kind standing there, and we were shouted into it by a fat official, a little like reluctant prisoners hustled into an execution van. We heaved and pushed each other up into it (for there were no steps). We sat on our luggage, stacked on the rotting floor, inadequately blocking the holes in its planks. Once we were inside, welded into a conglomerate mass, some wooden bars were thrust across the wide aperture through which we had clambered, and tied with ropes by two gray-clad soldiers with the puffy faces of hookworm victims. There for another hour we sat, stifling, with the soldiers on guard, trailing the butts of their long melodramatic rifles behind them. And such is the suggestibility of the human mind, so malleable the human conscience, that there was unease among us, a furtive sense of guilt, hushing into subdued chatter the recriminations of my fellow travelers at the heat, the flies, and the delay. We were all slightly frightened, for we were now behind bars, and felt that we had done wrong, though we could not remember how we had offended.

We finally arrived at the air terminus, a cement structure by the side of the wide sweep of road which scales the hills that are Chungking. Below the road, six hundred feet down, is the river. Half of us were sick with the jolting, and all of us had sore bottoms. And as we

crunched to a stop the well-remembered face of Fifth Brother, unchanged save for a more strongly modeled nose, now appeared at the
absent window of our vehicle. "Third Sister," he called. "Oh, Fifth
Brother," I said, delighted, "but you have not changed, and it is eight
years."

"Yes, one cannot realize it is already eight years. You have been to
England, and are now a doctor, and I have wandered in Burma (for
so he described his four years with the armies fighting in Burma), and
here we are meeting in our old home."

I replied with a quotation from a Chinese poem: "How often have
I raised my head and gazed on the moon, lowered my gaze and thought
of my home."

Fifth Brother smiled, showing the perfect family teeth of which we
are all inordinately proud. "You have not changed either," he said.

"No," I said, very pleased, "I have not changed. England has not
changed me." England, and medicine, and a career and the many decisions which had seemed to drive me away, none of these things had
changed me. Everything that was the immediate present — only this
morning acknowledged as the moment now — appeared of a past more
remote than the past of eight years ago in Chungking. I gazed at the
river, the impassive tranquil greatness dividing China into North and
South. Had I ever left it? It wound and turned and twisted like the life
of man, and I quoted these lines from Li Ho Chu:

Ask my lord how much sorrow can one hold?
Just as much as the great river in full spring flood, flowing eastwards.

"For," I told Fifth Brother, "in Europe each river flows to the sea, but
in China rivers flow eastwards. And perhaps there is meaning in that,
and perhaps there is not. But anyhow, I am back."

Fifth Brother and I went to a shop which belonged to our family.
The shopkeeper brought out black lacquered stools, and cups of smoky
Tsing Cheng tea, so fragrant that it quenches one's thirst before it is
sipped. I was back. I had not thought that I could be back so completely. Things have changed, yet I am back, rooted as firm, planted

deep as ever, my life moving here in harmony, geared to the same endless patience as the slow flow of the river. I am back.

In front of the shop ran the main road, and across the road there
were stone steps going down to another street, on a lower level. Up
these steps came the people I had always known. Not small Cantonese
with light bones and clean faces, but squat, ugly people with flattened
faces and heavy peasant legs, the varicose veins standing out in twisted
knots like a brood of snakes. Men and women, dirty and poor. Nearly
every one had a physical defect of some kind or other: harelip, a
finger missing, deformed chests; and on all those naked coolie shoulders one could see the large round lumps raised by the pressure of the
bamboo pole. A few of these lumps carried ulcers on them. I saw what
I had seen before, years ago: the straw sandals on their bare feet, the
abdominal muscles jutting out with effort, the heaving chests, the
loads. A load of firewood, a load of charcoal, then a man with two
pails of excrement, then a man with two baskets of fly-mottled pears,
then a man with a load of salt, then a man with red watermelons cut in
neat red and green pyramids dripping with juice. Then another load
of excrement. Then a man with two pails of water slopping down on
the steps . . . up and up they came, one after the other, a relentless
procession that would only end with the darkness.

Fifth Brother and I sat, and fanned ourselves, and talked of the
weather in Hong Kong and the hotter weather in Chungking; and the
improvements to Chungking since I had left it eight years ago; and
of the great fire which had destroyed the business section of the city
and had burnt for many days, and was still smoldering. It made Fifth
Brother laugh to talk of it, in the way we have of laughing at disaster.
That disparaging ironic self-laughter, which comes after we have shed
all the tears that we can shed. The laughter that seizes all the Chinese
when tragedy has become comical and ridiculous, as it often does.
Fires and floods, accidents, deaths and revolutions. It is quite true that
the direct impact of a personal catastrophe afflicts us with sorrow, and
that for a time we too wear the trappings of grief, and weep as genu-
inely as anyone ought to, and mourn as fervently. But it is also true

that we can laugh at the same things a little later, and at ourselves for grieving; for we have not the convention of privacy and the hidebound silence that Europeans have. We do not mope in seclusion and our friends do not spare us; for we must fit what we can into the pattern of living, and everything must be fitted with laughter, for laughter alone will show us the enormity of our grief. We treat sorrow-bringing and joy-capturing experiences on the same footing, for one day we shall laugh over both, counting them well worth while, and equal under Heaven, which equalizes all things; remembering them as part of our treasure of life, and the portion allotted to us by Fate. All men learn to do this, but we do it, on the whole, slightly more than many another people.

I too laugh at things which ought to shock me, even at accidents, when the smiling ambulance drivers bring in yet one more run-over after a hectic day; a nervous giggle, which may be accounted callousness, or cruelty, but it is not; it is a happy protection which keeps me balanced. And later I taught Mark to laugh at many things which ought to have hurt us, so that we were not hurt, and never shocked or bitter for very long.

And so it was with twitching mouths and convulsive amusement, although we had lost so much in the fire, and so many had died, that I listened and Fifth Brother told how six hundred measures of cotton bale, our family property, had gone in about ten minutes, and how many thousands were homeless. "The blaze was so bright," he related, "that I took a ferryboat over the river and climbed the First Range to watch it. There was no water and nothing we could do to help. It was a fascinating sight. The fire spread down the slopes to the river. The people at the tip of the peninsula were trapped, there was fire advancing behind them, and the river in front. Many were burnt; many drowned; many jumped onto the boats moored alongside the crumbling mud bank, and then sparks fell on the boats, and they too were burnt. The blaze stopped just two houses away from our Bank. Heaven has been kind to us."

"It is due to the accumulated virtue of your illustrious family," said the shopkeeper, who sat with us. In China we profit from our ancestors' good deeds.

We now turned solemnly to the topic of The Family, an inexhaustible one, for our clan numbered three hundred mouths.

Great-Uncle had died the year previously, and owing to this calamity, the offspring among his twenty-odd direct descendants had been considerably reduced. They were the most old-fashioned branch of our family, and it was not considered good taste for them to procreate during the period of mourning. But other branches flourished and numerous new babies had appeared. Fourth Sister expected her second, Fifth Brother himself was married but his wife had had a miscarriage, and was not allowed to step out of the house for a month. The old maidservant, Liu Sao, who had come as a child to The Family and was now sixty-two, would not enter the room for thirty days, for fear of becoming unclean, so Fifth Brother himself cleaned it. He loved his wife, and would not let her exert herself. As he spoke the world fell more and more accurately into place. I knew all this. I too had lived like this. Somehow, in my mind the oldest superstition stood equal with the latest medical discovery. And they were truly equal under Heaven, in whose eyes all things are of the same height and value. For Heaven equalizes all things.

And a strange word came into my mouth. "Mark." I said it again to myself. "Mark Elliott." The word like a pebble on my tongue, a loose fragment, out of pattern. Would it ever fit into the pattern? It was so funny, he was so far away. Did he really exist? I was not sure, now, that he was not a dream. What was reality, and what was dream? I would have to find out.

# CHAPTER 11

# My Sister Suchen

*September 1949*

AFTER ABOUT TWO HOURS OF WAITING, WHEN IT WAS GET-ting deeply dark, the car arrived. The driver explained that he had had another puncture and had stopped to change the tire. It was a very battered Ford, but for Chungking at that moment, waiting for the communists to take over, it was the height of capitalism; except for diplomats and important government officials, very few owned a car. The car was old, the driver new, a man from Tientsin in the North, arrogantly drawling his northern dialect, determined to condescend to less civilized provincials.

The river rolled dull lead to our right as we drove through the dust, making full use of the horn. Nothing had changed, in spite of the communists being so near. Here and there along the road were those agglomerations of wooden shacks with sagging uneven walls which I had seen eight years ago. In the red glow of their oil lamps, faces conjured out of darkness ate, talked, and stared at us, flat, two-dimensional faces passive as portraits.

Up the old winding road, up to the cobbled lane where our house stood. The car heaved and tossed like a boat riding a stormy sea over the oblong stones of the lane, tilting from side to side and up and down like swollen waves. Some mysterious underground honeycombing, referred to by the driver as "the sewer works," had produced this agitated appearance of the roadway. We drove on at full tilt until with a final hurl and screech of brakes we were flung to a standstill, and there we were, home.

The nail-studded door with its old-fashioned inside wooden latch and bars had not been painted for years. Like everything else in Chungking, it was dusty, decrepit, and peeling. It opened with the long melodious roar and squeak that Chinese hinges have, and inside was the courtyard, fenced on three sides by the veranda of the house. A few scattered lamps like glowworms interrupted without lightening the darkness around us, and in it I heard the well-remembered voice of my Third Uncle:

"You are there," he said.

"Third Uncle, Third Aunt."

Two dim shapes in the night, to whom I bowed. We were upset with simple emotion. We stood quite still, silent, our faces white blurs suspended in mid-air, our clothes merging with the opaque darkness.

"Come in, then," said Uncle. "Open the lights," he shouted, and the servant's obedient voice repeated the words, and all the lights were turned on. We went inside the house.

Tea was brought. We sat in chairs covered with fine bamboo mats because of the heat, and sipped it. Uncle and Aunt looked exactly the same. I said:

"The years have rolled away smoothly. You have not changed."

Uncle replied: "Your face is fuller and calmer. Some of the Family thought you would be extremely foreign after so many years in England. But I said you would not. You have not changed."

Third Aunt sat up very straight in her chair, as she had always done. Her legs were so short that her feet, tiny bound feet, did not touch the ground. I knew from the slight contraction of her forehead that she had one of her headaches, so I sat next to her, and fanned her. This I used to do in the hot sultry afternoons when we both went to our ancestral village to tend the graves of the ancestors and to collect the rents from the farmers. Ten years ago. For hours I used to fan her with a gentle relaxed motion, an effortless turn of the wrist. And to-night in Chungking I could still hear, outside the door, the silence of ten years before, shrill with the cicadas' soaring cry, and near us the light brief singsong of a mosquito circling to avoid the incense sticks we burnt to ward them off. But that was a lifetime ago, when I was young, unwise, easily hurt, and believed in such abstract notions as happiness and unhappiness.

Third Aunt remembered too, for she put out her soft white hand, and patted my arm. And we could not speak for the love that was in us.

Uncle and I did not ask each other questions. Questions would only elicit description of happenings, and happenings would not give us a clue to each other's meaning. So we apprehended each other with our instinct, smelt each other out with tentative trivialities. We did not talk about the communists who might be here any day now, next week, surely next month. What is the use of saying the obvious? In our family of bankowners, landowners, in our feudal family, of course one did not hope that they would come and take away everything we had but we knew that we could not expect a reversal of Destiny. And we could not expect the Nationalist government to win. There were many like us in Chungking who waited, not starting anything new, letting things stagnate and run down, waiting for unswerving Destiny to perform its task. And so we did not talk of what was actual and would decide our lives, since that was already decided and talk was futile. We talked of The Family, and the children growing up, the crops, last year's flood, and the fire. We did not talk of my sister.

Then we had supper. Third Uncle and Aunt, Second Brother, Fifth Brother and his wife, First and Fourth Sister and their husbands, and two or three girls of school age, distant relatives living in the house in Chungking — for a few months, or a few years, no one knew quite for how long and it did not matter — and a few of the new babies. The servants were all the same, with one or two additions to replace those that had died of old age or were resting their years in the ancestral village, near the graves. They had remembered the dishes I liked and put hot strong red peppers in everything, the way I want it, tearing at tongue and throat until one has to smother it in brown sugar. And we were all very happy together, first because it was the right attitude, and second because we were really happy.

When we were drinking the soup, at the end of the meal, Third Uncle assaulted our discretion by shouting: "Too bad your sister, our Seventh Daughter, does not like red pepper as we all do."

I knew the fight was on. I professed mild interest. "Really," I said, "she has always had a delicate digestion."

Third Uncle and I enjoy those swift parries and thrusts.

"I am not a Western doctor," said Third Uncle with a touch of dignity slightly overdone; "but her body is big and strong, bigger than yours, and I do not think that she is more delicate than a woman is entitled to be."

Second Brother said: "She does not have our manners, she is foreign in her manners." He always was a hasty young man, and being my older cousin, was the only one allowed to pass an opinion on those younger than myself.

"I believe her baby has been very ill," I replied.

"The girl child was born feeble," said Third Uncle.

Liu Sao, the old servant, refilled my cup of tea, and then we had a long discussion on various kinds of tea, which gave Second Brother, who knew he had hurt me, an opportunity to say my taste in tea was excellent. It was a lie, and I accepted it to show that I had been hurt. Then Third Uncle said, as the hot towels to wipe our faces were passed, that it was late, nearly the middle of the night, and that I must be tired. But I said, a trifle firmly:

"I am not very tired and now I shall go and visit my sister."

Third Uncle accepted this immediately. "Small Liu will light you on the way," he said.

Small Liu was the son of Lao Liu or "Old Liu," the husband of Liu Sao. Lao Liu had been Third Uncle's personal errand man and was now spitting out his last days and the remainder of his lungs in peace, in the sun of the ancestral village. Small Liu, a scabby, runny-nosed boy of eight when I had last seen him, was now a lanky, alert young man, with muscular legs, an intelligent smooth face and beautifully sleek hair. The lavender smell of the brilliantine he used hit you about five yards away. He wore khaki shorts, a blue shirt, and from his waist depended a formidable contraption, a latest model flashlight. He looked like so many of the younger generation, efficient, as if he knew how to handle machines, swim, play basketball, and still write a good letter, and keep his counsel secret and his tongue quiet before his unwiser elders. He lit me to the large compound up the street, and on the other side of the lane was the foreign business concern where my sister Suchen worked and lived.

The doorkeeper was sitting by the door, enjoying the late coolness, smoking his yard-long bamboo pipe with a soapstone mouth tip and a copper tobacco holder at the other end. The gate was neat and freshly painted, and there was a large copper plate on one side with the name of the foreign firm on it.

"Mrs. Chang is at home." The gatekeeper answered Small Liu's inquiry.

"We come from the Han Palace, Third Eldest Young Lady has arrived and wishes to visit her sister Mrs. Chang," said Small Liu with an impressive manner.

The porter was intelligent, not surly and bad tempered as are some foreigners' servants towards their fellow countrymen. He knew, perhaps, that the times were against him. He rose and bowed at me respectfully. "Going directly," he said, "please to come inside. This is a business concern, alas, and the guest room is locked, but the garden is pleasant and cool."

"Many apologies," I replied. "It will be pleasant to wait in the garden. Many thanks."

I looked at his knowing back swiftly swallowed by the dark night. He knew. All the servants talked. My sister had lost the family face for them, going and living by herself in a foreign house, her own family only twenty-five yards up the street. I swallowed hard. It was a big loss of face. I felt their shame as my own, and I was angry and hardened my heart against her. For at the moment I was all

Chinese, thoroughly old-fashioned, and conventional to the marrow.

It is rather frightening to be so many different people, with so many dissimilar and equally compelling emotions, affections, ideas, *élans,* apprehensions, aware of so many differences in restraint, nuances, of phraseology in the enunciation of a similar mood in three different languages, always so aware of shades of meaning that life becomes occasionally unbearable. Other people are faced with a choice between two courses of action. I am usually torn between at least two worlds, involving different ways of existence. Tiresias, Tiresias to the core, if a core is left to a being so much like Peer Gynt's onion as I.

And as I stood in the garden, smelling the full soft night, I heard Mark's voice again, clear and tender and light: "The multiple *you* — I never know which *you* it is going to be next time I see you — do go on being unpredictable, and I shall stick to my predictability.". . . the gay, mocking, true words. Would anyone else ever find me out so quickly, accept me so completely? For this I would open all my worlds to him, the thousand and one ways of looking at the one thing, the many-faceted, the rainbow diffraction that magicked splendor into every fragment of life.

I stood, gradually peaceful, filled with tenderness, in a dream of taking Mark to Third Uncle, smiling to see how solemnly they bowed to each other, and agreed with each other, or rather with what Third Uncle would say; and climbing Mount Omei with Mark; and visiting all the restaurants I knew. I was pulled out of it into reality with the porter's return, whisking the grass with his long pipe. "The lady's sister is asleep," he announced, "and says she cannot see her before the morning."

This was a rebuff. It was midnight, by Western standards too late for a visit. But Suchen knew that I was coming. By our standards she was younger than I and should welcome me at any hour. In China there is no such thing as set hours for visits. I had often flung myself out of bed for latecoming friends. For a moment I pondered. Should I retrieve my half-frayed dignity with a semicasual gesture, as of straightening a fold in a curtain, and go? That would be the right thing to do. Or should I insist? Small Liu and the porter waited and watched.

Since we are, each one of us, unequal, and equal opportunity does not exist, I have never been able to understand why one should not accept to do evil as well as good, and with just as much clarity. I believe in relationships between people, devotion to friends, sticking to principle and the pursuit of the absolute in oneself, not of perfection to impose upon others. I am feudal and a Taoist, and use despotism with enlightenment, for I am a doctor. One has to impose upon the sick one's own will, and anything else is hypocrisy and nonsense. Doctors use power so much and get so much pleasure out of it. They stalk in their white gowns, like prophetic kings; the stethoscopes round their necks are the badges of their magic knowledge; they survey the prostrate forms of their patients, lying helpless in neat rows on their beds. They lay healing hands and save lives. This is arrant, orgiastic power, the most corrupting one to the soul, that of doing good. For it is so easy to believe that one is good. So I said, knowing well that I was wrong, that I was compelling another person, and had no excuse: "Tell Mrs. Chang that I shall see her tonight."

The bungalow where Suchen lived was at the end of the garden, and by feel and smell I could tell that the garden grass was mown, like an English lawn. In front of the door was a clump of white scented flowers hanging in clusters on a bush. The porter held the door wide open into a room with an old-fashioned oil lamp on the table, the wick turned very low. And from the door opposite where I stood came my sister in a dressing gown, her hair done in two plaits above her head. Her voice was low and contemptuous, she hated me quietly. She had suffered much, and known it all the time, adding her every pain and making a sum total of it.

"Would not tomorrow have done?"

"No," I said. I could feel her contempt. It was well earned. "I had to see you tonight. My plane was late, the car was late, and we had our food late."

"And so you came to wake me up, and my baby . . . late."

"I did. I would rather see you tonight than wait, to clear the matter between us."

"You made a mess of things, as usual. Because of you I shall now be killed when the communists come. My baby and I."

"It is not so. It is fifteen years that we have not seen each other. I have no clue to you. I do not know what has happened to you, except vaguely. I do not know you . . . I know a few facts, but not their meaning."

"I wrote to you."

"Only facts. That The Family were ill-treating you and the child, and that your baby was dying. Something bad has happened, but I did not understand it until I saw you. Please tell me."

"Because of you," she said, "I cannot get into Hong Kong. I have no residence card for Chungking. Third Uncle will not give it to me without your consent, and without a card I cannot get an airplane passage to go away. I am sick of Chungking, I never want any more to be in China, with the dirt, and I hate The Family. Now the communists will come, and many people are leaving for America. I am sure The Family is getting ready to leave, abandoning me and my baby here. They have already tried to kill her, because she is only a girl child. And now I've been working in a European firm, and the communists will put me in a concentration camp as a traitor or shoot me."

"Don't be ridiculous," I replied. But somehow I had not thought of all this. It was true that many people were running away. Hong Kong was full of refugees, people with panic in their hearts. America was the goal of those who had enough money to run further than Hong Kong. But I had failed to understand it for my own sister. How odd it was.

"The Family is not going," I said. "I want to return to China myself. Politics are like clouds, passing things. What matters is the work to do."

"You may be a communist yourself," she retorted. "You always were different from other people. But I want to get out, I want to live, I want to go to America."

As she spoke I had a queer sensation of shrinkage, of becoming younger. I turned up the wick of the lamp, and now I could see her face plainly. The lovely forehead, smooth and broad with the hair springing from it, like ebony wings. The two long eyebrows, tapering gently, very dark. The large soft eyes with that double light in them, the whites clear like fine china. The nose straight and well shaped, without that cruel sensitive flare of the nostril, the inquisitive slight hook which Third Uncle and I have inherited from some predatory and certainly criminal ancestor. Her nose was kind, her mouth wide and generous, soft over her perfect teeth. Her lips lacked that pucker, screwing up the face with intensity and purpose, which Fourth and Fifth Brother possess. I knew then that she was kind, soft, and cling-ing, made for love and a normal life with a good man and many children. Not like me, hard, unfeeling and savagely alive now that I had been made alive by Mark. She was a woman to be looked after. No wonder Third Uncle disliked her and she hated him.

As I stared, the fine creases of suffering between her brows, the shadowed hollows beneath the beautiful cheekbones, the defeated droop of her lips disappeared, and she was the lovely child I had watched with a heart full of tenderness one night, asleep under her padded quilt, in the bed next to mine, in Peking twenty-five years ago. But this she did not know, for even as a child I was careful to show only anger and callousness.

And gradually my hardness towards her melted and vanished, and as it went so she recovered the assurance with which, all our years together, she had treated me, the amused condescension to the odd scrawny wild thing that I had been among our lot. Again, as when I was a child, I felt myself wrestling desperately against contempt, the imposition of a vision not mine, the assumption of unearned superior-ity. "You are ugly," I had been told as a child, and with these three simple words my mother and Suchen had pushed me out of their feminine universe; and so I had driven myself desperately through my youth, to open many worlds for myself, since the only one that was valuable in their eyes, the world of personal beauty, had been denied to me.

Now for the first time in my life a man had found me beautiful, and told me so, and insisted that I should know it, now that I had so little beauty left to give. And with the thought of Mark and his arms round me, suddenly filled with delight as my body remembered him and stirred, shaken with memory, I told myself: "Don't let them get you. You are beautiful now. Don't ever be bullied again. Remember what happened, and how few would have survived. You turned your weakness into strength."

But Suchen said with unconscious arrogance: "Well, now you had better straighten the mess you have made and get me out of here. I'm going to sleep now. I shall see you tomorrow."

I went back to The Family. I climbed the stairs to the veranda. They were waiting for me, Third Uncle, Third Aunt, and all my numerous cousins. Third Aunt poured a special tea. Third Uncle went to my bedroom to arrange on the night table, with his own hands, a clock which had been taken out of a cupboard, where it had lain for years, and wound it up specially for me. In a moment I was wrapped in affection, never cloying, never demonstrative, always restrained and courteous, devoid of gesture. They loved me. They comforted me. They told me funny stories, just as Mark had done, in Macao, holding me in his arms so gently that I did not know I was in bed with him. The story that made me laugh most was one about Uncle's German dog. He was supposed to guard the house, but one day the thieves came to steal the new winter quilts. And the dog liked the thieves so much that he went away with them without uttering a sound.

And so, though I knew that in one way they were a little afraid of me, of my judgment between my sister and them, yet I loved them in return, and I went to sleep laughing lest I should begin to cry with weariness and with love.

# CHAPTER III

## *Acedia*

*September 1949*

It was my uncle's habit to wake up very early and go for a long walk round the city before it became astir and confused with people; I never knew whether this was dictated by his Chinese love of emptiness, or whether it was part of his system of physical discipline. I liked to walk with him, watching the cool half-light seep slowly into town, and the breeze wing across the gray silver of the river, gentler than any bird's wing could be. Soon the hot day would be here, pressing down as an iron gin upon the sordid city. And so in the dawn, between the lift of night and the effulgence of the sun, Uncle and I walked the sleepy streets, bloomed with gray. His mole-colored silk gown swung behind him, his soft cloth shoes lifted at every step, shedding a fine sift of dust from their edges. I remember how the light slit between the crest of the hills and the thickly banked clouds above them, like a knife blade working away at a crack. Uncle and I walked, he in front and I five yards behind, for two or three hours at a time. Sometimes we spoke, sometimes we did not say a word.

The day after my return Uncle and I were up before dawn, reestablishing without comment our custom of eight years ago. We walked down to the river's edge, until we could hear its muttering against the moored boats; around the town wall, parceled in haphazard fashion between fragments of habitations; across the larger streets, pursued by the dying flutter of the morning wind. A few dusty sparrows chirped sleepily. Here and there the shuttered houses yawned as their wooden boards were pushed back, showing unkempt slatternly women squatting broadly, fanning with a palm leaf the crisp dry twigs in a dark stove. Little sparks of fire would rise, turn blue, and vanish; at last a flame burst out. Carefully, with the wind of the fan, the women would direct the flame towards the heart of the wood. Here and there on the sidewalk stood ambulant kitchens wrapped in an odor of frying fat and the marrow-warming smell of congee. Opposite the bank buildings on the business street, there were five or six early rickshaw pullers, spitting, talking, slapping their hard cushions into place. And suddenly all the raucous noises of morning came upon us, and we slackened pace. Uncle turned to me and said: "Let us go through the burnt quarter now, and come back to the Community Restaurant for breakfast."

Along Tou Yo Kai, past the forlorn buildings of the Salt Bank and the Meifeng Bank, we walked towards the triangular tip of the rocky peninsula jutting between two rivers, which is Chungking, that tip which had blazed so lustily for a full week. Uncle pointed out how the air which hung over the destroyed area was still stained with a smell of smoke. Beneath the stones, here and there, smoldering continued, and they were hot to touch. Uncle explained, with a wide sweep of his silk sleeve, how the wind blew the fire first down one side of the triangle, then across to the other. He pointed to the empty insides fenced by disintegrating walls, the erect carcasses of the godowns once piled high with cotton bales, the crumbling heaps of stone. This had been the business section of the city, stocked with goods, noisy and gay.

Already squatters were camping amid the ruins, and out of the rubble and a few mats had erected shelters and were breakfasting out of round iron pans placed on a few stones. "Exactly like after the bombings, do you remember?" said Uncle.

Measures, estimates of losses, in tons, pounds and U.S. dollars (in Chungking at that moment there was a craze for American gold), rolled in his pleasant strong tenor. His eyes glowed. I was in for a long monologue, just as in the old days.

I wish I could recollect all of Uncle's many discourses, having been the recipient of at least a score, and on such diverse subjects. I remember the first one he ever attacked for my benefit was Love (the Married kind, the only possible kind), and the necessity of concubines; then there was one on How to Make Money, and one on Friendship. Food, the Bank, The Family, other nations' shortcomings, and the superiority of Our Province over every other in China, were among the topics which Uncle assaulted and conquered with monologue on our ambles together.

Back we went to the Bank. The brass-studded doors were rusty, the walls were cracked, what remained of the window panes was thickly caked with dirt. I had remembered it shining and clean, its large entrance hall thronged with people, bells ringing, boys hurrying, the merchants and bankers of Chungking in their long silken robes pacing sedately across the shining marble floor between a double hedge of respect, the rickshaw coolies, naked to the waist, steaming with perspiration, standing at the polished counters clutching packets of banknotes in their hands during the inflation. But now, like everything else, the Bank was derelict. The elevator did not work, the floor had not been swept. We climbed slippery stairs foul with grease and dirt. "We can get a full view of the fire damage from the Bank roof," said Uncle. So we climbed six floors to the roof, and looked down upon the gutted streets and the charred godowns, and the straggling, dusty, squalid city sprawling away beneath us.

As we stood there, we did not speak of the future. We knew inside our bellies why nothing was painted, nothing worked. There was no need to talk. Chungking was waiting, waiting to be liberated or waiting to fall, depending which of the two equally meaningless words one chose to use. It had given up before it was taken. It was waiting in turpitude, in sloth, in corruption. The place had lost heart. Acedia, the sin of the soul, the spiritual torpor that Mark so dreaded, here it was, infecting not one man but a whole city. The people had lost faith in the faithless government that was now announcing its last stand, a fight to the finish, but whose efforts other than vocal were entirely concerned with preparations for flight to safety. Everywhere was oppression, extortion, and execution — execution of real communists, but also of sympathizers and suspects, which meant anyone that the government did not like. Szechuan is a very conservative province, the people the most feudal-minded in a feudal land. They talked of the warlords that oppressed them as one talks of legendary beings, heroes of the Three Kingdoms, above the common law. They had gone from one oppression to another, sturdy, patient, occasionally flaring into cruelty and violence, for the weapons of the weak are always too violent. They had never wanted the Kuomintang government to come back, and now part of it was back, dragging back with it its load of evil. They had lost heart, and now they waited for the communists to arrive. "They are also Chinese," they said, "and they may bring a better government. All we want is to be left in peace." And the wily banker warlords thought: "They are Chinese, like us, and we shall make a deal with them. We have always been able to make deals. We shall negotiate. It's just another revolution. Every man has his price." They were waiting for the time when it would be convenient and advantageous to proclaim that they too, in their hearts, had always been deeply imbued with love for democracy and communism. Meanwhile they negotiated, made terms for their own sale to the victors, haggled for the sale of their troops. And we, who had no power because we were not warlords, yet who were wealthy enough to lose what we had, we could not go against the inertia of the people and the corruption of the rulers. The people wanted a change because any change was better than what was, and very few realized that this time it would not be the same, after the change, as it was before. But we could not battle the future with the past. And so we would take what was to come, and endure it, for who were we to go against the inertia, or the will, of the people?

Suddenly there was a great uproar in the street below us. We saw a whirlpool of people, running in a circling movement and then pouring straight in one direction, and we made out a small platoon of khaki-clad steel-helmeted soldiers.

"Ha, ha," said Uncle, "another execution."

"Of what?"

"Communists, who set fire to the city. We've had four or five lots of executions already."

Fourth Sister, Sixth Brother and a few servants now appeared, flushed with excitement. They wanted to watch the execution, and they thought they could see it better from the roof. We bent over the parapet and looked down. The shooting was to be performed on the left side of the Bank, in a cleared space amid the burnt rubble.

We caught a glimpse of the victims aligned against an upstanding spar of wall, and the crowd thick and milling about, and suddenly there was a small rushing sound and a crack and then another and another, and a muffled roar from the crowd. Then mats were thrown over the sprawled bodies which were swiftly roped on bamboo poles, and like parcels the loads were carried away. Fourth Sister wiped the sweat on her face. "We saw them as they were walked here. One of them was only *that* high, he couldn't be more than twelve years old. I can scarcely believe that he could set fire to anything," she said.

But Sixth Brother replied: "The communists dope them to do it."

How often I was to hear this. The Japanese had been doped. . . . In Hong Kong, when the Chinese troops won in Korea, the papers said: "They have been doped . . . that's why they fight. . . ." And in the fiery pro-communist Chinese papers of Hong Kong, they said: "The Americans are dope fiends. . . ."

And these executions were part of the pattern of disaster, the last careless cruel days before the change-over, the outrages that a dying despotism orders, for a diversion. But it did not even create the expected diversion, because the people did not care any more. They had lost heart.

After the execution we had our morning meal at the Community Restaurant. It was a dirty place, with its tables of unseasoned wood, wracked and splintered where the wood had cracked with heat. There was an overwhelming prevalence of spittoons, pink enameled ones, with a red peony pattern embossed on their bellying middles. I saw a large Chungking rat with a long, scaly, hairy tail creep out from under a chair and come and drink out of one of them in great draughts. No one shooed him away. No one cared. On the wall was a beautiful reproduction of Yueh Fei's memorial to the emperor, written nine centuries ago, when he decided to disobey orders to retreat, and to continue fighting. Uncle and I went into a trance over the rhythmic magnificence of the words and the beautiful calligraphy. We forgot the rat and the filth.

That afternoon I saw my sister again. I had sent a note by Small Liu to say I would come about three o'clock, and as I stood within the gate of the business concern, I saw her crossing the garden, with her long hair spread over her shoulders and down to her waist, uncurled, shot with red gold in the sunlight. She walked so straight, she was so slim, with her thin hollowed-out cheeks and her fine-drawn features, and her long legs. She wore a red European dress with a low neck, and I realized again how beautiful she was, how incongruous on this English clipped lawn with the tremendous Chinese river flowing two hundred yards away, shouldering the massive hills and the unclean sky. She did not belong. There was something fragile in her spirit, in spite of her tallness. In a moment I understood how alien she was although she had been born here and was my sister. She could not help it. She was not born tough.

And this strong, terribly alive China was to her unreal and far away, a tedious long-winded novel with dirty covers. Where I saw with a passionate lift of the heart the ecstasy of the monotonous river, she saw how muddy it was, how inconveniently wide. Where I knew the sullen waiting of the people around me, waiting for Destiny, and not a word spoken, she saw only the danger and the dirt. Where The Family meant to me affection, respect and mutual help, she saw hostile intent, she read malice and annoyance with herself.

She heard the lofty sentences sedately used to give the moralistic poise, the equitable balance required in general conversation, and found that they did not apply to her. She missed the hints and subtleties, forgot that human beings are many-layered, and stoop to practical gestures out of keeping with the words they use. For in China, as elsewhere, sound is more important than sense, sincerity is relative, and self-deception prevalent.

She knew that there was only one bathtub in the house where the family lived, that the beds were hard wooden boards with a mat on top, that no one had any sense of time. It was so natural that she should hate it all, and so right. Not only the material arrangements, but the spiritual hemming-in, which she could not escape and which oppressed her. For we are all riveted to our own physiological landscape and the climate of our minds, unable to pry ourselves loose from the emotional evocation of the words we use, more important to us than their meaning; confusing feeling with thought, in this highly emotional and dangerously uneducated twentieth century in which we live.

I belonged. My roots were here. If I chose personal salvation, freedom of the individual spirit away from here, fleeing to a safer, gentler world, I would slowly wither and die, for here I was rooted. No matter how far away I strayed, I would come back. I would always be coming back. I could not help it. But she was not thus made. She belonged to an orderly civilization, rows of neat houses, mild weather. She was vulnerable and un-Chinese in a non-European fashion, too gentle and suave for a European woman, too good-natured and easygoing for a Chinese. There was nothing stark, vigorous or mad about her. She must leave, go to America, to the ready-made life and the orderly time-keeping day. For she was a realist where only a strong dreamer would survive.

We were having a revolution, not only in China, but in the whole of Asia. And the old isms would go and new isms would come, and clouds of politics obscure men's visions until they died willingly for that which they knew not. And the nations of Asia would find their way out, some in peace and some in war. There would be bloodshed, and waste, hatred and destruction, terror and brutality, madness trampling everything down. Perhaps a new world would emerge, and perhaps not. But it was useless to turn back, it was foolish to refuse knowledge of the flood, for the flood was upon us already. Many of us would be stripped, not only of material possessions, but of our familiar virtues and favorite faults, our ideal principles and our practical prejudices; the ways of our thoughts and the loves of our souls would be violated and defaced. We would have to burn what we thought we loved, adore what we had been taught to hate. Nothing would be left but dreams, if we had strength enough to dream. And dreams would win in the end. They always did. But in the meantime those who could not dream their world out must go away to save their souls. It was right that it should be so.

Till then I had not understood. Standing in the garden watching the sun filter gold through my sister's long black hair, I understood. But alas for our fitful understanding, we forget what we know, and in a moment it was all gone, I was blind again. I kept only one fact clear: that my sister must go away. No mad dreaming for her. No brave new world. She must go.

"Don't stand there dreaming, go in," she said to me. "Go in and meet my boss. His name is Franklin."

I went through the outer office where a supercilious Chinese employee looked up, prepared to be rude because I was dressed as a "native," and tried to speak English to me. I spoke to him with the voice of my uncle, and he crumpled up and went in to tell Mr. Franklin that I had arrived.

# New East, Old West

*September 1949*

Mr. FRANKLIN WAS NOT ONLY PORTLY AND TALL. HE HAD the surly offensive manner of the white man dealing with the inferior races, the old China-hand long in the Orient who has always considered it beneath his dignity to learn anything from the native, whose intensive knowledge of the Far East extends as far, perhaps, as his No. 1 boy, and who prides himself on his firm handling of situations. He was, in short, a wonderfully preserved specimen of a dying genus. His welcome to me was distinctly freezing. Reasonably so, since from his point of view I was a wicked cruel woman and had treated my family very badly . . . only he did not know at all what the word family meant in China. He thought it meant my sister alone.

After twenty minutes of what I shall euphemistically describe as moderate insult, it was obvious that he and I did not talk the same language. What he called disgusting I found natural, what he said was right seemed to me bad manners. He accused my Chinese family of ill-treating my sister. She had to live in a dark room. There was no running water. Meals were irregular and at all hours.

"But that is how we all live," I replied. "She was not treated differently from the others."

"I couldn't stand it, she was so unhappy," he replied, "so I gave her the bungalow to live in and a job. It saved her sanity and her child."

"But in doing so you've lost The Family's honor for them. The house where we live is just up the street. What do you think people say?"

"Damn your family," he said. "Your family is your sister. Her life, her child's life, depended on her getting out of there."

"I am sure your statement is right," I replied. "I am merely explaining to you what you have done to The Family and what they resent."

"Your uncle wanted to kill that child — they tried to poison her."

"In China the life of a girl baby is not so valuable as all that. They did not see why she should not die if she was weak and could not pull through. So many babies die, you know."

"But how callous you are!" he exclaimed. "And you a doctor trained in England!"

Suchen, who had not said anything, now told us that one day she had found a strange man bending over her child. He had brought with him a tube full of pills of his own invention, and was trying to get the child to swallow one. My uncle later told me it was a Chinese doctor friend of his, who had been asked by the family to have a look at the child, and that he was just looking at her tongue. Who was I to believe? Explanations are of no avail when both parties are determined to misconstrue. The most normal gesture becomes a threat of violence, a sentence in a slightly louder tone (and most people raise their voices when they think they are not understood, an illogical, but natural, thing to do), is taken as an insult. I had seen it happen before.

This was the sort of thing that never happened to Mark, because he was never on the defensive. He would never try to misunderstand others, for he was gentle and mild of heart. He had the courage of humility and patience. I felt such a wave of pride and delight and love for him, because I thought how valuable he would be in a world blind with hatred. He was a man of good will, and good will and tolerance and selflessness and vision were needed now as never before. And I saw then that it was not race that made men different, but the quality of their souls, for Mr. Franklin strongly reminded me of many a bullying, petty Chinese official.

"Do you know any Chinese?" I asked him. And he replied: "No, thank God I never tried. I wanted to keep my sanity."

Sitting in the low chair by his desk I held my head between my hands, and laughed with exasperation and futility and love for Mark. Suchen, ill and excited, believing that The Family to which she had come to escape from the communists in the North had evil intentions towards her. And now the communists were here, a bare six months later. Her husband had been shot for collaboration with the Japanese. In Chungking the grimness, the squalor, the aloneness had been too much for her. And then this foreigner had stepped in. Here was his opportunity to be noble and unselfish, and I knew that he had been noble and unselfish.

He had saved the life of her child and her own health. He was kind and good and her savior. In his eyes my clever, gentle uncle appeared a sinister, long-robed Asiatic, and the mild opium smoking which he had given up thirty years ago must have added only one more terrifying detail to the picture Mr. Franklin held in mind. There was even, to round out this story of beauty and rescue, a shady financial deal. My sister had been well supplied with U.S. dollars when she had arrived, but my uncle had changed it all at such a bad rate that it had vanished.

The whole episode was tragic and comical. However, it could be fixed up.

"You are a hardhearted, unfeeling woman, laughing like that at all this cruelty and misery," said Mr. Franklin. "Your sister is in great danger, and you laugh."

"We always laugh when things are sad and emotional," I replied between gusts. "We all do, you know."

"A cannibal race, you Chinese," said Mr. Franklin, spurred into wit by his indignation. "You seem to have a poor opinion of foreigners in general. Why do you side with the Chinese when your own mother is a European?" and he bent his nearly bald head and his weak blue eyes on me.

"I have, alas, identified myself with my Chinese side. I do not place

foreigners above the common run of humanity. Perhaps I do have a
poor opinion of them. I don't know."

"Your poor opinion is based, no doubt, on your own personal experiences," he said, heavily sarcastic.

A charming swallow skimmed over our heads, rushing in and out
of the room. I longed to be away, for I had other things to do. Why
had I been pinned down to this talk anyway? I sipped my tea to indicate I was preparing to go.

"You must not be so selfish," said Mr. Franklin, now adopting a
conciliatory tone. "You have always had a wonderful life. We all
know what a splendid success you have made of your life, how well
you've done. You're young and beautiful. I can see you've always had
a very good time, you have been happy and lucky and had no troubles,
and it has made you selfish and hard and unfeeling. Your sister needs
help, and only you can help her. Do it now."

And he wanted me to sign a lot of papers he had prepared. For
Europeans never trust a word unless it is written down, which is so
childish. For if one is prepared to break one's word, why should it
make a difference whether it be spoken or written?

"I won't sign any promise," I said. "I came to tell you that I was
going to help. I know that Suchen is not Chinese in feeling and is
unfitted for life here. Life in China is pretty awful and it is going to be
much worse."

"Thank God," he said, "you see that at last."

But he would never know that my mind was made up when I saw
Suchen in the garden. All his life he would carry the pride of having
changed my heart. Well, that was all right, too.

Now we all relaxed and said appropriately sentimental things. I left,
and the garden, the hills, the river, the sky and my dress were pow-
dered with the gold of the western sun. "Oh, Mark," I said to myself, and smiled. For I had learned a lot, I had learned so much, I had
not come to look at him from Chungking in vain.

And wearied to death of the thousand tangles in my brain, the thousand ways of explaining one thing, the mischief of words and their

many-faced interpretations, I went to bed and slept till the next day. During the night Third Aunt hovered gently into my room to see that all was well. To Third Uncle I said: "All is well. Seventh Sister (that was Suchen's title in the family) will come to the banquet tomorrow and all will be smoothed over. Uncle must give her a residence card so that she can book an airplane passage to Hong Kong. I shall leave a little money with her." He asked no questions. We did not discuss it. It was well that all was now smooth. Third Uncle did not defend himself, for we knew each other well, and we needed no words between us for this knowledge.

# CHAPTER V

# *Moment in Chungking*

*September, October 1949*

MY FRIEND YING CAME EARLY THE NEXT DAY TO VISIT ME. She was the first concubine of one of Chungking's important men. His wife had died eighteen years ago. He did not marry again but took two concubines, and Ying was one of them. Ying always had a good head, and an avid desire for knowledge. She herself was a power in our society, and still her husband's favorite.

Ying was good to me twelve years ago when I was a frightened young bride, doing and saying the wrong things. She and I used to make dresses of the same material and cut. Chinese women think it not at all disturbing to wear the same gown as another woman. Ying is small and exquisite, and I am tall and big-boned. We set each other off well. Ying took me everywhere. With her I used to spend hours listening to operas, shopping, fingering silks and jewelry, having our hair done in her bedroom by her hairdresser, teaching her a little English, embroidering small butterflies and tiny bats on our slips and our slippers, going to the horoscope man and the physiognomist to have pleasant things told to us, buying presents for friends and silver lockets for our friends' new babies.

Ying was sitting in the dining room waiting for me, calm as if she had seen me yesterday. She said: "You have not changed."

"You have not changed at all. Last year's flowers were beautiful, they are better this year, next year they will be more so. . . ."

"Alas, with whom shall I see them!" said Ying, and we both laughed with our eyes moist with tears after this quotation.

Third Uncle honored us with his presence and a long peroration on the Value of American Money. That morning gold dollars seemed uppermost in his mind. "Do you want to change any money?" Ying asked me. "Yes, I want to change a few American dollars," I said, "as I want to leave some money for Seventh Sister's air travel to Hong Kong." (For I too had bought American money on the free market in Hong Kong to carry with me to Chungking.)

Third Uncle nodded amiably. "Aunt Sheng [that was Ying] is able to get the best rate in Chungking," he said, "better than I can."

"Not at all, not at all," said Ying.

"She'll give you the best rate," said Uncle. And he added offhand, "Your sister wanted some money changed a while ago, but I was unable to get such a good rate for her."

Thus I knew that he had probably not made any effort to change at the black-market rate for her, but at the ordinary rate. Everyone changed at black-market rates, both in Chungking and Hong Kong.

Ying smiled at me. "I'll change it for you." So I handed over the money I had. She would also fix my return ticket on the plane. Getting an airplane ticket was tricky in those last days in Chungking. In view of the "uneven situation" there was a considerable amount of bribery in order to acquire permission for a plane passage, and it was hopeless to try for a ticket to Hong Kong if you were just an ordinary citizen. Big Shots left every week. But I would have priority because Ying was my friend and she practically ran the local air office. Meanwhile Ying's car would be mine whenever I wanted it.

It is nice to belong to the top class, even though one knows that in a few weeks nothing will be left of it. It is comfortable to have a car and to have one's plane ticket fixed. It is privilege, graft and corruption, but I enjoyed it, knowing it would soon be gone. For I too belonged to this corruption, which had made possible my expensive hybrid education and which in turn had made it possible for Mark and me to meet, to comprehend each other, and to love.

In a few weeks it would not be so. Ying's little parcels of special goods, nylon stockings, gold filigree bags and U.S. dollars, would no longer be smuggled by obliging friends in the Hong Kong airplanes. My uncle, sitting there so benevolent and carefree, had said to me casually at breakfast between sips of tea: "Sinkiang is talking, it will be on the other side in a few days." It meant the provincial government of Sinkiang, next door to our own province of Szechuan, had opened undercover negotiations with the communists. (Sinkiang was officially liberated about three weeks later.) We waited for what was to come, and while waiting, relaxed, drank tea, entertained our friends, drove the car sagging on its last tires, and arranged the use of our endless leisure, that true hallmark of our class.

That night with Ying and many friends and relatives, we played mahjong the Szechuan way, a very fast game, for the generation above us had played so much that they no longer looked at the carved ivory dice, but felt them with the pulp of the third finger as they picked them up, and did not bother to turn them for inspection before tossing away the unwanted ones. It made the game so quick that I could not follow. Ying and I sat together and smiled at each other in silence, happy to be together. Ying said to Third Uncle:

"You are indeed lucky. So many children in the family, and all virtuous. Look at Third Daughter" — that was me — "widowed for years, and yet not thinking of marriage. A virtuous and chaste widow, a wonderful thing indeed in this lax modern age."

Uncle threw me a keen look. He replied: "Headstrong and bad-tempered. But she knows her limits."

Ying turned to me. "An example to all of us. You were a model wife, now a model widow. You bring great honor to The Family."

"Oh, Mark, Mark," I groaned to my inward self, while my outward self blushed in a subdued and becoming manner.

My uncle now started another of his monologues, to which we listened respectfully, as was befitting. What was wrong with modern young people, he said, was chiefly their lack of virtue. This was their parents' fault, he said, throwing the sentence down like a hand grenade, pleased with the shocked silence which greeted it. In modern families, no sooner were children born than their mothers thrust them into the arms of a wet nurse, an unlettered rude country-woman, more often than not an imbecile. The mother herself, until her next labor, idled her time away, gambling and chatting with neighbors and concubines. Along with the healthy milk of the wet nurse, the child imbibed her level of intelligence and her character. By the time it was three years old and due for weaning, it might be physically healthy, but its heart was rude and untutored, its mind suffered from the nourishment it had derived, and was mostly composed of crude bone, lacking in those finer parts which could be molded by education. Later still, the child was in the hands of servants, who spoiled it with self-indulgence. Small wonder that, grown a man, it was ungovernable, stubborn, full of country-bumpkin curiosity, unable to concentrate its spirit. Upon such soil fell the rank seed of corrupt and immoral ideas, and so women became unchaste, and men left their families for other women, parents went uncared for, and great houses decayed.

His speech over, we all had an energetic and sweat-provoking dinner with plenty of red peppers in everything. This gave Uncle another opportunity to point out how different my sister was. She did not like red pepper, yet all our family did, all true Szechuanese did. I began to understand how Suchen must have disliked me. All the time they said to her: "Third Daughter likes this, Third Daughter said that . . . Third Daughter does everything the way we do it. Wait till Third Daughter comes back." No, they had obviously not been kind to her.

"Of course," said Suchen to me after the feast, to which she had arrived late, too late for the monologue and the red pepper remarks, "I don't think you can be very hygienic, eating so much of all this stuff. And you are getting fat. I think you ought to know better."

The next few days Ying and I went visiting relatives and friends, giving and receiving presents. We went to the Chinese opera and to banquets and feasts. I slept very little in those crowded days. Everybody was very happy, and I was happiest of all. Third Uncle made many another peroration. In one he expatiated at length on European food, how bad it was for teeth, hair and sinews, and why it made all Europeans stink so badly. I listened to Third Uncle, fascinated by the pomp of sound, the thunder of his rolling sentences, and thought him as full of honest heartfelt prejudice in this and many another subject as Addison's Sir Roger was in those which naturally cleave to the heart of an Englishman. And I nodded and agreed with Third Uncle in everything, so that by the end of my stay he was well satisfied that he had always known more about the West than anyone else in our province of Szechuan.

And Ying smiled her lovely smile, and made me admire her new dresses and her Peggy Sage American nail polish. We went in chaises up the Second Range to her summer residence, we went to the theater, we went to the cinema to see American movies, and one day she showed me how to dance the conga and the samba, which I did not know. For she was a well-informed woman, and kept abreast of modern developments in the world.

Everywhere in Chungking I was aware of neglect and squalor and decay. Everything that had not been bombed years ago was in the same place, and that was just the trouble. It had not been moved, dusted, or washed since the end of the war. Grime lay over all. The only new objects I remember were two shiny brass spittoons in Ying's bedroom. Some people spoke of a new stadium and a new bazaar and some new houses, but as if they were unreal and had nothing to do with them. And of course they seldom spoke of what was coming, except in offhand references.

No one of the society I belonged to professed in my hearing a belief that the Nationalist government would try to withstand what was coming. A few businessmen had moved part of their affairs to Hong Kong and some to Formosa, but the majority did no business outside of China and so they stayed. One young businessman, a distant relative of ours who ran a pig bristle company, had changed all his assets into U.S. dollars. Uncle thought this very foolish. "It will all be confiscated," he said. A prediction which proved correct.

Uncle summed it up one day. "No government," he said, "can carry on the business of ruling when it has abandoned virtue. This Kuomin-tang government lost its virtue and so it must go." And that was that. No other reason was needed for him. For although he was imperfect he knew that it is not money, nor arms, nor numbers, but virtue, to which the world belongs.

The time of my departure was approaching, and I wanted to talk to my uncle about Mark. For I wanted him to be accepted by my people, as himself, and without pretense.

Two days before I left, in the evening, Uncle and I sat as usual on the veranda after dinner. We stretched on our bamboo chairs, fanning. The night was thick on our faces. There was hovering smoke from a charcoal brazier in the next house where a woman was sick of malaria. From the courtyard rose a cicada's occasional stanza. The river stirred faintly in the darkness. Uncle knew I wanted to talk. He inquired about Hong Kong, which gave me an opening. I spoke of my job, and the prospects for a woman doctor, and my urge to come back to China. And I said abruptly: "I am thinking of marrying for the second time. A foreigner."

Uncle's fan did not show any feeling. He continued its steady strok-ing of the miasmatic night around him. He said evenly: "Tell me what he is like."

I thought it best to put the worst first. I said: "He is an Englishman. He is married. He wants to be divorced by his wife and marry me and thinks it can be done."

"You will not be a concubine?"

"No."

"Is it because he wants to marry you that he will put away his foreign wife?"

"He says so. Foreigners think a great deal of what they call happi-ness. And they believe that love is important."

"Do you respect as well as love him?"

"Yes. He is stronger than I. He is quiet and gentle. I would like to obey him and follow him always."

"I always thought you had a good eye for choosing people."

"He knows our country well, and wants to work here. We both want to work in China."

Uncle remained a long time without saying anything. There was weariness in his silence. And though I hoped against hope, I knew what he did not say. But in that moment in Chungking I blinded myself thoroughly, shutting my eyes, not wanting to understand Uncle's silence. Oh no, no, my heart said, it is not so, it is not so . . . I would not accept it. Not yet, not yet. I would not know. I bent down to slap a mosquito feeding on my leg, and the night was so black on the veranda that I was surprised, on looking up, to find the sky crowded so thick with stars.

Uncle stood up, and I knew he had made up his mind not to speak, since I refused to think. Perhaps he too did not see clearly. "Time flows, customs change; things remain, the people who used them are already departed. We kept your husband's clothes for years when he was already no more. Who knows what next year will bring, for now the world is changing faster than we are. You may marry again."

I said shyly, for I was very moved: "I would have liked him to come here one day, and stay with us. He is so English, yet he will not offend you. He is different. He has no fierceness, and he is not afraid and therefore not arrogant. He is always gentle and courteous. He has great virtue, and the only thing that makes me suffer is that he has to suffer in order to marry me, and make other people suffer. But so it is in his world, alas. If it were fifty years ago and he was Chinese, I would so gladly be his concubine and serve him and his wife, for it would be an honor to serve a man like him, even as a slave."

My uncle said: "Yes, all these Western arrangements are not practical, but since it is his world, it must be so."

And the next day, the whole family knew. There was the same affection, the same love. But they knew. However, the communists were coming, they were near, everything was changing and this was a sign of the times. They would not perhaps erect a monument to my virtue

as a widow, but then, who knew whether the ancestral graves themselves would now be kept?

And so, when I left, among the many presents, they gave me satin
quilt covers, which are always given to brides for their marriage bed.
One was imperial purple with two rows of green and silver butterflies
and peonies, and one was red and gold with dragons and phoenixes,
and one deep blue with pines and plum blossom and bamboo. For a
marriage bed. And a bolt of heavy white silk for a man's underwear,
and a man's fan, and two boxes of Szechuan cigars for a man, and a
heavy jade seal for a man, and tea, and bamboo scrolls. . . .

And they never said a word to make me change my mind.


The bus from the air station to the airfield left at eight in the morning. Uncle, Aunt, my luggage and I left the house at seven in a car
which one of our numerous cousins in the Foreign Office had lent us,
for in our week of festivity Ying's car and ours had finally died
of overwork. At six Third Uncle had walked to a shop famous
for its mooncakes. In another ten days it would be the Moon Festival. He knew I did not like the bloated, Falstaffian, Cantonese
mooncakes, with their thick walls and monstrous insides full of duck
egg and ham, sugared fruit and nuts. I liked the small, flaky mooncakes of the North, with the white wafer envelope and their thin
pounded almond, nut, and date filling. Uncle had ordered them the
night before, and went to fetch them himself, anxious lest the servant
should make a mistake. Glistening with sweat and triumph, he sat
next to me in the car, holding the cardboard box with the mooncakes
in it. Third Aunt held my hand. I had come with two suitcases containing the presents I had brought from Hong Kong. I departed with
the same suitcases stuffed with presents for my friends, Mark and myself, and a basket full of pickled vegetables, ham, bean curd, and two
stone bottles containing Maotai wine, the wine which Third Uncle,
my father and I would sell our souls to drink. "Your father," said Third
Uncle, "used to drink wine in a rice bowl. Then he would lift his
brush and write poetry."

The hills beyond the river were blued with mist and between the hills and us, two hundred yards below our feet, the river spread the large lazy undulations of its silken body. The morning breeze had died, already the heat was clamping down, but the dust was still gold-speckled and there was morning tenderness left in the faces of the people walking on the road side.

We arrived at the Station and got out of the car. We waited for the bus to convey the passengers to the airfield seventeen miles away. I rubbed my back reminiscently and Third Aunt laughed. Uncle was wearing a long gown of fine black wool, Aunt was in black silk, her hair smooth as jackdaw feathers. Uncle and Aunt stood against the low stone wall banking the road. Behind them the cliff dropped un-evenly to the water below. A few mat sheds and huts stuck crazily, perilously, on jutting pieces of rock here and there down to the river's edge, like the squatters' shacks crowding the slopes of the hills in Hong Kong.

I shall always remember Uncle and Aunt standing there, smiling a little sadly, making no gesture, just looking at me with gently sad eyes. We did not know whether we would meet again. There would be a great change. But The Family would not go away. They were staying on. No haven of refuge, no America for them. Come what might, they would not go away. Not for them the outer world, for China was their world. Not for them the heroics of the fleeing, the talk of personal free-dom when here men died of hunger. For them the acceptance and the faith in the earth and its people, and the steadfastness which is not writ-ten about in the newspapers. They did not know what democracy meant, but they knew that this was their country and it was their busi-ness to remain. Riches and happiness were in the hands of fate, but man's destiny was to take what Fate gave him, and not to run away.

The bus roared, spluttered, spat, hissed, then settled to a roar. "Third Uncle, Third Aunt," I said, bowing at them from inside the bus. Uncle and Aunt waved me off with a little gesture of their fans. My eyes pricked, and as the bus lurched forward I opened the box on my knees, and, childishly, I ate a mooncake to stop my tears.

# CHAPTER VI

# Hong Kong Profiles

*October 1949*

OH, MARK, A BUTTERFLY IS PERCHING ON YOUR SHOULDER. Turquoise and ebony. Such a good omen for us. Please do not move."

"Is it still there?" said Mark, very pleased and careful not to turn his head. "I hope it settles on you too."

The butterfly circled away, lazily volplaning above the long, seeded grass, leaving our hearts as light as its touch upon Mark.

"So I wish my love, if it be love that I bear you, to rest upon you no heavier than a butterfly."

"Darling, no one will say these nice things to her lover in your New Democracy," said Mark. "Everyone will be so busy with work, self-criticism and dialectics."

"Politics don't stop love. He will say to her: 'You are as beautiful as our new hydroelectric plant.' And she will reply: 'Comrade, how progressive of you.'"

It was hot on the hill slope. The sun slid into each corner of our bodies, palpable like hands, deft and loving, so much like love that I could scarcely bear it. Merged into the earth, the green tea scent of the grass, and the tobacco smell of Mark's pipe. His eyes very near and wide open. "You and the sun," I said to him. "I never knew that blue eyes could be so attractive."

"Look," said Mark, who had decided to be purely intellectual, and had brought papers and magazines and *The Times* crossword puzzle to help him: "Paragraph 7 of the Marriage Constitution of the New People's Government of China: 'Widows may now remarry.' Isn't that good? Your family won't lose face with their neighbors now, because of you."

"Widows have been remarrying, 'unvirtuous' ones; and divorce by mutual consent we've had for years. But we, like your people, are more bound by custom than by law, and old customs die hard. China is such a hodgepodge of things new and old. Anyone who tried to write a book about the Chinese of today would contradict himself at every step."

Mark said: "Anglo-Saxons are muddled with wishful thinking about your country. To us it is still a wonder land of hidden wealth and subtle wisdom. We say: 'How awful of you to give up those dear old customs, that wonderful family system we admire so much (since we did not have to live under its yoke). It's not you we want, but your traditions, your culture, your civilization.' We are collectors of a glass-incased past labeled: *Do not touch*. But some of us, I think, do understand the present."

I said: "Foreigners have such rigorous ideas of how Chinese should behave, speak, display at all times fatalism, inscrutability, serenity, figments of Western imagination so wrongly attibuted to an earthy, extrovert race. They don't want the uncomfortable truths about China, its enormous and collective hunger, its exorbitant poverty, its violence, its urge towards assertion, and the inevitability of its revolution. The civilization they admire, who but they destroyed it? Who but they broke down the dikes of institution and tradition which used to contain our exuberant and vital spirit?"

Mark said: "You ought to write something about the soul in torment of the Chinese today, since you are one about whom lingers fragments of the past, yet who wants to fit into the new and yet unknown pattern that your country is shaping. I predict great suffering for you, my dear."

"If I should write anything, my critics will say: 'This is not Chinese. There is no inscrutability, serenity, fatalism, and mighty little philos-

ophy. This is savage and violent and perverse and decadent all at once.'
People will read politics into my nonpolitical statements, and dispute
the meanings of my words, because all meanings are distorted. The
independent mind is a dangerous thing, for it belongs to no party, and
is suspect to all. No, I'll go to China and stick to my medicine. They
are my people, and what does it matter to me that they may be blue,
red, or dark green? For, like all Chinese, I am spellbound by my
own country."

Mark said: "In two months your year in Hong Kong is ended; and
go you will. I shall try to follow you, for I, like many foreigners, cannot get away from China. I too am spellbound. Like you, I have faith
in the common sense of your people. But I think it will be difficult for
you to fit into the new pattern. I still think you ought to go back, but
I am afraid you are already too mellow to participate in your country's
brash adolescence without cutting out great pieces of yourself. You are
too detached and undeluded, in spite of your love for it, to be possessed
by those burning faiths, and those fierce angers; you are too balanced,
the multiple *yous* holding delicate equipoise in courteous harmony,
to undergo again the abrupt divided mind, and the appeal of a
simple mystic to hungry idealism. Truly, you will have to be born
again.

"The West is old, the East is new. Our roles are reversed. It is only
too clear that China is young, agonizingly so; with its aspiration after
human perfection and social brotherhood, its belief in machinery and
achievement, its intolerance, its black and white universe, and its
slogans."

"You make it sound too simple," I replied. "There are all kinds of
people in China, all as complicated because they are as alive as you
and I. The early Christian Chinese, with their confessions, their repentance, their conscience searching; the patriotic Chinese, that hard
core of strength in all Asiatic communism which is ardent nationalism:
my country, right or wrong, but mine. The historic-minded Chinese,
haunted by the past and memories of the Great White Injustice; the
Chinese *émigrés* who go away, hoping that one day they will return.

Those who are here, in Hong Kong, waiting to let the dust settle, to see clearly what is going to happen before they make up their minds. And the many fence-sitters, who will go with the victor. And who can blame them, after all? For very few people have the physical means at their disposal to choose what is called *Freedom*. A word I do not understand in Asia, where hunger is absolute and freedom so relative."

Mark said, a little sadly: "Shall we be able to choose?"

"I don't know," I replied. "At the moment we are, like so many others, subjects of destiny. We want to go to Peking, you for your paper, I to do medicine. It does not depend on us whether we can go together. It depends on politicians, and economics, and markets, on all these things which I do not understand."

"Do you think that your new regime will allow newspapermen like myself to come in?" asked Mark.

I replied, "Wait till the dust settles. You are such a nice person, Mark, everyone will like you. I bet, though, that if you write anything in favor of New China, people in London clubs will frown over their paper and say: 'Is that chap going Red?' And if I say anything good about England (for I learned freedom of speech there), they will say: 'She is corrupted in her thoughts by that British imperialist newspaperman.'"

Mark was silent for a while, then he turned to me, and we laughed, pleased with the sun and each other, and in this pleasure thinking that we had hope in this life, hope for life together.

Around us lay Hong Kong, basking in the sun — Hong Kong, tiny excrescence of the Chinese mainland, rock of exile to so many — poised, expectant, waiting for the future, just as we were.

I I

The men sitting around the long polished table in parliamentarian attitudes now relaxed. The Chinese opened their cigarette cases, each took out a cigarette and presented it, Chinese fashion, to the Americans and the Englishmen sitting with them. They were Lucky Strikes. The Chinese wore sharkskin suits. They had fountain pens in their vest pockets. "Goodness," thought Suzanne, who had taken notes for over an hour, "they look just like the others."

Humphrey Palmer-Jones was genial. He rubbed his hands appreciatively and shuffled from one foot to another. Under his good-humored clumsiness he still managed to convey an impression of withheld power. "I think we shall be able to supply all that you need," he repeated to the more magisterial-looking of the bespectacled Chinese. "It's very good of you to think of us first in this connection. Our firm is small but very mobile, very mobile."

Mr. Parrish was conversing with the second man, who had the long thin face of an idealist. "We shall have to cover ourselves, of course . . . the risks of the blockade . . . and our boats come back empty from Tientsin."

"We pay cash," said the idealist in a crisp business voice. "We pay American dollars."

Humphrey nodded with obvious satisfaction. "Mr. Parrish will handle all this. I hope, gentlemen," he added in a slightly louder and more solemn tone, "that this marks the beginning of a long and prosperous era of friendly trade relationships between New China and ourselves."

Mr. Parrish and the smallest of the three men suddenly shook hands with marks of mutual pleasure. They turned beaming faces towards the others. The smaller man explained:

"Mr. Parrish is my teacher," he said. "I had the honor of being educated in his school in Hankow. I was under your care for three years," he added, bowing stiffly in Mr. Parrish's direction, and exhibiting all the Chinese symptoms of respect due to a teacher from a pupil.

When they had gone Suzanne snapped her shorthand book shut and turned towards Humphrey. "Mr. Palmer-Jones," she laughed, "I really couldn't believe it. But they're just like other businessmen. I thought communists would look so very different."

Humphrey idly worked the Venetian blind up and down. He always did that after a good deal. He said: "Oh, you can't tell by people's looks, Miss Howard. But there is a difference. These haven't spoken of commissions, they know what they want, they pay cash, and everything is above board. In all my years of dealing with Chinese governments, I can scarcely believe that we have an honest one, especially after the last . . . but it's early yet," he added. "Let's wait and see. This is only the beginning."

## I I I

"If he does it again," thought Oh-no, "I will revenge."

Oh-no was small, squat, and a slave. Who her father and mother were she would never know. She had been sold in a famine, very young, to the Hsu family. How old she was she would never know; probably between twelve and fourteen. No one cared how old a slave girl was. Oh-no knew only that she was not yet a woman.

Six months ago the Old Master, Old Mistress, and the four taitais (secondary wives) and all the young masters and their wives had left their palace in Szechuan and come to Hong Kong in an airplane. Oh-no belonged to taitai Number Three. "But she's not a person, only a slave, how can I buy a ticket for her?" Number Three had screamed at the ticket official at the airfield in Chungking. Oh-no had gone as luggage. In the plane she had no time to be frightened, because Number Three had been so sick. Oh-no had rubbed Tiger Balm on her mistress's forehead and temples, placed slices of fresh ginger and sour olive in her mouth, undone her high collar and pinched and pulled the skin until three dark purple marks had been raised on her neck; it made the sickness better.

Now here they were. Old Master had a large new Western-style house on top of a hill. Each taitai had her own room; Old Mistress had her opium. She had feared that opium would be difficult to get in Hong Kong under the foreigners, and had smuggled a few ounces inside each of six Yunnan smoked hams brought as luggage. But opium was easy to get; a regular channel had soon been established. Only two police officials to "help" for keeping their eyes towards the sky. Old Mistress was happy. Number Two and Number Four were happy. They played mahjong all day with their friends.

But Number Three was unhappy. She had been an actress before marrying the Old Master. In Hong Kong she went to American films and to Chinese operas. She smoked cigarettes good for the throat. She took singing lessons. She bought many new dresses, and lipsticks and nylons and gold kid shoes and pearl handbags and figure-improvers. She nagged Old Master to introduce her to friends of his, who would turn her into a "film empress." She often lost her temper. Then she beat Oh-no. Number Three worried and upset Old Master, who was already upset and worried by the communists and by the future.

The communists advanced so quickly. The South had not held at all. Now they were on their way to Canton. Canton, the last big city. Only eighty miles from the border of the Colony. Old Master often wondered whether Hong Kong was safe enough. Some friends of his had gone to Formosa; they said Formosa was safer. "America won't let them take Formosa; it's included in their defense strategy," they said, wisely nodding their heads and quoting widespread rumor. But now it was said that the communists were training their troops to swim, and that even in the bastion of Formosa some high-up Kuomintang generals were wondering whether or not to "rise in righteousness." Old Master thought Hong Kong might be safer. In the hills of the New Territories on the Kowloon side, that land leased to the English for another forty-five years, many thousands of English soldiers were stationed. More would be coming. You could see soldiers drilling in the barrack squares in Hong Kong itself. Old Master stopped to watch them from the street, red like boiled prawns in the hot sun, sweat pouring from them, the sour, rancid smell reaching the street and the passers-by laughing and wrinkling their noses, pleased that the foreign devils should toil and sweat. "But the English will fight for us," thought those who had something to lose; and felt comforted. Old Master, too, felt better, watching the English broiling and stinking in the sun.

Business was very good in Hong Kong. The boom was on. There was a lot of building. Many factories had been moved to Hong Kong, many new ones were being built. The shops were full of American goods. There was much quick-profit making, and the traffic in gold bars from Macao was excellent. But what of the future? It was not possible to say what would happen next year. Supposing the communists did not stop at the border? Anything might happen. The only thing to do was to make a good profit, and get away. But get away where? Macao, Manila, South America? Where would safety for the future be achieved?

And in the midst of Old Master's worries there was his Number Three wanting to be a film star!

No wonder that one night, coming out from Number Three's room after a rebuff (Old Master was frightened of Number Three — she had such a quick loud voice) he stumbled upon Oh-no squatting under the stairs where she slept just outside the room. He cursed. "Women and slaves all over my house," he said. Then he recognized Oh-no. "Cook me a pipe, quickly," he ordered.

Oh-no cooked opium well, she had deft fingers; she turned the small round pellet quickly on its silver spike until it was just right to put into the pipe. She crouched on the floor of Old Master's room, while Old Master lay on his side on the couch and smoked. And then it had happened.

At first she had struggled and kicked and whimpered. "Be quiet," Old Master said: "Do you want Third Taitai to come and beat you?" So she had lain quiet, biting both her hands. And when it was done he had rummaged in his vest pocket, put a dollar bill in her hand and turned over to sleep. Oh-no had gone back under the stairs.

For two days Oh-no did not say anything. On the third day she was still bleeding, and she had no more rags that could be used. She had to tell Old Ching, the oldest Szechuan servant the family had brought out, with the heavy luggage, by train. Old Ching looked after Oh-no.

"Old Mother, Mother Ching, there is blood in my trousers."

Old Ching looked up. She was very deaf. Oh-no nearly had to shout.

"Blood." Old Ching bared her gums in a smile. "You are a woman now, it is natural," she said.

"Mother Ching, it is not that way."

Something in Oh-no's pale, froglike face caught Mother Ching's attention. "Let us take a walk," she said.

On her bound feet (for Ching was very old, and came from old, feudal Szechuan where one could still see bound feet), she hobbled down the forty-five steps in the terrace leading down from the house, and up the road, followed by Oh-no. All around them were the silent hills. In a gap between two hills lay the sea that Oh-no had never seen before coming to Hong Kong.

"Now," said Mother Ching, "who was it?"

"The Old Master."

"When?"

"Three days ago."

Old Mother Ching struck Oh-no across the face. "You egg of a turtle," she cried, "so young, already running after men."

"I did not want it."

"There is no excuse. Have you no shame, no virtue, to come and talk of your whoring to me? I should let you die like a dog."

Something that Oh-no did not know was in her came to life then. Something fierce and reckless, never to be put down again. Oh-no was a peasant, and you can drive a peasant too far. Even a peasant from Szechuan.

But Mother Ching was old. She did not see. She went on abusing Oh-no. And Oh-no stood still, and stared between the hills, at the sea.

When they returned to the house, Old Ching gave Oh-no some shredded tobacco leaf, and some brown ointment on a paper. "Put that on, it will stop the blood. Lie down on my bed. You must not move for a day or two."

The bleeding stopped. Oh-no went back under the stairs. But in the crowded servants' quarters they had seen Oh-no lying on the bed and they guessed.

Some of the menservants would have gone to Oh-no under the stairs, then, but they were afraid, because Old Master might want to use her again.

But they made fun of Oh-no, and told stories in front of her, and leered, and Oh-no thought she would die of shame; and she thought that she would kill herself; but she did not.

The fierceness in her grew and grew. She waited, and she did not know what she was waiting for. "I will have my revenge," she thought. And it seemed that the whole of her was growing into just one word, one shout: *Revenge*.

## I V

"Why can't I go to see *Murder under the Moon?*" said Mei. "Ginger says it's GOOD."

"You can't go to the movies every week," I said. "Let's walk round the Peak with Ginger, collect ferns, and have cream cake and chocolate ice cream at the teashop afterwards."

"Ginger is going to see *Murder under the Moon* again. Some children are lucky; they go to the movies every night. I'm not brought up like the others," said Mei.

"I won't have you going every Saturday," I said. "It's bad for your eyes. Other children's parents don't care; they're so overcrowded at home that they are glad to let them go to the cinema."

"My friends," said Mei in a superior tone, "chew bubble gum and buy film star photographs, and all the comics. They read *Films Weekly*. We're going to America, Ginger and I, when we are big."

"Even in America people don't go to the movies every day," I said. "They work sometimes."

"All Americans are rich," said Mei firmly. "They all have cars, and they dance a lot. American ladies are much fatter in front than Chinese," said Mei, looking critically at her mother.

"Oh heaven," I said, worn out; "I'll buy you both bubble gum. I'll buy you a picture of Ingrid Bergman, and one of Lana Turner for Ginger."

"When I'm grown up," said Mei, "I don't want to work hard. It's silly and it makes you look old. I'll marry a rich man, just like the others."

"Wonderful," I replied. "Maybe I can come and help your amahs look after your children."

"Americans never have children," said Mei. "But they are always in love, which is boring. Are you going to marry Mark? Is he rich?"

"I don't think he is rich, but would you mind if I married him?" I asked.

"If you marry him," said Mei, "and we live in a house again instead of living in a big hospital, shall we have Chinese food or English food at home?"

"We'll have Chinese food one day and English food the next."

"There's a girl at school," said Mei. "Her mother has married an Englishman. The children all make fun of her. They say her father is a foreign devil. They say he smells bad. They laugh at her."

"Nonsense. Anyway Mark can't be your father, because your father is dead. He can only be my husband. So there."

"I'll tell the girls," said Mei. "Other children don't understand these things," she said and her face assumed the same conceited expression that her mother often had. "That girl is stupid. She cries when we tease her. I'll tell them an English friend of MINE wants to marry my mother, and they won't laugh at me, because I am never hurt."

## V

Lily Wu lived in the Chinese Wantsai district, but her beat, like so many of her profession, was the business sector of Hong Kong with its staid Victorian edifices, the wide main streets round the Gloucester and Hong Kong Hotels, the Post Office, Cable and Wireless; from the imposing Hong Kong and Shanghai Bank to Whiteaways on one side, and from the China Emporium to the Mercantile Bank on the other.

Lily was also a refugeee. She had worked in Peking for the last six years, in a second-class house of the Western City. Then the communists had come.

The business had been stopped, the houses closed. "You are no longer the slaves of men, you are The People," said the communists. The girls had been examined, their blood taken by doctors for the "flower and willow" disease; the sick sent to the hospital. The others had gone to girls' camps for rehabilitation. No perfume, no lipstick, no permanents, no manicures, no banquets, no men. Lily thought it was frightful.

Lily lived for three months with many other prostitutes from all over Peking in a converted school. They slept in dormitories that had once housed students, in two rows of orderly camp beds. They wore plain gray clothes, trousers and tops. They cut their hair, wore forage caps like the soldiers of the People's armies. They lost their slim figures on the coarse food. They rose at six and did physical exercises till seven. They attended classes: reading and writing for the illiterate, political tuition, history of the country, duties of the citizen. They swept their floors, made their beds, washed their clothes. In the afternoon they had sewing lessons. They sang patriotic songs as they planted vegetables. They played volleyball.

Fiery young men and women, students in ungainly uniforms, came to talk to them. The girls discovered how terrible their lives had been. At weekly meetings, tears streaming down their faces, they talked of their past; how they had been sold; how cruel their "mother" was; no matter how hard they worked all night, they were always in debt; they told of beatings they had endured and perversions they had practiced to please. They told how they went down the scale with age and wear, from first-class to the fearsome fourth-class that lay on mats in the blind alleys and in doorways, and dragged the rickshaw coolies to them, twenty, thirty, fifty a night. Some of the thirty-year-olds were broken-down old women without hair.

After three months many talked of the future. Now they were like everyone else, and would help to build the great New Democracy. Lily felt jealous when she saw them changed, shining with inner fervor, striding sexless in their trousers. Many became factory workers; two would train to become agricultural engineers; one to be a doctor. Some were left, like Lily, an intractable residue. They had another three months' course. "Some take longer to become new," said the political instructor.

Lily was born a slave-spirit. She liked the excitement of hearing the slave girl shout: "A guest has arrived," and seeing the strange man come in from the street. She missed the occasional rich banquets, though she might starve between. "You have no character, Lily," said her friends. "You never had any character. Why don't you want to be a self-respecting, honorable woman? The country needs all of us for its rebuilding. Life is going to be hard, perhaps, but we are no longer slaves. We are free. China stands on her own, great and honored; no one will ever oppress us again."

Lily knew that she had no character. It was her fate. She did not want character; she wanted her old habits. Lying in bed till noon, dragging her slippers till her hair had been combed by the slave girl, dressing and waiting for the guests. She did not mind how erratic men's tastes, how curious and amounting to pain their desires. She was stolid and healthy.

In those six months she did not learn anything. Rehabilitation went through her like grains of sand through a fowl. She absorbed none of it.

The political instructor sighed when Lily came again before him. "Comrade Wu," said he, "I urge you to stay another three months and have your thoughts rectified. You have not progressed well."

Lily looked down at the floor. "I would like to join my friends in Shanghai," she said finally. "They will find work for me."

The instructor knew the type. Some people could not be saved. It was hard to admit that some people could not be saved, for the instructor had great faith and patience. But so it was. He did not insist.

"Perhaps it is better for you to go to your friends in Shanghai. If you do not find them in Shanghai, they will be in Hong Kong. Hong Kong is a very mixed place, all kinds of people go there. You will find your friends in Hong Kong I think," said the instructor, knowing that she had no friends.

Lily came down to Hong Kong. Her beat was the best section of the town, and she sat, when she was not walking about, in the lobby of one of the best hotels.

## V I

The house on Conduit Road was fragrant with carnations in pots along the garden wall. Through the windows the harbor streaked with ships lay seemingly within hand reach. "How beautiful is Hong Kong," said Fiona Manton, back from Europe a few days previously. "Every time I return to it I think how lucky we are to have lived here many years, and to have had enough money to live well."

It was peaceful in the drawing room with Fiona's detached, undemanding friendliness. It was not necessary to act a role, to wear a mask. Ah Sun, the old servant, ritually poured tea, passed sandwiches and cinammon biscuits. Evelyn Walsingham came in with Tattybogle, fresh from a long walk. Tatty barked cheerfully, advanced towards me sitting in the striped chair, and with his front right paw scratched my bare leg, which was quite painful. "There," said James, "he likes you. Tatty only does that to people he really likes.'

Mark, absurdly handsome with his brown face and very blue eyes, held his pipe gently between two fingers. Evelyn sat next to him, in green linen, serene, precise. I imagined Mark thinking: "Evelyn is my favorite middle-aged woman. I am very fond of her. I long to tell her about Suyin and myself. We owe our meeting to the happy inspiration which prompted her to invite us to the same party, and after God I must be grateful to Evelyn. Would Suyin mind if I told her?" He looked towards me, and I turned my head.

"This is where it began, in this house, in this chair. He was only a foreigner to make small talk to, and now I faint and melt within because he has looked towards me. If Evelyn had not asked us to dinner at the same time, I might have missed him, forever, all my life . . . how terrible, and I would not even have known it."

I liked Fiona as I looked at her, the large brown eyes, the humorous mouth. "She's not pushing her kindness down my throat, it's nice." A delightful voice, something Irish in its softness, her words not coated with that acid mixture of condescension and curiosity displayed by many Englishwomen in Hong Kong. They seemed strangely bent on proving their entourage the best in the Colony, too casual in their frequent recalls of dinner at a particular house, cocktails with a certain general; pursuing gentility with extremist measures, and too careful with certain inflections. "How come," I said in a burst of that occasional appalling frankness which brought me many invaluable enemies and some good friends, "how come you are not Colony-minded after your many years here, Mrs. Manton? It seems to me you have successfully escaped the mania of hearsay and the Hong Kong way of thought."

Unperturbed, Fiona replied: "But not the Hong Kong way of life, for I think I'm utterly spoiled with good servants and comfort. But I still like people as people."

"I know what you mean," said Evelyn. "The English Hong Kong is a small place, and *très potinier*. Many of those who come here suddenly find themselves faced with a standard of living incomparably above the one they endure in England. House, servants, car, leisure all the time, which they never had before and do not know how to use — can you blame them if they feel lost and insecure? They have been, they think, lifted in the social scale, and must live up to it. They are afraid to lose caste within the narrow circle to which they are confined by the scope of their interests, to be rejected from the social herd for any peculiarity of thought, to lose in the struggle for conformity up the nicely graduated steps of the island hierarchy. Their aim is to attain that chimerical upper stratum of birth and financial security which only exists in the English middle-class mind, but which, in the Colony, is still doubt-fully symbolized by that eminence called the Peak."

"Your people are also exclusive," said Fiona, "because they resent us at the same time that they admit how useful Hong Kong is to them, especially at the present time. There are exceptions, of course, but they are always individual. The barrier is there, each race with its own social structure, its hierarchies, its customs and its prejudices. It is quite impossible for anyone to belong to both worlds at once."

"I know someone who does," said Mark, "but then, as you say, it is quite exceptional."

"What is happening in China?" asked Evelyn. "I was reading in the papers of another batch of Chinese students from the United States re-turning to Shanghai. And the first thing they did was to launch into fiery attacks, in the newspapers, against the 'imperialism' of the coun-try where they had studied. They confessed to having been seduced by corrupt, perverse reactionary thoughts. It makes frightening reading."

"Oh I suppose it's a phase," I said. "The attacks are propaganda, part of the policy to eradicate the hold of American influence on our edu-cational system. All our revolutions have been marked by antiforeign feeling; xenophobia is always latent in China, and is due to our ever-present recall of oppression and humiliation; we, like the Irish, have historical memories. I think all missionaries will have to go, for today China is fiercely pro-itself, and will not let its higher education be under foreigners again. It's as if Oxford and Cambridge were run by Chinese dons and Buddhist monks."

"But it seems ungrateful to us," said Evelyn, "especially to the Ameri-cans, for they have engaged in extensive philanthropy in China, and many of your universities are subsidized with American money. . . . I was wondering," she added smiling, "if one day when you go back, you too would have to write a confession, and whether you would complain of the evil you had suffered at our hands; whether you too, Suyin, would one day revile what you had seemed to love?"

And I looked around, and then said: "I do not know."

## V I I

"Chinese people," said Mr. Kam, "only need two meals a day."

The new government servant looked at Mr. Kam from behind the double incognito of his thick glasses, which shielded him from the stare of the unknown, and masked his own reactions.

Mrs. Palmer-Jones gave a smile like a purr to Mr. Kam.

Around them the vast reminiscent room spread the trophies of the Kams. A granite hearth from a Scottish castle saturated one end with gloom. On either side, the life-size wax effigies of President Roosevelt and Dr. Sun Yat-sen sat in episcopal converse on stalls of carved oak. On a table with devious legs, a Grecian urn's unflustered mourners stalked near an ivory centaur, and the Tour Eiffel in shining steel reared towards the perpetual tremolo of the crystal chandeliers the un-wavering accusation of its spike. Along the paneled walls encrusted with mother-of-pearl planets, stood marble replicas of the statuary upon which the Kams had unfalteringly gazed in the Louvre, the Brit-ish Museum, the Vatican, and other places. Venus de Milo and Queen Victoria in full dress presided over this concourse of hardened nudes. The colorful depravities of the ceiling, inspired by a view of the Sistine Chapel, in an American painter who had taken up reincarnation, de-lighted Mr. Kam and dumbfounded even the highest British govern-ment officials.

Mr. Kam had noticed the eyes of this new, and young, government servant, wandering round his house; from the moment when, in the hall, he had greeted the man and Mrs. Palmer-Jones between the stuffed lion with the ingenious Swiss machine inside it that roared when it was wound, and Lady Godiva pale on her wilted horse. He had seen those safely goggled eyes immobilized by the four-foot brass eagle pedestaled upon Mr. Kam's marmoreal coat of arms, with fleur de lotus, phoenix rampant, and a comet. The white sun of the Kuomintang in its center was now superseded by five quiet stars, for the new Chinese flag was out, and Mr. Kam, after all, was Chinese. He had no doubt but that the young man admired everything wordlessly, as the English are prone to do.

"Chinese people," repeated Mr. Kam, "never eat more than two meals a day. It is not necessary for them to eat more." His hand touched his favorite lamp, placed on the lacquered table near the flowery teacups of transparent porcelain, two hundred years old. The lamp was a camel's dried stomach, inflated and shaped to stand without support, purchased from a British Colonel of the Indian Army, retired.

"Once upon a time," thought the young man, "I was told that the Chinese had good taste; that they lived in beautiful courtyards with lotus ponds, and were surrounded by exquisite old curios."

Mr. and Mrs. Kam were justly proud of their home. For this they had painstakingly voyaged in ships, resided in grandiose and uncomfortable European and American hotels, acquiring expensively the best that Western knowledge of beauty offered. Guides and friends had taken them to Buckingham Palace, Holyrood, Washington's Home, Oberammergau, St. Peter's. They had crawled through countless museums and famous sites, and Mr. Kam had nodded all the way. If at times his horrified inner self rebelled, his well-controlled round face showed no trace of it. This was the best; he made sure of that. This was all that Western books and educated Westerners agreed in admiring. These statues they erected in public squares, for the education of their young.

Mr. Kam would have only the best. It was a fair exchange; since many foreign friends of Mr. Kam, asking for something "typically Chinese" had received jade figurines, scrolls, and porcelain, it was only right that he, in return, should gather in his house these proven and sumptuous manifestations of European art.

Mr. Kam had amassed his wealth during thirty years of British peace in a Hong Kong safe from the troubles of the mainland. And he was grateful. Benevolent causes and charitable organizations, those outstanding features of Hong Kong social life, had his patronage. Mention of his contributions could never be omitted from the newspapers; he had by now given enough to entitle him to more than a hint of a possible honor.

The government servant remembered what his unpleasant and cynical predecessor had said, a parting defamation which he had withstood with the frigidity of shock and the supercilious idealism of the Englishman new to Hong Kong's little ways. "Voluntary contribution, the British way . . . There are a few reliables, but for others, it's charity at the sword-point of an O.B.E."

Welfare, thought the government servant, dismayed by greedy charity. "Look at Adeline Palmer-Jones. There she sits, suffused with patronizing benevolence, more regal than Queen Victoria, unencumbered with need for tact, a poker player with all the aces in her handbag. She achieves grandeur, a corpulent Britannia not come to beg, but to confer upon Mr. Kam the honor of parting with another million for the benefit of a column in the Hong Kong *Post*. I must hand it to her; she levies well."

"I think," said Mr. Kam gravely, "that it is bad for Chinese youth to eat three times a day. They do not need so much food. They are not used to it, the poor. It will produce much illness in them."

Mrs. Palmer-Jones agreed; she couldn't agree more with Mr. Kam. The Chinese were an extraordinary race. They could work longer hours and sleep less and especially eat far less than English people needed to. She, Adeline, had been in China for so many years. She loved the Chinese. All those dear little children.

"Mr. Kam," said the government servant, "the food for these one hundred and forty orphans comes to one hundred and fifty dollars a day, including staff salaries. I don't think it can really be cut down."

Mr. Kam shook his head sadly. "I am not rich, not any longer," he imparted, buttoning the young man with his distress. "My father is getting old, very old. I shall need a lot of money for his funeral. Very expensive, funerals. My father feels that his tomb should be enlarged, and of course I must please him. You know how we are, we Chinese" — he switched to a beam, producing Ye Olde China for the benefit of the foreigners — "filial duty, filial respect. Confucius."

Mr. Kam knew that the English think highly of Confucius.

Mrs. Palmer-Jones now tackled Mr. Kam. Such a fine new project, a large hotel to relieve the overcrowding in the Colony . . . air conditioning if possible, electric cookers and laundry. . . . Sir Madison Tam had given the site and a great deal of money for the building. It showed such confidence in the future of Hong Kong. It showed the wonderful spirit of Hong Kong's Great Men. Someone would be greatly pleased if a public-spirited person like Mr. Kam came forward with a donation for the furnishings and interior decoration and for the garden. The furnishing would be specially designed by a world-famous architect, and the garden — they were importing a specialist from America to do the garden.

Mr. Kam invisibly pricked his ears. This sounded like a good thing, a fine big building showing from many miles out, nothing to do with those uninteresting tenements and slums down below. In Mrs. Palmer-Jones's mellifluous tones he read again a promise. But he hesitated. Was it not known that the Palmer-Joneses, too, were in the running for letters after their name? If Mrs. Palmer-Jones could not arrange a diminutive alphabet for her husband or for herself, how could he, Mr. Kam, expect her to arrange one for him? And with the communists so near, was it wise to co-operate too visibly with the English? It was all very vexing. He decided to wait until a definite offer should be made to him.

"Times are not good," he announced. "You see Hong Kong. It looks so rich, so happy. But there are many refugees, many communists here already. Tomorrow there may be an invasion."

"Hong Kong is quite impregnable," said Mrs. Palmer-Jones. "Quite impregnable. Our soldiers are the finest in the world, Mr. Kam."

"Sure, sure," said Mr. Kam. "But we, the poor people, we don't understand about fighting. What shall we do? We shall have no money. Already business is so bad now. Tomorrow I may be a beggar," said Mr. Kam, shaking his face with a tragic downward wrench.

It was obvious that nothing could be done. Just like dear, cunning

Mr. Kam, to ask both the young man and Mrs. Palmer-Jones, with their different requests, at the same time.

Mr. Kam had invited them to dinner. They must stay to have a meal, only a very few friends. They could not say no.

In the large dining hall presided over by "The Last Supper" and the Statue of Liberty brandishing a red light, the guests sat round rosewood tables and eighteen people consumed delicacies amounting to two thousand dollars. Mrs. Kam, knowing the prejudices of foreigners in favor of hygiene, washed the bowls and cups and plates in front of them in boiling water disinfected with Dettol. After dinner a hundred dollars worth of firecrackers were let off near the swimming pool. Mrs. Kam showed the women guests the new diamonds purchased from South America. Three hundred and sixty thousand dollars. "It's so easy to take away if you have to go by airplane," said Mrs. Kam. Their eldest son was fond of dogs and had two Dalmatians and two chows. "My son spends thirty-five dollars on their food every day," said his mother. The son owned one of the largest cars in Hong Kong, that city of enormous cars. He was thinking of buying another one.

Under Mr. Kam's bed reposed his coffin, made of finest lammu wood, awaiting its predestined occupant.

"I don't understand," said the government servant new from England. "Godiva in the hall, the coffin under the bed. The diamonds, and he wants to cut the orphans down to two meals a day. Thirty-five dollars on four dogs, and one hundred and fifty for as many humans. I wonder if I'm not dreaming all this . . . but I mustn't go on like that, otherwise I don't think I could stay very long in Hong Kong."

# CHAPTER VII

# *The Moon Feast*

*October 1949*

MARK AND I HAD MANY FRIENDS, AND ONE OF THEM WAS
the moon. *Les dévots de la lune,* we called ourselves, amiable lunatics
pervaded by moonbeam madness, fervent disciples, docile unfettered
captives no longer disputing our surrender to her enchantment. In
China, poets have become the lovers of the moon, and one of them
lost his earthbound life attempting to embrace her in a lake. As for
ourselves, it was quaint sharp distress to sit in careful curtained houses
that shut out the moon-inhabited night.

"Once in Sumatra," said Mark, "I journeyed alone with a guide and
two elephants, sleeping through the hot day and traveling by night.
The moon was about, at first an elegant curved blade; waxing, perfectly bisected; round, and full of cold lunar birds and flowers. The
night I remember the moon hung alone in the sky, an opal great with
fire, dominating the silence of the earth. The flanks of the elephant in
front of mine were washed with silver. His legs were swathed in man-
high grass blue with moonlight, and we advanced through the phos-
phorescent flat plain in indolent sea motion. Except for the swish of
grass in the wake of the elephant, there was nothing to mar this purity
of moonlight and silence. And suddenly rose a racking echo, half
bark, half screech; it was my guide who found the sway of his beast
too much for him. How wise is God, who gives us forever the small
flaw, the slight outrage to perfection otherwise unbearable and stifling
to our mere humanity."

The autumn moon impassioned me. Only autumn moons, to me, were love moons. "I remember an October night in wartime London: the blackout curtains drawn tight and I was reading in bed. My husband came in late. 'Oh come, let us go out,' he cried, 'for the beautiful moon is in the sky and we cannot miss her.' So we went out into the street, and walked down the Strand, and onto Waterloo Bridge, where we stood, holding hands, and looking at her, hard-shining, bright and round. And the Thames was solid silver. But the moon in London is smaller than in Hong Kong, and in Peking she is biggest of all."

Mark protested, his blue eyes astonished. "But how unscientific of you. The moon is always the same size, everywhere."

"It is not. The moon is bigger in some places than in others." And whatever Mark said of exact measurement, of span and circumference, I would not be moved.

"You are quite right," he wrote from Singapore, the next spring. "The moon here is smaller than in Hong Kong. Now I believe you when you say the moon in Peking is bigger than in Paris or London."

And from Taejon in Korea, much later, he wrote: "I saw the moon tonight with her attendant clouds, larger and more brilliant than I have yet seen her."

We climbed up the Peak to watch the evening moon, heavy, orange, and opaque; we stood below various trees to capture her late brightness tangled in the black lace of foliage. We compiled a moon anthology. We talked about her to our friends, and our judgment of them varied as they appeared glad or restless under our moon talk. Mark would turn to me: "What a pity, the chap has no moon feeling at all." But what our friends thought or said of us for our lunar intoxication we never knew.

Now the moon feast was come, the fifteenth day of the eighth month, the Harvest Festival which was also my birthday in the Chinese calendar style. "Let us celebrate the moon and you," said Mark. "We shall drink the Maotai wine in stone bottles which you brought back from China, and I can look at you, and as always, become unlucid and delightfully muddled."

And so with friends we went to look at the moon on the water at the fishing village so prosaically called Aberdeen by the English. There on an arm of sea between the island of Hong Kong and a tiny islet called Aplichau, Duck's Tongue, strung along the main road circling the island, is a fast-growing townlet where live the fishing people. Along the coast of the island, and the New Territories and Kowloon on the mainland opposite, are dotted the villages, temples and fleets of the sea-peasant, separate from the land-bound toiler by customs and religious rites exclusive to his profession. It is a beautiful sight from the hills, the deep blue, narrow bay at Aberdeen compact with close-huddled junks at rest. The boatwomen are strong and dauntless, and among the careless children who get run over by the drivers of Hong Kong, the Aberdeen fishermen's children are many. Unused to the dangerous land, they play among the road's intermittent stream of cars as they would on the safe planks of their family junks.

There in a row in the middle of the small bay are strung the houseboat restaurants, expensive and popular, where the tourist and the rich spend on one meal enough to feed many a boat family for a month.

Through John Tam I invited Ernest Watts, wanting to see him and Mark together. Ernest Watts conferred the honor of his company on very few. Father Low, the tall Jesuit who knew Chinese so well, was coming, and with him he brought a friend, Dr. Goh, a spectacled Chinese psychologist. Dr. Goh brought two of his children, explaining that his wife and the other five were at another party. My dearer-than-sister Maya Wong came with her youngest daughter, the other two having returned to school in Shanghai, and with her came a friend, a student just out of China, Eileen Cheng. I have always thought it one of the better customs of my country that one's friends should as a matter of course bring uninvited guests, and especially bring children. For what greater pleasure than to please our friends? And how can one enjoy a feast without the happiness of children? Mark brought François Perrin, a young Frenchman slight of build, the owner of an enormous Cadillac. I brought my daughter Mei and she brought her friend Ginger, one year older than herself. And thus, a goodly company, we set forth early in the evening to go to Aberdeen.

The Cadillac took six of us, with four children haphazardly disposed among our knees, through the swift dusk; Mark, John Tam, Ernest Watts and Ginger followed in Watts's car. The ships at sea wore sparse lights when we started, and the half-clear sky seemed empty. François said: "Heaven is waiting for the moon, as we are." We went past the University with its hodgepodge of buildings on the hill slope; up Pokfulum Road, past forbidding Mount Davis, its flanks dappled with the crescent graves of the Chinese cemetery; past the deep hollow where stood the Coffin Hospital and the Leprosarium; the promontory on which a hundred women had stamped a wide flat plain where a hill had stood; the House of Wisdom and the Hospital; the Dairy Farm; the semi-squatter settlements groveling between the hill and the cattle pens; past the new huts housing the refugees and their chickens. At the turn of the road we caught the moon, emergent from behind a hilltop, wreathed in gold-fringed cloud. François and Mei on his lap both gave a shout. "Look, look," said Mei, reaching for the moon with her hand, as she had one day reached for the sun, because it was pink as her plate, and she was four years old. And now at nine she made the same gesture. Heavy and arrogant, the lonely amber despot sat on top of the dark hill, and then the cloud swept over her. "She shall come out again." Father Low's voice, pitched to prophecy, wafted from the black depths of the back seat.

We reached Aberdeen, and parked in a spot forbidden to private cars. "*Mais ça ne fait rien,* of course," said François in his talented mixture of French and English interspersed with Chinese expressions, "*c'est fête aujourd'hui.*" A surging crowd of boatwomen, black-trousered and black-aproned, with round woven straw hats on their heads, pressed round us, pushing and catching us by our clothes to pull us into their sampans and row us across the hundred yards of water to the restaurant boats. We saw Mark and the others and went towards them, flicking away with movements of our fingers and our fans the human bodies pressing on ours. A large red-cheeked boatwoman, with parted legs planted in front of our group, held all the others at bay. We followed her down the stone steps to her sampan, and sat on rattan chairs. Under the round mat roof of the boat hung colored paper hare lanterns and lotus lanterns in honor of the festival. A little girl, as pale as her mother was red, helped to row, a fascinating movement, with the single oar held sideways wriggling in the water, the woman revolving the oar in her hand and rocking back and forth on heel and sole of foot. So effortless seeming, so smooth, so difficult. Across the polished ebony water shone the gaudy neon signs of the restaurant boats — Chinese characters a foot long and wide, in red, blue and green — constellating their landward side. The restaurants were loud with human voices and the relentless smack of endless games of mahjong, the playing of which is traditional at festivals and celebrations, including funerals. All over Hong Kong one can hear mahjong played day and night, and from the staff quarters of the coolies at the Hospital, the click of the dice goes on long after every other noise has stopped. "But in China now," said Eileen Cheng, two days in Hong Kong, "it is a crime to play mahjong. It is a sign of sloth and waste. Some of my friends played and they were sent to sweep the streets for a week. It is a capitalist vice. I think it is right to punish them," she added in a loftily moral tone, "for gambling is a dangerous excess with us, as alcohol is with foreigners."

A sleek, pomaded young man, the manager of the restaurant we were heading for, stood at the foot of the steps along the houseboat side, and greeted us with smiles as shining as his hair. François and John and I walked towards the floating pantry and kitchen moored to the seaward side of the houseboat, while the others sought a table from where the moon would be seen. Four large wooden pens were fastened at water level to this side, their walls bored with holes for fresh sea water; inside swam the chosen fish. At right angles to the boat was the kitchen, a floating platform lit with hurricane lamps and peopled with braziers, small and large stoves, and a long array of cooks. Round baskets, dipping in the sea, hung from the platform. They contained shrimps, crabs, lobsters and squids. A giant like a fat sea god, bronze of skin in the brazier glow, rode the water on a little shell boat, hovering with a short net over the fish tanks. He snared the ones we selected — pert red spotted garoupas, iridescent blue-banded lentjans, two silvery pomfrets and a grass-green wrasse — and tossed them one by one towards the platform, where a little boy with a complete harelip caught them expertly in another net and flung them in turn to the first in the line of cooks. The first cook with the flat of his chopper stunned the fish on a large round board, a slice of camphor tree trunk. He passed it to a second, who split it with one stroke of a sharp knife; the insides came out, and he gave the fish to a third. And so our fish went on, down the belt of cooks, whence it would emerge on a flowered porcelain dish, with ginger and spice and sauce — delectable, delicious, and still equipped with that wide round-eyed look of passionate, speechless surprise, which a fish carries to its final destination on the Chinese dinner table.

The harelip gave a shout, and we looked, to see an enormous lobster held in his hand for our inspection, its cream belly towards us and the symmetrical projections of its limbs like a many-branched candelabra. A convulsion shook it and all its legs came together in multiple sup-plication. Quickly it too was approved of and taken away and chopped to be cooked in red pepper and sweet sauce. Crabs speckled with blue and gold, shrimps pearl-gray and translucent we looked on and nod-ded, and execution was done on all these lives. And then, pleased with the ordering of our dinner, we turned to join the others seated at a round table, talking and fanning, cracking melon seeds, and drinking green tea.

Heaven establishes amity even among barbarians, but a common gentle madness, a subtler, long-lasting bond fastens upon us in genial company. This is a friendship. Friendship cannot be exclusive or self-centered; as a light in a garden, illuminating ampler space of trees and flowers the brighter it shines, its very essence is the discovery of sim-ilarly attuned objects, the calling into being of delightful fancies and noble thoughts in others. How impoverished and meager a world without congenial spirits to share the dream of miraculous agreement, in pursuit of splendid truths! And so Mark and I had many friends, alive in our age and dead in the past. Companions of beauty, intimates in joy, and in sorrow. How good is God, and how lucky I; for among the friends of Mark I was one, and his gentle friendship released me from the shadow of terror at the bottom of myself until I no longer knew fear; until in the sensuous enjoyment of each enchanted instant we transcended ourselves, and found our immortality, although we ourselves should certainly die.

That evening devoted to our friend the moon, we felt subtly exhilarated, even before the Maotai wine had started its amble round the table, and deeming ourselves more than usually witty, wise or eloquent, said words and thought fancies that otherwise would not have been. And immediately I knew that Ernest Watts and Mark Elliott talked to each other; like well-matched horses their minds ran swift and joyful together, while John Tam, in dual adoration, listened with fierce attentiveness.

"How beautiful his speech," I thought as I listened to Ernest Watts, "and how, like a skillful merchant showing jade, he spreads the jeweled anecdotes, revolving the gemlike words in that low clear voice, and how they glow with him!" And John Tam, like myself, enamored of beauty, but with no words to say it, slapped me on the shoulder, like a brother. "You're getting fat-ter, man," he said, putting the accent on the second syllable as all Malay Chinese do. "Ought to play some badminton to keep the lipoid down." And then lower: "You were right to ask them together. They're having a good time. I don't know what they're talking about, but I'm going to read up all these books one day, for I feel a fire within me when I listen."

"Yes," I whispered back, definitely adding Ernest Watts to the many-faceted, the glittering world which went round Mark, the snare of beauty wide, so wide that he would never feel it. John Tam and the goldfish, Ernest Watts and his precious conversation, Maya's fragile, exquisite looks, the Maotai wine, the moon, all the loveliness of earth for Mark. And to make it quite perfect, who should be sitting at the next table, who rose to walk towards us with both hands outstretched and peal upon peal of tremendous laughter, like the deep bronze bay of a monastery bell, but the large, charming Portuguese manager of our hotel in Macao? He drew a chair and settled on Mark's left, and beamed at him through admirably shining glasses, looking as pleased with himself as if he had engineered the moon, the houseboat and our meeting; and immediately started talking of Fear.

"Fear," said the Portuguese, "is a funny thing. Take me, a big tough guy, 180 lbs. stripped. I like a good time, and I'm never scared except of going to hell, which is natural, but that's in the hands of God. Not afraid of the Reds either, though they've taken Canton, and all China is theirs, and they'll be on the border in no time. Yet I remember one time when I knew what terror was, and it was seven years ago today.

"I was in the Volunteers in Hong Kong during the last war. The Japs sent me to work in the coal mines in Hokkaido. Four years I was there. We used to eat the same as they did, balls of rice and a little salt fish and vegetables. Hefty fellows they were, the Japs; they'd take the drill with one hand and swing it over their shoulder. And all this time I hadn't been frightened once. Some of the other fellas got neuroses, and they faked accidents so they'd go off work. One or two of them pushed the drill through their foot so they'd stop working down below. They'd jab hard, push, and *scrunch* their foot would spread out, all churned up like a red cauliflower with the bones in little white bits. And the guy would look at his foot for a long time as if he didn't understand it.

"One day I let the drill drop on my foot. Just drop, I didn't push, and I immediately lifted it up again. I didn't feel anything. In the evening I had my shower and as I undid my shoe I saw a hole through the top. When we sat to our meal, cross-legged on the floor, I noticed that the hole went through my foot and I saw it on my sole a little black hole. No blood. I fainted right away. After that I could not work down below any longer, I was so frightened of the drill. My heart beats hard whenever I think of it," said the manager, applying his hand to the left side of his shirt and looking imploringly at Mark. He was a little drunk.

And Mark said in his most lovely voice: "But I am very frightened too. In airplanes. I always have to get slightly *beschwippst* before I climb into an airplane; and I climb into them so very often."

John stared at him respectfully. "Gee, Mark," he said, "did they shoot you down or something during the war?"

Mark became acutely uncomfortable. He said finally, "There was a crash."

"Fear is an odd thing," said Maya in Chinese to me. "One starts by being afraid of something definite — bats, one-eyed men, night, leprosy, being beaten. Then one gets into a habit, going from one fear into another, existence punctuated by its lapses."

Eileen Cheng said with a beaming smile, also in Chinese so that the others would not understand. "I do not fear the communists, they released me from my misery. My husband was rich and old, and I was forced. My family would not allow me to divorce, for fear of loss of face. Five years I endured it, always in fear. I became frightened of everything, seeing friends, opening letters. When anyone smiled at me, I thought they were scheming to harm me. I could never do anything, because I always questioned my motives, and other people's intentions. Then the communists came and I had my divorce. We put a notice in the paper and it was done. And now I am a student again. I am going to America to study English literature. I am no longer afraid."

"Fear is our natural state," Watts was saying languidly to Mark. "Alas for the white man that the time of the great plague is no longer with him. He reads about the flood and the earthquake in the morning newspaper, and by lunch time has forgotten how many thousands died. He has lost his collective memory of hunger; though he may starve individually, he is no longer driven to the cannibalistic state of Asiatic famine. City-bred man makes perpetual light to negate his fear of the dark, and he cannot hear the thunder because of the traffic roar.

The cataclysms of nature are no longer his, and he must forge his own disasters as outlets to his fear."

"When the Chinese peasant has a son," I said, speaking for Mark to hear, but addressing myself to Dr. Goh, "he dresses him in girl's clothes, and gives him a girl's name, because he is afraid that the jealous gods may take him away. When the crop in his field is bountiful, he stands in the ditch and shakes his head, and cries aloud: 'Bad rice, bad rice.' He does this to propitiate the gods, and to deceive them. And this memory must be with me still, for I too am frightened of the supernatural powers, and dare not believe my luck."

Dr. Goh nodded. "It is the same with a large proportion of the insane and mentally deranged of Hong Kong," he said amiably, "who have their roots in the adjacent country. For only six per cent of the island's Chinese claim to be Hong Kong born. And their ways are peasant folk ways, their thinking not founded on abstract notions; cause and effect are not related, and their belief in control and external influence so very like schizophrenic ideas that it is often extremely difficult to differentiate them."

"Among the so-called Westernized, educated young men and women of Asia," said Father Low, "you often find this split, divided personality, which is very puzzling. At one moment the well-educated young Asiatic will behave and talk in a manner which seems reasonable and very much like one's own, and in another he will revert to another mode of thinking and behavior with such startling suddenness that one can scarcely believe that it is the same man."

"Yes," said Dr. Goh, "people in times of stress revert to an older pattern. I have known an old man who had lost his money suddenly perform what seemed to his son incomprehensible gestures. His son was a 'marginal man' brought up in modern Chinese schools, no longer acquainted with the old rites. He took his father to the mental hospital, thinking he had gone mad."

François had imbibed a certain quantity of wine, and it made him loquacious. "Not only individuals revert, but nations revert, under the stimulus of fear, to a primitive pattern. The thalamic, decerebrate reaction. And for keeping this fatal fascination geared to high intensity," he said, turning to Mark, "whom have we to thank, but your esteemed profession? Fear, the pleasurable anguish of the masochistic masses, marshaling today, one against the other, two economic systems. How subtly your profession titillates the quasi-sexual excitement of their reciprocal alarm. How deftly it chooses for the front page that item which will more surely provoke the colic of fright, the diarrhea of panic. How undeniably correct its knowledge of the morbid taste of the multitudes, that passion for strong emotion which must be exploited collectively, since it can no longer, under our Western codes, be satisfied in private violence. We all get death in the bargain basement, cheap and second hand, in our thrillers, our films; and work ourselves up to such a pitch of expectation, that we shall not rest content until terror has overwhelmed us all with its fecal odor of an immense cloaca."

The shrimps were *sauté*, the lobster was delicious in red spicy sauce with brown sugar and red peppers, the crabs were stewed with mushroom and chicken; and words fail me when confronted with the culinary excellence of the other dishes. We had my most excellent Maotai wine, and then hot yellow wine. The children were very happy. They ran about the houseboat, and the guests at other tables were delighted, as Chinese always are, to have them about, and made them sit and talk to them. "How nice to be a Chinese child," said Father Low. "You always have your children so much about with you. You do not make them a race apart, shielding them absurdly from life so that they will have a terrible struggle afterwards getting out of the nursery world into the world of reality. We train misfits, but you train men and women for a grownup world. They do not interfere with adult talk and behavior, because much is not hidden from them, and they do not believe that grownups know more than they do."

It was nearly ten o'clock, the most propitious hour at which the moon should be seen. The moon was still hidden by cloud and by the roof of the next houseboat. We sat and ate, and, satiated, talked of Li Po, and Shenfu and other moon lovers, and we envied them.

"Alas," said Father Low, "that the purity and single-mindedness of their lunar passion could not be devoted to some higher object."

"I disagree so much," said François. "What better death to die than with the beloved in ones' arms? Thus Li Po drowned, holding the beautiful moon close to him, and thus would I perish, wrapped in the illusion of a splendid love." And since Father Low also had the soul of a poet, and could not be moralistic for very long, we were soon quoting Chinese verse in praise of wine and moon.

Meanwhile the toil of cloud in which the moon had stayed perturbed the fishing folk of Aberdeen. I looked at Mark, who was tapping his thigh with his black fan, and smiling in a half-dream; for such was my passion, that I had made the night a sign and an omen for us, and even the moon must give me her approbation by coming out at the right hour. And we were perturbed, the fishermen and I, for now another shape was traveling moonwards, a cloud like a menacing dragon with outstretched talons. Suddenly there was an onslaught of firecrackers from all the junks, one after the other. It was the fishermen, frightening the devils of the air and the clouds away, that the moon might be free. They beat gongs, at first a few, then more and more, and from the boatwomen in the many junks around us rose strong wails, derisive railing against the devil cloud. Their incantations flowed across the water and hurled skywards. The water rippled its thick smooth scales, stippled and striped with the reflections of the lanterns and the neon lights. François and John Tam were also infected by the anxiety of the fishermen, and the three of us rose and stood at the prow of the boat. I turned my back on Mark, refusing the knowledge of him, so that the evil gods, the jealous ones, would not guess that he was most precious, and would turn their wrath elsewhere. And this I did, not in pretense, but with my deepest self, for at that moment I was a Chinese peasant, knowing devils and gods, incantation and sacrifice, with fear knowing I must ward off the threat which was on Mark. François shouted encouragement to the fishermen in French, and John Tam translated into Hokkien dialect, and soon we were joined by groups from the other tables. The fisher people became excited, seeing so many of the rich helping their rites, and fired more crackers, and beat their gongs louder, and the women wailed higher, many more of them. Suddenly we all shouted, for the moon, the moon was up, she was up and out of the cloud, her proud vacant face so brilliant and so cruel. Solitary, feline and glaring, liquid light pouring from her, so beautiful, the autumn moon, and we forever caught by her beauty. The fishermen cheered, the women laughed, the children clapped their hands while the baffled cloud tore its last shreds away pursued by a final jeering crepitation of firecrackers. We now called for another catty of hot yellow wine to toast the moon.

> Do not laugh if I, an old man, wear flowers,
> The six-string harp is struck, the goblet passes round.
> Where in man's life is there a moment
> Better than the one before a full wine-bowl?

"For sages and wise men have been mute for many centuries, and their names are forgotten, but drunkards leave a resounding echo after them."

And now at last we could look at each other, Mark and I, across the table our eyes on each other's face. And the slow throb of our confusion.

"I hope," said Dr. Goh, "that the people in the moon have an earth festival, and something comparable to the Maotai wine we have drunk in her celebration."

"I hope they peer at the earth's face, and in its geography see a fairy tie red string round the feet of a boy and a girl when they are babies, so that they may get married later on," said Maya.

"And a hare pounding with a pestle in a large jade bowl the magic for the pills of immortality," said Mei, who had bought a hare lantern that morning.

And Father Low spoke of the "Song of Unending Sorrow," the poem celebrating the love between the T'ang Emperor and the beautiful Yang Kuei Fei. Kuei Fei was so beautiful that one could speak of her only in metaphors of spring nights and fairy palaces, cities emptied for a glimpse of her loveliness, and couriers killing their steeds beneath them to bring her flowers from far-off Yunnan. And all this beauty negated, when the rebellion rose, and the soldiers of the Emperor would not move until Kuei Fei had died. So at Mawei slope, in front of the armies and their horses, she was destroyed. The Emperor could not save her; he could only hide his face with his sleeve. Forever afterwards he saw her, in the curve of a leaf her eyebrows, the glow of petals her face, for she was beauty incarnate. Eileen Cheng liked this poem, for she believed in the superiority of man-and-woman love over every other emotion: "To abuse the pathos of death and the emotionalism of love is an error of judgment not confined to the Western romantic tradition of literature," Ernest Watts, "but then you are going to America to study." "Yes," glowed Eileen, "I shall read, I shall find my soul." I could not refrain from smiling, and I thought:

> Weaving your tendril fingers in your hair
> — Hair a dark cloud bewitched about your face —
> You sit deriding idleness, and bear
> A thousand palsied doubts, that clot the pace
> Of your heart's motion. O marvel, you shall go
> And peer at buried loves and enmities,
> While sparrows pester the green-blossomed trees,
> And say, a wise child sad with newest fruit
> Of information gained: "I have no root."
> When pertinacious worms grow fat and mellow
> On the fair flesh that once was love to touch,
> Will you both sigh and smile, then further burrow
> In some grave ponderous tome that says too much?

We went back to the shore in the same sampan. The boatwomen always waited to row back their clients. The little girl was eating the remains of our dishes, as it was customary for the restaurants to give the leftovers to the sampans. We landed and found ourselves face to face with Reality in the guise of the Palmer-Joneses, who had honored a large party on another restaurant boat with their combined presence, and were waiting for their chauffeur and their car. Adeline immediately separated the sheep from the goats by completely ignoring Ernest Watts, John Tam, Maya and myself, and concentrating her recognition on Mark and on François.

"The Reds are in Canton, Mr. Elliott," she announced. "I hear, though, that there's been a great Nationalist victory."

Mark looked at her with the enormous, deep blue eyes he turned on those who amazed him. He forgot to answer and François came to his assistance.

"*Toujours la même histoire,*" he said. "They always announce a victory when they abandon a city. I wish they would not do it every time," he added plaintively. "It is very boring for me."

"Oh," replied Adeline, with that shudder of dire enjoyment which tragedy at a remove gave her. "How perfectly ghastly. Poor, poor China. We must keep our heads of course," she added in a normal, practical tone.

"You will," said François. "*Ne vous en faites pas, Madame.* Mr. Palmer-Jones will carry on as usual, *j'en suis certain.*"

"A miraculous people the English," he said to Watts later. "They never insist that two and two should make four, because in real life two plus two makes any number you want, provided you want it strongly enough. *Ils s'élèvent à la logique de l'absurde,* and they are so often right."

Mark and I walked to our stone, and sat down under the moon. Now that the excitement of the feast was over, we were sad, because already we saw each other in everything, we were too near the center of ourselves to be joyful. "We have eaten and drunk, honored the moon and talked with friends, we have seen children at play and now we shall love. Is not this life, and happiness?" said Mark. "God is very good to us."

We gazed upon the moon, and were enchanted again.

# CHAPTER VIII

# Mark

*October 1949*

Mark was in my room when I came back from cleaning the abortion. Four days the woman had bled at home before her husband brought her to the Hospital. Exsanguinate, her eyeballs rolled up, she lay unconscious on the operating table. We gave her blood and worked fast, and when it was done she was well enough to whisper a word or two. It was with that sense of well-being which a doctor gets often, and often so cheaply, that I opened the door of my room and found Mark waiting for me.

"Mark." He had not been to my room since the day we had spoken of marriage. He looked different from his urbane, courteous self. "Mark," I said, a little frightened, "what is the matter?"

"I shall have to go back. Back home to Singapore."

We sat down on my bed, he on one side, I on the other, each turned facing the other way. To touch each other with our eyes would overcome us, and we would not be able to think or to talk.

"Has someone gossiped?"

"I do not know. I was going back, later. But this is not the sort of thing one settles in a letter. I must go back now."

"Have you had dinner?"

He had not. He forced down a mouthful or two of the food I brought from the kitchen of the Residents' Quarters, and drank coffee while I told him about the abortion. I did not feel anything at all.

Detached, truly calm when Mark was so upset. "You are schizo-phrenic," I told myself. "This is probably tragic, and involves you. But you are finding it hard not to smile. In fact you are smiling now." Then I saw his eyes looking at me, and I went dark inside. He was not upset, he was unhappy. He had been hurt. He had been hurt and I filled up with darkness. I would always be dark and pitiless when he was unhappy. I suppose all women are like that about their man. No one is allowed to hurt him, except themselves.

"Darling," I said, "please do not worry. It had to come. We were borrowers of time, and perhaps better now than later."

"If I were free," Mark said, "I'd marry you tomorrow. But . . ."

I knew. "But now you feel such a cad," I said consolingly. "Now you are not sure. Because you do not like hurting other people, and you find that you are. Of course you are."

Suddenly this was a play, and we two actors on a dusty stage, among cardboard scenery, thrust into roles, mouthing words, making gestures. Much depended on the words and the gestures. Actions one performed with certain intentions, but the spectators did not know the intentions, neither did they care; intentions were irrelevant to the play. What mattered was the audience's interpretation of one's actions. Not what we meant, but what they thought we meant.

What to us was the kingdom, the power and the glory, was something very different to others: to the pious and the narrow, an indecency to be expurgated with vocal indignation from the world in which they moved. To some of my Chinese friends, a pity that I should succumb to this infatuation for a foreigner, which would prevent me doing what I ought to do. To Suzanne, a charming bit of fun. I had no doubt what a few of Mark's friends would call him for his folly. One could not shrug it away, saying: "Don't worry about gossip. People always gossip." Should we in time become respectable, our adverse critics might be the first to congratulate us; there is nothing a crowd likes better than to drag its procession behind a victor. But at the moment we were vulnerable, we could be hurt. My many-splendored thing smeared across the lips of the complacent and the righteous, fouled with innuendoes, muddied with moralities, until we too would doubt, feel guilty, defeated and absurd. We would be swerved from our intent towards each other. We would become ashamed; furtive, sneaking shame muffling the splendor and the delight, making us wary, watchful, attentive to discretion, desirous of the cemetery odor of concealment, resigned to the stealth of stolen hours in secret. We too would parade due respect for propriety; until one day we would confess: "Yes, it was a mistake. And now it's over. We can be proper again. It did not exist." We would forgo the vision and the dream, refuse the many-splendored thing.

I could not justify us with motives; motives interested no one. All I could do was to make what seemed to me, at the moment, the appropriate gestures in this play which Mark and I had to act to the end. I felt no emotion, and would scatter none. In an instant the formulae were there. My mind went back to the old books, to the Classics I had droned:

*The Master said: "Yu, shall I teach you what knowledge is? When you know a thing, to recognize that you know it; when you do not know a thing, to recognize you do not. That is knowledge."*

Back, back my mind went, to the Book of Rites and Ceremonies:

*"Man and woman do not sit in the same room, do not hang their clothes on the same hook; they do not pass an object from hand to hand."*

The old books, prescribing so minutely, so rigidly the behavior of man in all phases of life, every hour of the day, from the moment of rising, and even during sleep. All life ritual, existence a ceremonial. *For animals are slaves of their impulses, but man has propriety to rule himself.* And I wondered what Confucius would have answered if I had approached him respectfully, and asked his advice on the way I should handle this situation. What would the Master have replied? I dared not think.

"Drink your coffee," I said. Flippancy is the attitude struck by my favorite heroes when tragedy and danger impend, and I had countered cruelty and pain before with laughter and a jest. "Drink your coffee.

You may give me up if you wish. I cannot care, at this moment, whether you do or not. But I shall be worried if you go away from me hungry."

He smiled, already calmer. "I was rather upset," he said simply, "Now you've made it better." Always Mark was to imagine that I could transmute suffering, seize and control it, strip it of its overlay of emotion and make it valuable for both of us. It was one of his illusions about me which I never dispelled.

"Have a cigar," I replied, moving quietly, sitting at his feet on the floor, my head against his thigh and his fingers in my hair. At first his fingers absent-minded, then aware, thinking of me. The cigars were the Szechuan ones I had brought back for him — short and stubby, black and strong. The band round them read: *Corona de Extra.* He laughed as he read the words aloud. "Would you really not mind if I should stick to my present arrangements and give you up? You say that it is infatuation on my part, and that you do not know what love is."

I parried smilingly: "At your age you should realize that no motive is pure, no feeling unmixed, no thought unsullied. Therefore I cannot answer whether I would mind or not. I expect my vanity would be hurt. I would lose face."

"We have never asked," said Mark, his fingers lingering in my hair, "we have never said to each other: 'Do you love me?' What is love? That I love you is happiness enough for me, and that I want to make my whole life with you. But I know well that with you it is all or nothing. I may rise, but I may fail miserably. Sometimes I become afraid. I want to run back to my neutrality, to the conventional life that means little and appears safer."

I said: "I do not know whether I love you. I do not know what love means, it is such a big thing. Should we be free to marry now, I would hesitate. For although I crave the sight and the sound of you, although everything I touch is you, yet it is not the aim and end of my feeling for you to become Mrs. Elliott. I want to look after you, cook your breakfast, clean your shoes, bear your children. But there is something else, something in me that wants . . . I know not what. China perhaps, I cannot explain it."

"If I thought I were doing you harm," Mark said, "I would go away from you immediately. If I thought I prevented you from fulfilling yourself in any way."

"And how would your going away undo what is already done to me? For your absence is even more potent than your presence to evoke you to me."

We looked at each other and burst into laughter, for we had been so very solemn.

"However worrying life can be," said Mark wiping his eyes, "I cannot remain sad for long when we are together. I soon get well. When God made me He must have left some pieces out, for neither injustice nor sorrow stay long with me."

And on his laughter we parted. "When do you go away?" I asked.

"Next week. . . . How gentle you are," he added, "aware yet tranquil. I like it so much."

Gentle? Gentle as a black panther, careful, soft-padding, relentless. I smoked and I thought. And when I slept it was soundly. I knew what I would do.

And although when I woke the pain which had stayed away from me the night before woke with me, full-sized and clamorous, I still did everything the way I had it thought out.

"Whatever you decide, I shall be content, since nothing matters to me but the affirmation of yourself. Your decision, your will. Not outside circumstances. You cannot hurt me except by being untrue to yourself."

Noble-sounding, dignified words; Confucius in an unclassical setting. Smooth-drawn, tranquil gestures, a ceremonial from the Book of Rites. A civilized Chinese play. I bowed my head when he speculated on leaving me; for he in his way played honorably too. He knew what he would face. He knew what he might lose. I showed no disrespectful sorrow, I bowed my head and he saw my hair, black, long, and all my submission to his will. And who could prevail against such humility?

For five days of that week I was peaceful all the time. Dark, form-less, water running softly at night. Tenderness. Passivity. I had never heard of self-assertion. I put forward no rights. A voice who quoted verse and made him laugh. An unresisting hand held in his, we went to peer at the skirmishing butterflies in love along Lovers' Lane. A teller of old legends, tales of love and sweet grief and despair amid the drums of death. A companion who translated the Chinese papers and expounded the meaning wrapped in the laborious, propagandist phrases. A debunker of pomposity, wherever it came from. A night wanderer by his side, stepping as delicately as he around the sinuous bodies of the street sleepers lying on their outspread mats in the cov-ered vaulted sidewalks of Hong Kong. Light, laughing easily, gay with friends and easy laughter.

"I think you would be happy anywhere. You are so gay."

And when he talked of what lay in front of us, tried to reason why he could not relinquish me, I spoke against myself. "But I have noth-ing to hold you, nothing at all. Is love reason enough to inflict pain and suffering?" I said it was Hong Kong, the beauty of it, the fortu-itous occasion, circumstance. "Had we met in London some years ago, we would not have fallen in love; we might never have plucked up enough courage to go out together in Chungking." Every word against our madness. Every gesture delicate surrender to his will.

I told him, beforehand, what would be said and used against me by some people.

"I am a Eurasian. It only means that my mother was European, my father Chinese; in China no one ever thinks of me but as Chinese, but it is not the same with your colonial English. The English of the colonies and the concessions made it a shame and an inferiority to be a Eurasian; perhaps because there are so many of them in India. They will jump at the word, and never think of me as a person at all. It may be bad for your career."

"But the English are the most mongrel people in the world," said Mark. "Only very stupid people think like that, Suyin."

I pointed out all the reasons against us, knowing that he liked to climb mountains. "You do not try to influence me," he said. "You never speak for yourself. You exact no promises."

Thus I played, taking advantage of his honor. I played with all of myself, reckless at every turn, bidding all I was every time. Thus he grew sure of himself, anchored in the certainty of his will. He learned to grasp the pain that was to companion our joy from henceforth until the end, to hold it incessant in thought as he held the delight of me, all the time, all the time.

On the fifth night at the House of Wisdom, I left him.

"Good-by now. I shall not see you again until you come back. If you do come back to Hong Kong."

"Why not?"

"Because it is not fair to take you right up to the last moment. It would be influencing you. You must be alone."

And I walked away, relinquishing two days of our time together, knowing that he would not follow protestingly.

At nine o'clock the night before he left, he rang again, and asked to see me.

"I said good-by to you, two days ago."

"I wish to see you."

"What for?" My brutality hurt me. I swayed a little at the telephone.

"Because I want to." He said it quietly and I knew that it was time to give in.

"I am going out," I lied. "I am going to Church Guest House to see Lucy Koo."

"I shall be with you in ten minutes. I'll take you to your friend in a taxi."

Ten minutes to dress, to lipstick; it was hot and sticky and outside the rain poured down. I stepped into the taxi and gave the address "Church Guest House."

Mark said: "I am sorry I bullied you. I wanted to see you."

"What is the use? What is the use?"

"None. I wondered if from tomorrow my life was to be like the 'Song of Unending Sorrow.' Because somehow I too see your eyebrows in the curve of every leaf, I hear your voice in me; I feel you in the wind and the moonlight; the night is your hair, and the daytime your laughter."

"And I. Not a moment but you are with me . . . all the time, all the time, until I want to die under the weight of this want of you."

"I have learned so much with you, so much about so many things. So much living . . . I did not know love was like that."

"You alone know what you have done to me. Made me so tender, so vulnerable. By the time you have done with me I won't be good for anything at all, I'll be so soft."

We spoke in the darkness enclosed within the moving taxi, and our voices were urgent and tenuous.

"What was your reason for not wanting to see me these last two nights, when we have so little time together anyway?"

"Because I wanted to train myself to your absence."

The taxi stopped. Mark got out, opened his Chinese oiled paper umbrella, and stood holding it above my head. "I may not come back to you. Have you thought about that?"

"Yes . . . I thought of that."

"Good-by, then," he said, and I walked up the steps to the barred door of the Guest House. I kept my back turned.

But I heard his taxi go away, all the same. I never knew that the noise of an engine could hurt so much.

Days without Mark. A smudge of pain in the precise October enduring still with me; a hole burnt out in the many-colored coat of autumn.

I who love the moon's downward look, the gaudy sunlight on the ships, the silver slither of raindrops scuffling among leaves, I cannot remember seeing them, feeling them, during those days without Mark.

The time a blank, a rent in the close-knit luminous mesh of awareness which I wrought round the knowledge of Mark. The time was never mine. All I know of it amorphous information, an arid stretch of word and attitude, a dimness of heart.

Days without the hum of the sea, the stir of a dragonfly's wing, the patchwork glory of sunset and moonrise to etch into the living autumn I have hoarded against death.

Uncounted, unknown, days without Mark.

We lay, Maya Wong and I, in the hot grass in front of the Hospital. A palm tree pitched behind us its spurious privacy. Maya had a cold and coughed. "You must look after yourself, you are getting thinner, Maya."

"When will he come back?" asked Maya. She hated me to notice her colds; beneath her eyes were dark fingerprints of weariness.

"I do not know."

"He will come back."

"I cannot expect anything. Only to wait, to see what is going to happen, not to think overmuch. I often wonder that I should want so strongly a man so different from me. Why not a more available person? An inoffensive young bachelor, English, with a relic of the staid island about his voice, and a car, steady and dull, like Diana's friend? Why not a Chinese, a burly Northerner with great laughter in his belly and sheaves of humor gleaned through the years of poverty and compassion? Why should this man touch me, and no one else?"

"Perhaps because he was born free, and not even you can cage him. He is simple, and no one can deceive him, not even you. You weave a tight close web with skill and competence, but his simplicity will encompass you in the end. He does not know it. He does not know himself well, does he?"

"He does not know himself. But he is learning, he is finding out. Perhaps it is more important than love. I do not know."

"You are finding out, too, you cannot stop. You must be unafraid, all the way."

"How wise you are, Maya," I said, burying my face in the grass, sud-

denly smelling the autumn-ripe earth, Maya and I become sun-warm
fragments of earth pressed upon the grass with all the sky's blue above.
(And how right the Book of Rites' saying: *When a man sorrows, his
body is pressed to earth*.) "I think Heaven is unfair, and is preparing
for Mark and for me a great sadness, because now at last I am acquainted with fortitude."

"You are childish, there is no such thing as fairness or unfairness
under Heaven," said Maya. "And life is always sad if you stop to think
about it. Our old poets were enamored of bitter-sweet sorrow, because
the permanence of the beauty we love is the transiency of its creatures.
You can only wait, ungrasping of the future, holding the present lightly,
withstanding cupidity for happiness, relinquishing fulfillment to be fulfilled. He will decide, you will accept. It will be right, do not fear. Because love cannot do wrong."

"Suzanne, were you ever deeply in love? Really deep?"

Suzanne looked at me, her mouth hidden by the cake she was biting.
In her candid cunning look I read that she knew. Secretaries always
know. Secretaries and clerks, talking Cantonese, and English, recog-
nizing the handwriting on envelopes going through their hands,
remembering voices on the telephone, piecing scraps of knowledge together with minute stitches of half words and hints and forgotten fragments in wastepaper baskets. Suzanne knew.

"Many many times," she said, "but never so much as this time.
You?"

"Very very few times, and never like this. I don't understand it."

"I always think the last time is more than the one before and is going
to be the last time," said Suzanne.

"There's not going to be anyone else, ever," I replied, full of smug
conviction.

Suzanne's favorite subject being love, she continued. "I am always
in and out of love. Hong Kong seemed so dull and suburban at first,
after gay Shanghai. Everything shuts so early. Not the Chinese, of
course, they never sleep. But the English. But in two months I had a

boy friend, and now I think Hong Kong is nice and cosy. My present friend is a pet."

"Are you going to marry him?"

"Oh no." Suzanne spilled laughter on the white tea cloth. "He's married and a pretty Big Shot, you know. We've got to be discreet. You know how the English are. So long as it's well hidden, it doesn't matter *what* you do. So long as it isn't too obvious. I could tell you some tales about the nice women here, you'd be horrified, my little cabbage," she added maternally. "But then, you're so naive I feel like weeping when I look at you. It's bad, you know. You'll have to grow up or be hurt. You can't go on idealizing love forever."

"Suzanne, I'm not. But I hate hypocrisy. Don't you?"

"No," said Suzanne meditatively. "It's the way things are. Now you see that blonde over there, sitting with the two men? One's her husband, the other her boy friend. Tuesdays and Thursdays for him. You can get away with a lot if you look respectable and you aren't found out. It wouldn't be good for my friend if people knew. But he says I've spoiled him for any other woman, and that he'll never love anyone else."

My fingers stiffened on the Coca-Cola glass, remembering the words, the words until this moment mine alone, never spoken to any other woman in the world. Did her discreet Big Shot hold Suzanne's hand in the darkness? Did he smoke a pipe, keeping it delicately poised between two fingers, as did Mark? Did he talk in a low, quiet voice, half mocking, half tender?

Suzanne pulled some more shreds out of my cloak of exclusiveness. "He is very handsome. He is a little sentimental. He says he feels all funny when he looks at me. He was always a good boy until I took him in hand," concluded Suzanne triumphantly.

The Coca-Cola tasted of Lysol, the cheapest and favorite poison of Hong Kong's numerous would-be suicides. Suddenly I felt very tired.

"Well," I replied feebly, "I suppose love is always the same thing. I just don't know enough about it."

Suzanne nodded. "It's only afterwards you will know. You can only tell by the amount that it will hurt when it's over. Not by what they say. The words are always the same."

I went to see Diana at teatime. She was living in Anne Richards's flat near the Hospital. Anne was away in Indo-China, studying Buddhism. "She'll probably become a Buddhist herself," said Diana. We sat on the small veranda. Diana had a towel round her chest and short white shorts. She wanted a smashing tan and her skin was getting purple in the strong sun.

"So Mark's gone," she said.

"He's finding out whether we can get married, some day."

Diana laughed in spurts. "Gosh, fat hope he has of getting anywhere."

"Don't you think we might? We want to go to China together, to work."

"I wouldn't have any hope if I were you," said she. "He'll probably change his mind, anyway."

"Diana, if you were Mark, would you give up so much to marry me?"

"No I wouldn't, I consider it quite idiotic of him," said Diana. "But don't worry, my dear rabbit, you won't get him, you know."

Diana says my nose wrinkles up like a rabbit when I laugh.

"I'm only afraid that he will come back and say he can," I replied.

"Why?"

"If he cannot, he will feel unfree, and I shall possess his imagination more than ever. If he can, I shall have to give him back to his world, otherwise he may leave me. Not bodily, but part of his mind. That's the most important thing. One woman is very much like another, after a while."

"What in the name of Hades are you talking about?" said Diana. "One minute so cynical, the next like a babe in arms. You've got far too much imagination, that's the trouble. Everything goes upside down with you. Far too much imagination."

"Not where Mark is concerned, I haven't got too much. I know I see many people not as they are, but wrapped in the shining garment of my own dreams. I grant them more subtlety of heart than they possess, and learn painfully how much cheaper they hold themselves than I hold them. But not where Mark is concerned."

"You're quite hopeless, you always were, you know. Next you'll be saying that you must give each other up because you are in love."

"Perhaps. But not yet, not yet . . . I could not bear it now. You see," I said, looking at the sun until the whole world went black, "neither Mark nor I can resist nobility. That's the way it is. That's what it amounts to. Do you see?"

"No, I don't," said Diana, decisively wiping the sweat off her chest. "I think you're quite, quite nuts. I'm glad I'm not temperamental. My relationships with people aren't involved. Now Alfred and I, you see, are quite simple, we don't get all tangled up like you. And he's got a car, which is more than your Mark has. Now for Heaven's sake stop crying in your teacup, Rabbit, and have some cake."

On red paper spangled with gold, good-luck paper, with a brush and Chinese ink, I wrote a spell to bind Mark Elliott to me.

I went to the temple in Hollywood Street in the twilight of an evening; in the pewter incense holders I burnt incense sticks to the peaceful gilded figures canopied in crimson satin, seated above the altar. I threw the half-moon clappers on the ground three times and then five times; I shook the joss sticks in their cylinders and those that fell out were favorable to me.

I waited for Mark.

Mark had not told me that he would come back to Hong Kong. I knew he would, because Hong Kong was such a good place for news gathering. One day I rang up the airline, and his name was on the passenger list of the airplane arriving that afternoon. I pawned two Wednesdays for the afternoon off, and went to Kaitak Airport in the blue-spotted Chinese gown that he liked so much.

The sun cantered in a wide open sky; the wind coursed across the harbor, unsubdued white horses; the hills shook with decorous mirth. Laughter was everywhere, in the hangars filled with grinning machines, in the airport's waiting room where uproarious pilots were drinking large iced beers. Everything was such a joke: the war, the speeches about mounting international tension, the doleful wireless announcing atom bomb tests and the news that Russia too had the atom bomb, the usual eager disquietude of the posters, and the Customs men making perfunctory passes into the heaped suitcases. "Look what a joke it is," said scudding wavelets bouncing like frolicsome puppies against each other; and "Look how gay life is," said a little yacht so absurdly tilted against the sea's back that I laughed aloud, and all the pilots were laughing.

Then his plane was in the sky, an elongated silver meteor swirling round above the pink smoke from behind the hills, and I did not know or see anything until I saw him walk down the gangway in his white shirt and his shorts and his hair flopping a little in the wind, and he ran his hand through it, throwing the thick hair back, not knowing he was watched. I turned away, it was unfair to look at him when he did not know it and was unprotected.

I stayed in the waiting room, upright against the wall, so that my dress should not wrinkle. He could not see me and I would not see him until he had gone through the Customs. A short pilot with a turned-up nose came up to me. "You were asking about this plane a little while ago. It's in." "Thank you, I know," I replied. His look said how strange it was that I should not rush out with the others to the wooden barrier, to the entrance door of the Customs hall, to see him walk slowly towards me, keeping pace with his luggage; to wave, to smile. But I could not have done it. I could never have done it.

Carefully flattened against the door of the Ladies', I saw him cross the Customs hall, greeted by a good-looking stewardess. He was outside the hall now, in the sunlight, waiting for a taxi. I walked out of the waiting room and stood behind him, five paces away. He walked about a little. He expected no one. I moved when he did and he could not catch sight of me. Until suddenly he had turned and was looking at me. And I knew. There was no smile on his face as he said politely: "Suyin, my dear, when did you arrive?"

"I have been stalking you for some time," I replied in similarly polite tones, "as a huntress stalks her prey."

It was six days before Mark could bring himself to say to me what we both knew.

It seems surprising that we should have behaved as we did. But I tell of things as they happened. That day at the airport after our greeting, we climbed into a taxi, crossed the harbor by ferry to the island, took another taxi to the Bay Hotel where Mark had booked a room. Meanwhile we talked courteously, ceremoniously, of the dimensions of the moon, of Su Tung-po's remarks about gentlemen and nongentlemen, and of Baudelaire; soon transported from the life extant around us into the intimate ageless wander of companion spirits, up and down the living books of the dead that we loved; noted the splash of autumn along the road our taxi pursued; savored the honey-colored sherries we drank at the rattan table on the hotel veranda; and turned to each other to share the sunset in one look.

I left him after one sherry. That night he rang up. "I'll meet you at the House of Wisdom," he said.

I had not thought that he would come so quickly. Down the steps and along the mortuary path swift with white coat on and my stethoscope knocking against my side. I met him coming up the steps. And I felt his sadness hit me as I threw myself into his arms, ardent, impetuous, yet cold and pitiless inside because he had been hurt. He had not slept very much. He was too quiet, too taut.

"Darling," I whispered, pressing him to me, kissing his white shirt at the shoulder, heady with the feel and the smell of him, pulling him down to me on our stone, damming back his sadness, making talk impossible until he lay slack and helpless and relaxed, released from bitterness and only sadness still in him as a quiet pool after rain. And of this I was impatient, nearly angry. It was so futile. I knew. But I showed him a happy face, crushed a leaf from a small laurel within finger reach, made him smell the peppery fragrance. We walked back together and he said:

"It seems to me that I should talk to you."

"There is no hurry. I have not asked any questions."

"I wish I were Chinese, and a technician. We could go to China and we would be together, always."

"If you were Chinese, I could be your concubine. But we'd have to stay in Hong Kong, because concubines are only allowed in your British colonies, Hong Kong, Singapore; not in China now."

"Would you?" he said, already amused. He would sleep now. The body is merciless, and the spirit is at its mercy only too often. We change as our body changes; our thoughts and feelings molded by hunger and cold and sleeplessness. Mark's body would sleep. That was all I could want for tonight.

The next night he came to my room with Diana Kilton, and we all drank a little rum which Diana brought with her and became what Mark called *beschwippst*. He ran his hand over the floor and the walls and the plaited straw mat. "I am so conscious of surfaces and their texture. I understand now the Chinese holding a piece of jade in their hands for the sheer sensuous feel of it. How much I have missed loving, how much more there is that we miss, all the time."

And the next, the next, the next, he wandered in and out again, always with Diana; until she, impatient of her chaperonage, said to me when he had gone: "Well, what are you waiting for? Why don't you ask him what's the answer?"

"Oh no," I said, "that would not be right." And added more quickly, "I mean, it wouldn't be the right tactics."

Diana scoffed from the bottom of her feet up and stalked out.

Saturday afternoon came. We went walking in the hills; we lay in the sunshine reading comic verse and Ou-yang Hsiu's "Song of Autumn." In the evening we walked down the hill slope, watching the crimson sunset relinquish the western sky. We saw two early moon moths flounder in the thick gloom beneath a Gordonia, their pale green wings gleaming among the dark leaves. The sky dug holes between some clouds, and a yellow moon slid across them so that the water of the bay was bright and dim in turn. Inside the hotel, in the large dining room, many couples were dancing. We sat listening to the water rubbing the sand, the honks of passing cars, and the gruff voices of male toads. The orchestra wafted conventional lamentations across the night.

Mark lined three liqueur brandies in front of him, drank them in quick succession and then said that he would never be free. Never. He sat clutching his black Chinese fan, his head a little bent, suddenly reinvaded by sadness, as near to tragedy as he would ever be.

I said: "I don't see that you could have expected anything else."

"You don't?"

"No. I'd probably have done the same. Refused to consider your request. It's logical, reasonable, and perfectly right. In fact, the only right thing to do. We must not be madly romantic. You may be losing your head over some cheap woman. I am Eurasian, and the word itself evokes in some minds a sensation of moral laxity. People never think about words, they only feel them. I am Chinese, and at a certain moderate middling level, people do not marry Chinese girls. Neither, in China, do girls marry foreigners. It's only big enough people who can afford, occasionally, to be untrammeled by ordinary prejudice."

I paused, counted fifteen and went on:

"You have only known me four months. Whether we love each other or not does not matter to other people. The thing that happened to us means nothing to them. Let us look at it from the point of view of your world, from the standpoint of other people's interpretation of our motives. People will always go for the worst, not for the best, in their interpretation. People are always convinced that they know others better than the others know themselves. It is possible that you are being saved from disaster, and that you will be grateful one day for being rescued against your whim.

"Perhaps I should not say this. Perhaps I should be sad. But I am not built for emotionalism, tears, tragedy. This is what I think."

(And Mark had given me six days to think it.)

Mark stared at his fan for a considerable time. Then he said, coolly, "It's quite extraordinary. I thought this was going to be tragic. All these days I've been dreading telling you. I do so dislike emotional scenes. I felt that I had done you a great injustice, deluded you into thinking that it would be easy for me to become what is called 'free.' I thought we would have to take a lot of decisions, and not see each other again. But now it's all so detached. I have no feelings left about it at all. It's all . . . a little commonplace. Not at all tragic."

"Slightly boring. But then I always find these overloaded emotional upsets boring in the end. Don't you?"

And we were off, talking about Flaubert.

And after a little while Mark said: "Since there is no tragedy, will you stay with me in my room for a while?" "All right," I said. We walked together into the hotel, past the slow revolving dancers, past some English people who stared. And though we were also defiant, nothing mattered, for neither of us could go back any longer. And now less than ever would I care what people said. I told myself I would not care. I would not care if they whispered to one another, "Who's that Chinese girl Mark Elliott has picked up in Hong Kong?" I would not care about anything at all.

# CHAPTER IX

# A Good Day

*October 1949*

IT WAS CROWDED WITH THE THREE BEARS IN MY OFFICE AT
the hospital. Big Bear would write a story with a human angle about
Hong Kong. He was spending a day in the Casualty Department to get
some first-hand life shots.

Medium Bear had a degree from the London School of Economics
and the *New Statesman* rolled into a soft stick under her arm.

Small Bear, a thin idealist moved by human suffering to rage and
self-castigating pity, was here to test himself against the instant, bio-
logical pitch of human pain.

The leper swayed gently in front of them. He was starving. He
would now be deported for the third time. In that winter lepers were
batted back and forth across the border with China. The Chinese
pushed them into Hong Kong; they were found, brought to the hospital, certified lepers, pushed back across the border.

Two hard-working missionaries had set up a temporary leprosarium
in some sheds; it was overcrowded. One day a site would be found on
some unwanted land, before some quick-profit speculator bought it up
and raised the price; contributions would come from someone very
generous; other contributions would follow with a general spray of
honors. Someone would lay a foundation stone, and a leper colony
would be set up. Meanwhile the lepers had a bad time.

Mr. Mok, the wonderful Casualty dresser, helped the leper put on his frayed blue vest. Fascinated, at a safe distance, the usual Cantonese crowd watched Mr. Mok. Leprosy frightens men, and when men are frightened, they do terrible things. They throw stones at lepers; fling food on the ground, because they are frightened. But if someone, neither afraid nor disgusted, handled lepers as human beings, they would lose their fear. Mr. Mok was heroic all the time and never knew it at all.

"Leprosy can be cured," he said aloud to the crowd. "Don't be frightened to come to the Hospital as soon as you notice it. You can be cured now of everything, if you come early. And especially the children. Bring the children early." Mr. Mok loved children.

Small Bear said. "How revolting. Can't the Hong Kong government do something for this poor man?"

He would be fed, then deported. Hong Kong was swamped with people from the mainland. Everything was strained — housing, water, food, hospitals. The Colony had done very well. It had withstood the shock of a doubling of population, there had been no epidemics, hundreds of destitutes were being fed; there was, of course, a heart-rending store of human waste, inefficiency, stupidity and bungling; but the system had not broken down, it was trying to cope. How odd, I thought, here am I, an Asian brought up as we all are to execrate colonialism, explaining how well this colonial government has done. And I hoped no Chinese would think me a "running dog," a lackey of British imperialism. But Small Bear, being English, found great fault with his own government. "We ought to do so much more, so much more."

"Doctor, a blast case," said Mr. Mok, beaming. He was upset. The ambulance men were bringing it in on the stretcher. An hour ago it had been a fisherman on a junk, holding some crude, homemade dynamite ready to throw into the sea, to blast the fish. The charge had exploded too early. One hand dangled at the end of a twisted white string which had been a nerve. The other forearm was off halfway to the elbow. There was no face. It was still alive, and moaned. Mr. Mok shot morphia into it. The operating theater was ready.

Small Bear disappeared. Mr. Mok, double chins tremulous with laughter, proffered brandy to Middle Bear. Middle Bear was very shocked, because Mr. Mok laughed. I explained. Mr. Mok was upset by the blast case; he had a soft heart; but instead of crying, he giggled. "I am like that too; many Chinese are like that." Middle Bear disapproved, unconvinced by the truth.

A dysentery, a fractured skull, a burnt child; then the man came in, a walking skeleton, his arm round the pregnant girl his wife. A look was enough.

"Tuberculosis. The plague of Hong Kong. Seventy-six out of ninety-two deaths in the Colony last week due to tuberculosis. One hundred and fifty-four new cases notified last week."

"I've seen the slums," said Middle Bear. "I've seen the tenements. In all my life I have not seen worse, and I have been round many slum areas in the world. My God!"

There is not enough money to pull down and rebuild. There are no cheap sites. These tenement houses ought to have come down twenty years ago. Then there was a war. Now Hong Kong is overcrowded. And now there may be another war. Poverty, dirt and disease are true internationalists.

There were not enough beds; there were not enough sanatoria. Hundreds of new cases went to the clinics, were seen, diagnosed, X-rayed, told to go home and to rest. How could they rest? If they stopped work, they starved. So they went on until they died.

"I can sell my son," said the girl. Behind her stood the little boy hanging his head, sucking his thumb. He was very shy. "We come from a good family," said the girl. "My little one is intelligent and well made. If I sell him, will there be enough money to cure my husband?"

They were refugees, the man an officer in one of those defeated army units that had drifted to Hong Kong. They were kept alive by the Hong Kong government, in camps. Formosa did not want them. China did not want them. Hong Kong fed them. There they lay, rotting away slowly in camps. But elsewhere they would have died.

We got the man a pallet on the floor of a hospital for incurables. Th

ospital was overcrowded; there were two patients in each bed and
)atients on the floor. But it was better than dying in a hut, or on the
treet.

"Revenue Officer," said Mr. Mok, popping his round head into my
)ffice again. "Twenty-eight suspects, Doctor."

"Gold bars," I told the Bears.

Crouching on the tiled floor of the Casualty main room were sixteen
women and twelve men off the Macao boat, suspected of carrying gold
ars inside their bodies. The traffic was brisk. Regular passers did it
or a livelihood, and many others, converting their savings into a gold
ar, hoped to smuggle into Hong Kong with it. In Macao a certain
pecialist introduced the bars, wrapped in fine tissue paper and a thin
ubber sheath, inside their human containers. The same specialist then
varned the Hong Kong police. He got his cut from both sides.

The suspects were X-rayed. Seven had gold inside them. The Rev-
nue Officer was pleased with the haul. Mr. Mok and I extracted the
old bars.

Lily Wu walked gaily in, smiling brilliantly at Mr. Mok, who never
oticed. Mr. Mok lived to give injections, pat lepers, scold would-be
uicides, handle children deftly, carry babies more gently than their
nothers did. Mr. Mok knew more human medicine than many doc-
)rs, and was a better teacher than any professor. He always knew the
iside story of every patient. He never lost his temper; I always asked
is advice. We were great friends.

After her penicillin injection Lily stayed on for her usual little chat
id a cigarette. "Miss Wu, from Peking," I introduced her to the
ears, who said "How do you do?" and "Pleased to meet you" respec-
vely. From sheer force of habit Lily's large dark eyes started sending
it code messages to Big Bear; then Lily remembered that she was, in
y office, a girl of good family, and her charming black irises slid back
wards me.

Lily had been brought to me one evening after some brandy and two
blets of aspirin; the combination had made her drunk for the first
ne in her life. "She bit me," the man who was with her kept on re-

peating, holding out his wrist in which Lily had embedded her healthy
teeth. The policeman who brought them paternally kept them at arm's
length from each other. Lily spent a night in our Prison Ward, and
I admonished her next morning. "You must not *bite* people. I had to
give the man an injection, it was quite painful for him."

Conscienceless Lily giggled without stopping, hiding her face in the
sheet. I liked her.

Lily, restored to freedom, gave a sedate tea party for me at her abode.
Several of her "sisters" had now drifted down from Peking, along with
the rich, the poor, the intellectuals, the doctors, dribbling out of China
with the slowly-tightening pressure from above. At the first turning of
the stair on the second floor, invisible throughout the day owing to the
prevalent darkness of the corridor, lit up at night by an electric bulb
suspended above it, was a fresco on the wall. A heavy, rotund eagle
with a banderole grasped in its talons. Upon it was the word WELCOME

The girls had been shy at first as we sat in the waiting room with its
padded chairs with faded cretonne covers and little tables and numerous ash trays; later, they had asked many medical questions. I hoped
they liked me. I learned a lot of statistics; the girls lived on statistics.
How much, and what was the rake-off to the "horse that pulls," who
brought the clients; and the thoughtful little presents, before Christmas
and Chinese New Year, that ensured peace and protection of the house;
and why Americans were best. "It's not a question of race prejudice,"
said the girls. "We have no race prejudice. But the English soldier
round the Murray barracks cannot afford it. One American is two and
a half Englishmen. We have to think of ourselves. We cannot work too
hard and get too tired."

And, of course, once the girls had been with foreigners the Chinese
did not like to go to them any longer.

Mr. Mok's face in my office was followed by a black-clad crowd, a
whole terrified family surrounding the mother who thrust under my
nose a bundle. It was a child, wrapped in layers of clothing. We undid
the layers and the abdomen appeared. There was practically nothing
else but glistening abdomen, enormously distended, semi-transparent

netted in a lace pattern of veins, looking as if at any moment it might burst like an overblown balloon. Around the navel were a dozen of those round brown marks, like owls' eyes, which the Chinese herbalist burns through slices of ginger root with a wax wick, to draw out the sickness. Above this monstrous sphere sat the chest, a tiny bird's cage; then the face of a miniature, querulous monkey, the blind wide eyes bleak with dying. "How long has it been ill?" And the invariable answer: "Oh, a long, long time . . ." "Then why did you not come earlier?" And again the same answer as always: "M'chee . . . we did not know."

And Mr. Mok, indefatigably teaching where teaching is needed, not in expensive lecture rooms to bored students, but right down here: "Come early, come early . . . you come too late."

The baby died in the elevator, on the way to the Babies' Ward.

"Well that was very interesting, very," said Big Bear consulting his watch. "Thanks so much, doctor, most interesting." I hoped he had had enough life shots for the day.

Middle Bear stayed; we went through the hours. More tuberculosis, more babies, more police cases. We talked. Of the squatters' camps, of the refugees, of the street sleepers; of malnutrition, and of hunger, the disinherited and the underprivileged, eight-tenths of the world.

The Social Welfare worker walked in with a child. The child's face was froglike, flattened. She was not a Cantonese. "Case of rape," said the worker cheerfully. "Would you please examine to confirm rape?"

"Heaven," I said. "She is smaller than my own daughter Mei."

"She does not know her age," said the social worker. "She is a slave girl belonging to a Szechuan family of refugees in Hong Kong. The X-ray of bones shows she is about twelve."

So far I had not been upset at all. Why should I be? I handled human pain every day. But because this child was smaller than my daughter, I was upset.

"She went to the police station herself," said the social worker. "Her master tried to rape her again, and she struck him, then ran out of the house to the police station down the hill road, and reported him."

"Heaven," I said again, lost in admiration. "What courage!"

Mr. Mok, the social worker, and I, all looked at Oh-no (for it was she) with our hearts beating, lost in wonder at her courage.

(When the police came for Old Master Hsu, all the taitais screamed, and fainted, and the servants hid in terror in their quarters, and locked the doors from inside; and Old Mistress nearly swallowed an ounce of opium to kill herself, but desisted and smoked it instead.

Old Master Hsu screamed louder, and fainted harder, and tore his clothes better than any of his taitais. He thought it was a plot of the Hong Kong police to blackmail him for money. He offered everyone money, and was horrified when it was refused. "How is it possible?" he shouted again and again. "It has never happened, that a slave girl dare to injure her master thus. It is an injustice." He became quite ill and thin with shouting, red-eyed and a little mad. "There is no justice and no freedom in Hong Kong," he screamed. "We are oppressed here.")

"Tell me," said Middle Bear, "why were you all so excited about this little girl? You all seemed so pleased too."

"Why? Don't you see why? In China Oh-no would never have had redress. Not in old China. She would not have run to the police station. If she had, the police would not have paid any attention to her. No one would listen to the word of a slave girl against her master. Not in old China. That's why we were excited. We all think Oh-no has the courage of a hero."

"A good day, quite busy, Doctor," said Mr. Mok to me, as I left. Sleeves rolled up, he was attacking a long queue of typhoid inoculations, talking to each one, getting a "life story" every time.

"How terrible," said Middle Bear. "One knows about these things of course, but to see it is quite different. What a lot of misery and pain there is in the world."

It was true. "And they are so much more important than any politics; for politics are passing things, but pain, and hunger, and poverty like the proverbial brook, go on forever."

# Amour Profane

*October, November 1949*

Nothing so delights a lover as the loved one's pleasure. For Mark I would have ransacked the world of beauty.

"Look," my eyes said, "look, is he not beautiful, this man? I sit under the Tree of Love we planted together, watching him, as one watches a bird on a high branch, a hovering butterfly — content with sight and sound, and knowledge of him on earth. And let me not want more, for more is murder." One thing vexed me, the fear that he might deny himself because of me. I did not wish him narrowed in any way.

"A European woman would find it difficult to understand that because you love me, you urge me to be unfaithful to you, Suyin."

"But it is so unfair to restrict, to hem you within the boundaries of myself. Your pleasure is my delight, and that you might miss or regret a particle of your life would sorrow me."

"*Elle ne fait rien pour exciter mon amour,*" said Mark, "*car elle a l'insouciance des grands enchantements.*"

"Did you read a book called *A Floating Life?* It is the story of Shenfu and his wife Yun; lovers of beauty, they also loved each other with delicate and moving tenderness. Yun tried to purchase a girl as a concubine for her husband. 'But our passion is so full,' said Shenfu to her, 'need we add to it?' Yun replied: 'She is beautiful and lovable. Let me arrange it.' Like ourselves, Shenfu and Yun looked at the moon, collected books, recited and wrote poetry, arranged flowers, drank wine and had many friends. As we do, they propitiated Heaven with sacrifice, strove for good omen, and went in fear of wrath from above, for great happiness displeases the gods. And theirs was short-lived, alas — only twenty-three years of married love together."

"Only twenty-three years," said Mark.

"It seemed so short to them. Shenfu says of his wife: 'I do believe Yun's sensitive nature never recovered from the grief she felt when this girl was sold to a boorish trader instead of joining our household, and this was the cause of her short life.' Shenfu and Yun lived in China nearly five centuries ago."

"I wonder what your pet missionaries, and Father Low, would say if they heard you," pondered Mark.

"They would moralize. But moralists have no place in an art gallery. Shenfu and Yun were moral for their own times. Yun's unselfishness and wifely generosity would be highly praised by the family and her husband's friends. 'A truly loving and unjealous wife,' they would have said. Love and jealousy do not abide together. How can one be jealous, when one loves?"

"I, like Shenfu, do not want anything else; it would be adding feet to a snake," Mark quoted the Chinese proverb. "Our passion fills me, and please notice," he said with the slight solemnity he employed to tease me, "that I use the word not in the narrow sense to which our uncouth and barbarous age has whittled it down, but to indicate that mixture of the elements converging towards one aim, *le transport total de mon âme envers vous.*"

Yet I was afraid that he would clip the wings of his imagination to my stature. I feared him diminished by wordless compact, as others are by that frightening apparatus of possessiveness and habit which established couples form between them. He was born free and I would keep him so. And by so doing, I bound him to myself with a tenfold chain.

"One of my first memories of hair," said Mark, "is of my amah in Peking. I remember her long pigtail, a thick vigorous braid depending from her glossy head to the back of her knees, and tied with black string. Alive and vibrant the strong coil I grasped in my six-year-old hands, twisting it once round my wrist as I pulled. I can still feel the many strands of that heavy rope between my palms, and like to think that my Victorian passion has its roots in that first sensuous recollection. All my life, until you, I have wanted, unavowed, a woman with long black hair streaming down her back."

"You continue for me the tradition under which I lived during my marriage," I replied, "perhaps because you were born in Peking, although you are so English. My husband being Chinese loved long hair. He would not let me curl, cut or show mine. I kept it in a tight knot, as now. He deemed it bad taste for a woman to flaunt, blunting the fine point of beauty in herself."

"I did not know yours was long until the night you combed it out . . do you remember?" said Mark.

"You must see my sister Suchen," I replied, cheeks hot with violent recollection. "She wears hers spread out as a mantle of grace upon her shoulders. It will give you pleasure."

Suchen had arrived in Hong Kong two weeks before, and lived on the Kowloon side in a room rented from a Portuguese family, awaiting her visa for the United States. Sitting in the Parisian Grill, waiting for her, and for Mark, I saw Suchen push open the glass door; she wore pink linen, her face rounder and happier than when we were in Chungking.

Then Mark came in, slightly unsubstantial, and walked in the opposite direction. "That is Mark," I said to Suchen, and felt turned to water. Suchen scanned him efficiently, beginning with his back, and when he turned and came towards us in his soft, unhurried way, from the thick hair through the old careless clothes to the shoes and up again. "Of course, you choose all your beaux the same type, don't you?"

I protested indignantly. "This one's English."

Suchen shook her head. "Ever since your University days, all the

beaux that took you out, and your husband also — all were the same
type as this Englishman."

Mark stood in front of us, waiting to be introduced. I stared at
him as if I had never seen him. He gave us both a disarming smile;
his eyes, friendly, went to my sister's face framed in a close crop of
curls.

Deeply miserable, I too gazed at Suchen's shorn head. She noticed
it and smiled, exhibiting once more our inherited enamel:

"Yes, I am glad I can look nice again. All that awful hair. I could
not wait a moment longer to get it cut and have a perm."

And then I met Margaret in Pedder Street near the Post Office. "I
was bitten by a centipede this morning, what shall I put on it?"

People always stopped Mark and me to ask the way, the time, and
even more startling questions; perhaps because of the lost look we had.

Margaret was a tourist; she was leaving for Bangkok next day. She
wore a lime-green dress, her eyes were cobalt with long dark lashes.
Her hair lay in plaited coils round her head. Her American accent was
delightful.

After the druggist she asked me to come up to her room at the
Gloucester Hotel for a drink. In ten minutes and two drinks apiece
we liked each other exuberantly and confided the salient facts of our
past lives. I could not leave off staring at her. "How lovely you are,"
I said, as her beauty grew on me, aided by the gin I had drunk. "How
beautifully made some of you American women are."

She sat in front of her tall mirror, looking at herself, her eyes dreamy,
her lips red and curved with pleasure in her own beauty. Then she took
out the little tortoise-shell combs which held the twisted coils of her
hair, and it fell in one silk wave down her back. A long sleek flame
still warm from folding close, stirred with the rich smooth swell of
undergold as she shook it, until it lay smooth and close as a goldbird's
wing. I cried with pleasure and pain, feeling the daggers of pleasure
run through me. "Oh Margaret, how I wish Mark could see this."

She sat, offered to her reflection in the long mirror her long white neck like a lily stemming from the green linen dress. "Oh let me fetch Mark to see you," I said. "He is probably in the eighth floor lounge. Please let me."

I went to the eighth floor lounge of the Gloucester Hotel, the haunt of newspaper correspondents, and there was Mark amidst a bevy of them, all talking shop. I swooped on him and took him by the hand and dragged him to the elevator without a word. He was a little astonished but followed unprotestingly. "My dear," he said, "John Tam erupted on me a little while ago, wading through the kitchens because he could not find the elevator, and demanding iced beer. Now you kidnap me in broad daylight from the bosom of my colleagues. Life is full of surprises with you doctors."

I pushed open Margaret's door; she lay on the bed blowing smoke rings. She smiled lazily at Mark, her hands clasped behind her neck. Her hair was up again. "Hi you two," she said.

"Oh Margaret, let down your hair."

She shook it down again, looking at Mark all the time.

"Don't you love it, Mark? Isn't it beautiful?"

I think that, being English, he was more than startled, perhaps a little shocked. But he showed no sign, and soon he too was caught, and he said gently, "Yes, yes . . . it is beautiful, isn't it . . . yes . . . it is."

Margaret and I laughed and laughed.

We took Margaret out to dinner at the Parisian Grill. In the night we taxied up to the top of the Peak to show her Hong Kong, the hoard of a jewel thief.

"I know a shop in Brussels down the Rue de la Paix, a narrow gray shop with a perfectly circular window cut in the stone façade," said Margaret. "Spread on unwrinkled black velvet lie the scintillating masterpieces of that arch-creator, Mr. Burmah. Rivers of diamonds, fountains and sprays of rubies and emeralds, cascades of brooches and galaxies of topaz, sapphire and aquamarine. And the inscription in small gray letters above the window reads: *Les Bijoux Burmah, aussi beaux que des vrais.* Hong Kong at night reminds me of that circular window cut out somewhere in the wall of a world, an escape into enchantment, a glittering mirage with the frailty of a mirage about it; as if it might disappear, swallowed into dark velvet night again."

We had shared the same joyful madness, we said good-by regretfully. I did not see Margaret again, but her hair would not leave my imagination for many days.

We would start early, dawn still arrayed in mother of pearl from shimmering gray sea to soft pink sky; inside this iridescent world, hushed as the inner wall of a shell, we walked, and saw the mist fall halfway down the hills and remain suspended, flat and white between water and sky as in a Japanese print. Up the footpaths among the hills we went, the mist smooth against our faces. We strode through the strong bracken, parting it with our hands, treading lava chips released under our feet. At noon we sat on warm, sun-burnished boulders, moss-flanked, or lay in the long, blue-glinted grass by a half-dry torrent scarring the hill slope with its downroll of stones. A little breeze would saunter with us, trailing a few rustling red leaves along the path. I walked just behind Mark, for his eyes undid me. I saw the world and he the man its center, vulnerable as all beautiful things are. Knowing that I looked, he would hold out his hand; sometimes he stopped and turned towards me, and there I would stand, biting my lips, my ears roaring, helpless as a young girl the first time in love. We never met anyone else.

All day we wandered, locked in our dream-bound world, armed with two apples, a small squat bottle of brandy, and one or two books. We lingered on the sun-bright slopes, watching the island contentedly lapped in the tranquil arms of the sea, the errant clouds drag their obedient purple shadows across the water, the day go its predestined way, the campaigning sun commit its final grandiose arson. Our throats tight we watched the scythes of dusk rake gold and emerald and turquoise out of the earth, and witless stars, anonymous heads at a theater balcony, peer numerous and cold from a vacuous sky.

In the unkempt seeding grass of the hollows we loitered and found the last lady-slipper orchids with their purple speckled lips, and the primrose arundinas wheeling into ocher and brown. Above us the beauhinias were in flower and seed at the same time, dangling their clusters of long green pods crowned with the pink and magenta contortions of their blossoms. Hawking through them went the last swallows. The flame of the forest, outwearing their scarlet splendor, hung gourds of black shining seed from each feathered twig. Mark would collect it, pouring the ebony round life into my cupped hands. I would keep it until we reached a stone pathway, then throw one handful and the other. We listened to the seed falling on stone, it gave us extraordinary pleasure.

Everywhere on the slopes the yellow luminous gordonia clustered like stars among their glossy thick leaves. The hibiscus swayed its loaded hedges and hinted at Christmas. Camellias pale as white flames upward flaming recalled the morning that was all day in their incongruous spring. Waxy, self-assured, snobbish damsels in snug rows, pink Melastoma, bloomed out of place in autumn's sweet disorder. In the high clear sky at noon swung a kite or two, and some francolins, and one day a small sea eagle with white barred wings. Along Lovers' Lane the orange tips would bolt precipitous from camphor trees, and painted courtesans and swallowtails, inebriate with sun, rush at each other in dazzling tournament and a great fury of wing. And one morning, after rain, we saw this marvel, a humble and lovely deer, rain sleek and wet-muzzled, delicately stepping, testing the path with hesitant lifted foot, and ears poised like leaves.

The Achatine Fulica sprawled their countless millions over Hong Kong. These voracious African snails we met every few steps — all sizes, and here and there girdled by teeming flocks of hungry red ants. On hot days their bodies melted in the sun, and the whorled shells fixed on top of the decomposing gray slime stuck to the heat-storing rocks. By night our feet crushed dozens of these omnivorous hermaphrodites, their shells were thin and brittle. "Is it not Mrs. Palmer-Jones who says that the human race will die of starvation in fifty years?" said Mark. "We shall die of overreproduction; our own, and

Achatina's; and all because your gastronomically ingenious nation cannot think of a way of making these snails edible."

There is something birdlike about Hong Kong encompassed by sea and sky. From October to January, when the glare of summer has given place to a lucid, tranquil luminosity, Hong Kong riots and shimmers, flaunts and struts in emerald, sapphire, cobalt and jade like a peacock's tail in the sun. It is surprising not to meet one of these intent shrewish birds stepping delicately down a hill path, and sudden and brusque as an Indian merchant unbolting brocade, wheeling its tail in a great circle skywards.

The kingfisher, uneclipsed by its surroundings, skims the blue water of the reservoirs, loops through the emerald disintegrated leaves of the flame of forest, and disappears behind a hill crest.

"In the next life," said Mark, following its flight from the grass where we lay, "let's be birds, Suyin."

"Let's be kingfishers. They are so beautiful."

"They live suspended between water and earth, carry the sky and the sea on their backs."

"And they are uncommonly faithful."

"I must find out more about the connubial habits of kingfishers," said Mark. "But in the next life, according to the laws of reincarnation, you must be the male and I the female."

"No, I won't. I'll refuse to be male. I want to be female again, for ever and always. You have reconciled me to being a woman, I who yearned to be a man until I met you. And since in the next life it must be you again, I shall want to be female from incarnation to incarnation."

"I too want to say forever, and always," Mark said, "but then you stop me, for you say they are words thought up by fools and believed in by the weak-minded. But then, are we not all weak-minded when we need to believe ourselves immortal? I cannot help thinking of Shenfu and Yun. 'Alas,' says Shenfu, 'my bosom friend is gone, alas and we only had twenty-three years of this life together.' The conceit of the man, Suyin, and his good luck! I cannot imagine being alive in two years, much less in ten. How much time, do you think, will be vouchsafed to us in this life?"

"The astrologer promised us eight years. Eight years in this life, Mark. No less than eight. That's very good for this world, isn't it?"

"Eight is enough then," said Mark, "since it must be enough. But I must have them with you. I'll fix it for this life, and you will fix us up for the next. For I want to be bound to you from incarnation to incarnation."

"I'll fix it for the next," I promised, and put my mouth in the palm of his hand. "We'll be kingfishers; we'll live together and arrange to die together."

That made Mark very happy. "I'm glad that you did not choose the mandarin duck and drake, so often mentioned in Chinese poetry as symbols of love. I would have hated it, because, although the drake is a rainbow of color, the female is such a drab, gray little thing, and you'd have to be that since you insist on remaining the woman."

"But you'd be such a nice drake, strutting about, rolling round black and gold eyes, and with a beautiful little crest on your head. I'd go as limp with love of you in the next life as I do in this one."

But Mark would not have it. He was not Elizabethan, and could not imagine himself in pink and purple and azure and gold. So kingfishers it would be, and we watched for them everywhere in Hong Kong, and when we saw one we looked at each other with rapture, and counted it a good omen for us.

Mark sent me a picture cut out from a child's book about kingfishers. A blue sky and a stream with green banks, and two kingfishers flying across it side by side. Gay and sunlit, I kept even the piece of cardboard he put in the envelope to hold it straight.

Now the picture hangs on my wall, and from the same book I cut another one: it is evening, the trees bear armfuls of gloom as they bend over the stream across which one little kingfisher hurries flying home.

To go on living one has to be occasionally silly; to cherish memories which in more detached moments exhale a pungent odor of embalming fluid; to finger old letters which the silver worm punches, to distort in the trappings of sentiment the ardors of love; to magnify into a saying the light, mocking word.

"But," he said, "I shall leave you."

He was still. From where I stood I could feel the warmth of his body. His eyes were searching the equivocal and troubled twilight folding the hills.

"I shall want to go on walkabouts of my own, alone."

Little boy with the bright rebellious hair, leaving for distant glorious realms the other side of a golden afternoon. His need to possess himself, away, cut off from everything, away from love, especially from love, in complete possession of his own dreaming, walking towards unreachable snow-clad mountains. Of course he would go.

And suddenly I knew how much a woman must suffer who wanted this man to live with her. To wake up with her in the morning and to return to her with the night. Who wanted to grow old with him; to feel the security of his routine round her: "Heaven, how much more love I must learn to make him free."

What a genius he was at going away. Like a child, he knew how not to be there; fading without a trace, evanescing as a cloud in one's hand. I had seen him do it.

And I felt pity for woman, any woman, who would try to tie him down with promise, or arrangement. Security hungry, wanting the future stabilized, formulated; giving up today for tomorrow. Of course he would abide by promises, but his soul would go away. Leaving an efficient outer shell, he would be gone, lost in the moment of acquiescence, vanished when the last lock fell securely into place.

He would be bound only by freedom, and to the faraway quest; nothing else would hold him.

I sat on the ground. It was very important, and I had to learn it again. I could feel him quiver a little with his own desire to be away, just to go away. Even from me.

And so because I loved him, in utter humility I laid my forehead against his knee, very light, scarce a touch.

"Oh darling, how lovely it will be, just waiting for you. If you so wish it, I shall wait for you in my heart always; for waiting where it concerns you is joyful dalliance. Go where you will, go clean away, it does not matter; you can never hurt me, for the world you leave behind with me is always full of you."

After a while he too sat down, and lit his pipe, absurdly reassured, back of his own will, smoking his pipe near me in the companionable silence. The curtains of dusk dropped around us, and crisp with death a shriveled leaf brought by the slight wind sat in my lap. We walked on, and sudden as a gust of laughter came the moon from behind a hill: Mark took and held my hand.

We could not hold back the day, and at night descended from the hills resigned to enter the other world again. The night roads were often raucous with big cars; their headlights, sniveling interpolations in the dark, swept and caught us conspicuous as malefactors. There were flowers in my hair and scratches on my legs as we ascended the steps of the Bay Hotel, and from our rambles we brought back armfuls of red and tan leaves, berries black and scarlet and gold, and told our friends, gravely, that Autumn was walking on the hills.

The tidy neat people who call their souls their own, sitting tidily at neat rattan tables amid potted palms and punctilious waiters, eyed us with disapproval. We were so mad. "Do you look like a competent newspaperman?" I asked Mark. "Your colleagues carry harried and woeful countenances, the world's troubles on their shoulders and insomnia embedded in the creases of their brow." — "You do not look like a thirty-two year old, efficient woman doctor," said Mark. "I feel like saying to those who stare: 'Pray forgive us, we are in love.' You are now sixteen, and have your after-love face on you." I fled to wash my face while Mark ordered dinner for two.

We reverted. In us awoke the oldest, most primitive instincts of our species. Our conscious civilized selves were often concerned with the absolute nature of the feeling which pervaded us, but other elements arose. Everything that happened in our sensuous world somehow or other entangled us in its event. Whether we wished it or not, the shape of a hill, the direction of a cloud, the fall of a leaf, the sudden call of an oriole, the passing of a shadow . . . all affected, swayed, or portended the destiny that we could not shape for ourselves. For everything was alive, even the stones under our feet.

Omens, portents, symbols, beneficent and malicious spirits, we were aware of them and half believed in all. Propitiatory, we invoked those supernatural essences that roam about, by the seashore, among the graves, in the woods; spirits of water, half-dry torrent shaded by skimpy casuarinas; spirits of earth, leaf, tree, flower, root. Reverence we exhibited towards their manifestations and a semi-earnest cult came to us spontaneously. We buried flowers. We picked beetles out of the nullahs where they would have drowned. One day we saved a lizard, and watched, fascinated, the fantastic animation of its snapped tail, convinced it held meaning. I remember one evening when a chill wind suddenly fell on the hill slope; regretfully we rose from the earth, and I searched for the two red combs that held back my hair. "Here is one, broken," said Mark. "The spirit of the hill must have it." Mark dug a hole in the ground for the fragments, then found the other one. "We've rescued one from the hill demon," he jested. I broke it in two and buried it with the first. For who were we to wrest an object from the benign earth upon which we had lain?

At night we would go to the Chinese Wantsai district. There, in an open space of land, amid the flare of kerosene lamps, astrologers and diviners, acrobats and mole removers, conjurers and ambulant restaurants, pimps, robbers, prostitutes, school children, refugees rich and poor, ambled among rickety trestle tables upon which hung charts of the stars, calendars of lucky and inauspicious days, and large drawings of hands and of faces, done in pink and black on sheets of linen. We moved with the crowds from one charlatan to another. We asked the future for a few small coins and they told us gorgeous lies.

We stopped to watch the excoriation of some virus-infected leaves on a tree.

"A Japanese woman would take these tortured boughs and make a lovely flower arrangement with them," said Mark. "How exciting and satisfying the blisters, the swellings and crevices, the variegated daubs of disease. Pustules of flaring scarlet, crusts of green gold, leprous ulcers topped with livid bubbles of gangrene. And the blenched hideous underbelly. Look at that mottled caterpillar's slow progress up the twig, and its sudden stop, half erect. How it twists its microscopic sightless head, and sensing dreadfulness, backs away from the sweet corruption, a sinister retreat precipitate with the confusion of its many hairy pads."

"Is not this like passion, the dread beauty roaming through me now," said I, "twisting me out of shape, working its will on me like disease on that leaf? I can remember the inception of my malady, when I could not sleep or eat, consumed with fever for you, and hating it; and then terror gone, hunger slaked, sadness turned to resignation; the flowering of my joy. Then backwards into childhood, the search into the past to compel the future; the quest for the appropriate gesture that could save tomorrow from disaster. And now, beyond these stages, deeply diseased, I can no longer resist, worry, or be sad. Whatever happens now, I cannot be too sad. Sadness is so ungrateful when this has been given."

"All my life," said Mark, "I thought that one day all things would spring alive and have meaning, not only those we see, hear and name, but those we leave in darkness perpetual; for to confine ourselves only to the seen and the named, how contracted our span of universe would be. Always I was pursued by that slight fear, call it emotional impotence, which afflicts many of my kind, because what seemed to move and stir others in the prescribed way, left me cold and neutral. It is the paradox of people like myself; half regretting their lack of deep emotion, they evade spiritual discomposure skillfully. I had escapes, glorious and rewarding, safe from the outrages of vulgarity. I could remain pleasant and detached; serene mountains and intricate jungles, calm desert and self-forsaking peril were mine. My body could wander among conventionally sharp bullets while my heart mused on the Heart's Journey up and down the tumult of massacres and the cacophony of wars. Like all men, I was half glad, half sorry of this stainless shield of composure, this dispassionate poise of the soul. Knowing with the head, unfeeling in the belly. Spiritual drought, the emptiness within, hollow the inward self save for its own reverberating echo of silence."

"This is the age of the Great Normal Delusion," I said, "when we dare no longer call ourselves sinners, selfish and mean. We all want to be normal, which now means Good. It is wrong to have strong personal passions, uncomfortable, unsocial, which is Bad. Passion puts one out of pace with the herd, and the herd is only to be prodded to collective frenzy, a disciplined stampede of panic, of hatred, of righteous indignation. This is the era of mass dedication to ill-understood Abstraction, hallowed by the verbiage of newspapers, sanctified by majority votes. The time of the public common man, whose private life dare only conform to a minimum of moderate virtue and timorous defect, whose spiritual quest is comfort and security. It has become ridiculous to die for love of one person. Love is only a sensible compromise, a democracy made safe by contraception. It has become nearly impossible to live for oneself, for we dare no longer be tender for fear of being cheated, and we dare never be damned."

"I held myself incapable of warmth or depth, and in thin neutrality like cold ash, sifted in a bleak wind of events which left me whole, I moved, undeluded by truths as various as the men who propound them, and deeming accuracy a better challenge to my integrity; doubting the heroism of causes, aware of the self-importance which incites men to extend themselves into inhuman fallacies. Yet all my life, while shrinking from it, I had wanted something beyond the figments of reality, beyond the specious solidity of this rock-bottom world. A steady, passionate flame. A singlehearted ecstasy. And now it has happened."

"Such a small thing has made it happen. An absurdly small thing. It could have been another woman; or a man; or even a cause."

"Perhaps. But it happened between us; because of this lovely and delicate counterpoise, which is neither sex alone nor love alone, everything has come alive, every moment a shooting star."

"It is not going to happen again," I said. "Never again. And I do not know what it is going to do to us. After the virus the leaf is no longer the same."

"I do not know," said Mark, "what God's intentions towards us can be. He has used us as springboards for one another, a long vast leap into life. And there is no going back from life."

"Every moment with ravished hearts we discover the implausible succession of miracles which God scatters in heedless, unastonished profusion. We cannot stop the eternal insubstantial change, demand a conclusion, fix with a name, presuppose an end; conclusions are ignorance arrested on the path to less ignorance, and even our slight wisdom knows that the final word is never uttered. There never is an end. Only a way."

"And so I thank God now and always, and ask for nothing else. There is not anything else. And even should the future cleverly intend to keep us apart, I shall still be grateful to Him, all my life."

And in that autumn our prayer was to love each other better and more perfectly; to be content and steadfast; not to want anything far out in the future, nor grasp too hard what was given. For even if the future were withdrawn from us, and the present treat us harshly, yet this which we had, already was enough. For it seemed to us then that our joys and our sorrows, our denials and our decisions, our faults and our virtues, and all of the past, were like the load at the end of a plumbline that led us straight to each other; and that our lives had no other aim but this moment of fusion, this instant of discovery between ourselves, and God. Before Him we stood, naked. Yet we were not ashamed.

# CHAPTER XI

# All Chinese Together

*November 1949*

"WE'RE REALLY ÉMIGRÉS NOW," SAID ROBERT. "ARISTOCRATS after the French Revolution."

"Or White Russians," said I. "Those who escaped."

In Robert and Nora Hung's house at Repulse Bay disorder prevailed. Fourteen friends and five relatives had lived in it since the fall of Canton in October. For a month Nora had not been able to plan a well-conducted party. The servants had increased to six. Serene amid the litter of the drawing room now part bedroom, Nora finished potting Saisai, her fourth child. Robert and I sat under a Chinese painting and he recounted the latest onslaught.

"We had taken the children to see *Pinocchio*. When we came back, there was the Minister, and all nine of his family, sitting on the doorstep. They had such a bad time getting out through Indo-China. Our new, foolish amah is Cantonese; she could not understand the Minister's northern dialect. She locked the gate and refused to let them in. She was terrified when the Minister laughed. He has such a big laugh."

"It reminds me of the old days, during the Japanese war," said Nora, "when we walked all day, and slept on the ground in farmyards, and rats ran across our faces. It was very uncomfortable; yet I remember those days with great pleasure."

"I discover again that my wife has the heart of a hero," said Robert. For him every event confirms his love of Nora.

"And now," he continued, "we still have with us my cousin Sen, who went to the University in your year; he remembers you. He is a scientist and is buying research instruments. Nora's aunt by marriage, Mrs. Cheng, with her daughter Eileen and her niece Rose, are in our bedroom. Mrs. Cheng comes from Formosa; her husband may become a general there. They have quite a few vacancies among generals. Eileen is going to the States to recover from her divorce and to study literary criticism. Rose is a communist, and has cut her hair short. She does not speak to her aunt. It makes our meals a little silent, but not impossible. After all, we all of us have friends and relatives on both sides; for we are all Chinese together."

"We may be all Chinese together," said Nora, "but I doubt if we could go back to live in Shanghai now."

"Oh, we're *émigrés* now," said Robert, sprightly. "Every revolution has its *émigrés*. Let's wait until the dust settles to see the future clearly; things are not so bad. Let's just see what happens."

"The White Russians," I said, "never went back. Those of us who run away now are the White Chinese, Robert. They will never go back."

Robert disliked this. To a Chinese, the idea of never returning to China is preposterous. Should he not return alive, when he is dead his bones go back. The Coffin Hospital in Hong Kong — comfortable, spacious and rainproof, not like the huddle of sheds next to it which temporarily sheltered one hundred and eighty lepers — was also crowded; crowded with carefully packaged, well-labeled boxes. In these lay the bones of many an Overseas Chinese who had died far from his country, awaiting settled conditions to return to that small ancestral village, somewhere in the endless yellow plain; back to the village where his dead ancestors waited for him.

"I was at the Kamling Restaurant last night," said Robert, dexterously shifting the talk to avoid becoming angry. "That's where all the big business dinners are given, as you know. The New China Trade agents were giving a dinner. It was like old times again; they certainly have keen, efficient business people," said Robert, proud of his own countrymen. "Mr. Parrish also had a dinner given to him, by one of the agents who was his pupil at the Mission School, years ago. Mr. Parrish was very pleased, especially when his ex-student, just before the shark's-fin soup, turned to him and said: 'Now, Reverend Mr. Parrish, would you like to say grace before we start?'—'That shows our Christian teaching has not been in vain, after all,' Mr. Parrish kept on repeating to me in the car when we drove home."

"How is business?" I asked, to get Robert away from anecdote. "How is the Big Hong Kong Boom? Isn't there a small depression now? The godowns are full of goods, but not much is moving out. There's nowhere to unload because of the blockade of the China ports, is there?"

"I would not call it a depression," said Robert. "That's not a good name for it; not a good name at all. Let's call it a stalemate. Yes, a stalemate," he repeated, pleased with the sound of the word.

"The way Suyin keeps up with business in Hong Kong," smiled Nora, "is by watching the lobby of one hotel."

I confessed that it was my barometer of trade and financial weather. In the lobby, red-seated, fawn-tabled, palm-festooned, of a large hotel in the business section of the city, there was a slackening in number and noise of the bustling Shanghai families disgorged at teatime from the cinemas. And was I right in thinking the businessmen a trifle subdued in their clamorous calculations over their fresh orange juice? Was it that the wealthiest had found permanent refuge elsewhere in the world? Was it that many had proved unlucky, and come to the end of their savings? The English still inhabited the higher stratum on the first floor. After half past six, the lobby became the strict enclosure of Lily Wu, from Peking, her professional colleagues from everywhere, and American sailors. Two grimly indifferent M.P.s mounted guard, while over iced coffee, Scotch, fresh milk and rye, the nations became acquainted.

"Good evening, Han," said a voice, "I hear you are going to Peking."

It was Sen, a quiet young man, and good-looking. He called me by my surname, we had been to the same University, and in the same year. I knew his sisters and his family. We all belonged. We wore the old school tie. And now he was a scientist of the New Democracy.

"Yes, I think I shall be going in January."

"Going to Red China?" said Mrs. Cheng, suddenly appearing with Eileen behind her holding a *Life of Shelley*. "They will shoot you, Dr. Han." Mrs. Cheng had a great many stiff curls round her well-shaped head, and her small feet plumped out from her tiny black American pumps. Eileen smiled ethereally, she had been my guest at our moonfeast dinner.

"Why would they shoot me?"

"You ask me why? You are the widow of a Kuomintang general, are you not? Your husband was killed in battle against the communists, was he not? You have been abroad, you are an intellectual, is it not so? Do you think you will escape? You will be suspect as soon as you are back. They will indoctrinate and reindoctrinate you. But they will never trust you, never. And in the end they will shoot you."

I said politely: "I am not intellectual, I am a technician. It is not a question of fearing what might happen to me. I only want to work for my people."

"I would not think of working for people who had killed my husband," said Mrs. Cheng. "I could never become a communist."

"Neither will Han become a communist," said Sen in his quiet voice. "She would be such a bad party member," he smiled, "but we are all Chinese together. Han is a doctor, and her duty is to the people who need doctors — the Chinese people."

I felt grateful to Sen. After all, that is why I had trained in England — so that I could be a doctor in China. Many people had suddenly become addicted to flinging violent political labels at other people. There were so many among the foreigners in Hong Kong whose automatic reaction, if one said "Peking," was to think "Red," where once they would have thought of imperial palaces and quiet courtyards. There were so many, hysterical with fear, seeing communists everywhere. There would be so many in China, denouncing reactionaries and spies in every corner. And no iron curtains to keep savagery, stupidity and fear safely confined. They rampaged freely over the world.

Mrs. Cheng's mind dwelt on the lurid and the emotional. While the new, foolish amah, an irregular comet, darted at intervals from the outer spaces of the kitchen into the planetary system of our supper table to refill our rice bowls, Mrs. Cheng ate and talked steadily. Her stories were of torture and rape, of well-poisoning and dope, of beautiful women spies and mass atrocities. Eileen returned to the *Life;* Rose, the short-haired communist niece, blew her breath fiercely in and out through dilated nostrils; Sen went on eating, never raising his eyes. Mrs. Cheng was evidently talking at him through me.

"And so," concluded Mrs. Cheng, "the Reds will only be happy when they have killed off a hundred and eighty million people in China. Everybody knows that."

"Dear aunt," said Nora, "have some more soup. You must not get so excited, it is bad for your digestion. We are all Chinese together: we all have brothers, sisters, cousins, friends, on one side and on the other. It is sad. We all want the good of our country, and a way of life for ourselves."

"What are you doing in Hong Kong?" I asked Sen.

"Buying and testing research apparatus," he replied. "It has to come from the States."

"The Americans," said Mrs. Cheng bitterly, sipping her tea. "Why do they sell to you? They give us money, but they do not respect us. We have lost so much face, and I wish we could return the money and get our face back."

"Trade is an instrument of peace," said Sen. "We want to do business with the whole world. Do you think that Russia and America do not buy and sell from each other?"

Mrs. Cheng was very bitter. "Only a big war," she said, "will make the world safe again."

"They have a lot of neuroses in Formosa," said Sen to me when Mrs. Cheng had left the table. "It is understandable. They have lost so much face. In China now," he added with a touch of arrogance, "we have no time for neuroses. We are all much too busy rebuilding our country."

"Sen," I said, "I am glad to see you again. We have been to the same University. We have many friends in common. I am glad to see that you have adapted yourself well to the new conditions. It is what I want to do. I would like you to come and have dinner with me and with an English friend of mine, Mark Elliott."

A change came over Sen, a change which was from inside and pervaded his outward appearance though not a muscle moved. His fingers, holding his pipe as deftly as Mark did (for Sen had spent two years in England on postgraduate research and brought back the pipe habit), did not even tighten on the stem. Yet he had changed. I knew him no longer.

In a perfectly normal voice, merely stating a fact, Sen said: "Mark Elliott. Ah, yes. A newspaperman. Counter-revolutionary, an agent from the imperialist camp."

And then, at last, I understood.

# CHAPTER XII

# The Squirrel Cage

*December 1949*

"Dearest," said mark, "how nice you smell. is it you, or a combination of you and Chanel?"

"Mark, what were you doing in China in 1937?"

"I don't remember. Let's go to our stone; let's see if the butterflies are all asleep on Lovers' Lane."

"Mark, when you were a financier in Shanghai, you were not doing intelligence, were you?"

"Dear one, what are you trying to tell me?"

"Mark, were you ever a spy?"

Strangers. Strangers whose paths had crossed in Hong Kong. Aloof in each other's arms, sitting in a borrowed green Morris car in front of a hospital one night.

We were back from an English party. A good party. I met officials who talked knowledgeably about rice, fish and China; traders who talked of finance, old books and China; amusing missionaries who did not fancy themselves immaculately conceived. Some were influential; a few spoke Chinese; here and there some even had Chinese friends. Whereas lower down it was not done to know Chinese or Eurasians, higher up it sometimes happened spontaneously.

Mark and I had come back together. What I had kept to myself must now be said, for in three more days he would leave Hong Kong. A New Republic in Indonesia; trouble in Indo-China; the jungle war

so charmingly nicknamed an emergency in Malaya, soon to enter its
third year. Countries where men sat in luxurious *boites-de-nuit,* head
turned towards the entrance through which one of these nights a
hand grenade would certainly be thrown; where villages under the
old dispensation by day, in the darkness belonged to a new order;
where men of property died for rubber with rifles in their hands;
where terror crawled out of the jungle in the name of freedom; where
there was no lack of white man courage, but a vast amount of stupidity. And fear over all.

Mark sat, relaxed, deceptively inoffensive. He was gentle, and carried no armor. He was never on the defensive, for he had nothing
to defend. I was in the crook of his arm, and he waited for my
words.

"Mark, I do not think we shall go to Peking together. Ever."

'My friend, did you really want to know my past? You have never
asked me questions, though I have asked a great many of you."

"You had to know me well; I belong to you."

"You do not really want information about me. For you I began the
day I came to you."

"It is so."

"Then if you wish to know — and under what compulsion I shall
not ask — I will tell you."

"Do not tell me," I said, my voice very small. "I do not want to
know. True or not, we cannot go to China together like this. You
are working for an imperialist paper in a bourgeois democracy. A
potential reactionary, a possible spy. You will probably get to Peking
if and when your government is recognized by, and recognizes, New
China. But you are a newspaperman, always suspect, always to be
watched. And if I have anything to do with you, we shall both be
suspected. It will be bad for your work. I too, am born wrong, a
potenial reactionary, a potential saboteur. I also am of that bourgeois
class which will have to be re-educated in the People's Democratic
Dictatorship. Not a proletarian, my saving grace is medicine, and
poverty. But my thoughts must be changed, my heart purified, my

soul renewed. It is as you said. I shall have to cut out great portions of myself. I shall have to give you up."

Mrs. Cheng had confined herself to the lurid and the emotional. I hoped that my words were a parched minimum, a summarized weather forecast. Cold, facing our private catastrophe with a bright shield of blandness, Mark drawled:

"Hmmm . . . yes, I see. It's rather a pity, isn't it?"

Our throats were sore with distress. Suddenly Mark looked very young. Already years younger in looks than his age, his face was now that of a little boy. I said:

"Some people will never believe that we just love each other. They will ascribe all sorts of motives to us."

"I see that the chances of sudden death for you have increased enormously."

"They cannot take chances, Mark. We must not be indignant about it. This is a revolution, not a parlor game. Saboteurs, potential spies, traitors, will be eliminated. For the future of the country, whatever that may be."

"I know that they will take no chances when the day of the purges is come."

"I could have fitted myself into the new pattern, and my past would have been forgiven me, for I never dabbled in politics. Like all middle-of-the-road liberals, I was against the Kuomintang. My Kuomintang husband would be forgiven me. But now I've done the wrong thing; I've fallen for an imperialist, and a newspaperman. And to save myself, perhaps I shall have to do all sorts of things. Confess certainly, repent, revile what I have loved, foul this thing between us — do you understand, Mark? And you would be in danger, too."

"Darling, you have got yourself into a mess, haven't you? Over here, Adeline Palmer-Jones, the moral commissar; over there the political commissar. I've messed up your life."

"I've messed up yours just as much."

"Have you?" He laughed shortly, and was out of the car and round to the other side, opening the door for me. "Get out."

I came out. He took my hand.

"Where are we going, Mark?"

"To our stone. The only home, perhaps, that we shall ever have."

We stood on our stone, feeling very desperate, looking at the blurred paler shadows of each other in the night.

"Paradise lost, my dearest," said Mark lightly. "Of course it could not be. I would have been too proud and happy with you all my life. Such things don't happen on this earth."

"We must be strong enough to go on dreaming," I began, but he cut me short.

"I am glad you spoke. How long have you harbored this in one of the *yous* that I know?"

"About three weeks."

"All the time, on the hill slope, in the enchanted autumn, you spared me. It was very wrong of you."

"I spared myself. I put it away when with you. I took it up again when you were not there. I made sure."

"Yes. Shut the door on one world, open one into the next. I do the same."

"We must not lose our heads," I said, an unconscious parody of Adeline Palmer-Jones. "We must be honest, and not hide anything. We must also be practical. It is better to know the truth, isn't it?"

"Dear Confucius," said Mark, "the truth is that I must marry you. Nothing else will do. I want it so badly, so much. Six weeks ago I was upset, and for a while, unsure. There seemed so many practical difficulties in our way. Now I have nothing left but moral certitude. I must marry you."

"Oh," I said, "must we go through it again? I can't bear it, I can't. I go black inside."

"Even if you were run over by a bus, tonight, I would not go back to the life that has lost heart."

"Heaven," I thought, "this is horrible. I'm caught in my own snare."

"With you I would not mind anything. I could be happy anywhere my paper sent me. Without you, I would not have the urge to accomplish very much. You set me free. You are so alive that I too become alive."

"Mark, stop. I am worse than anyone. I bind you with freedom; I play at honor, because you cannot resist nobility. It is a trick. The illusion of free will." I was very agitated.

"For an intelligent woman, you are occasionally very naïve. You swung me a line, a beautiful line. It was well done, and I couldn't care less. Don't you see that you could not have behaved otherwise? Both of us are indoctrinated with a certain behavior. We are both dishonorably honorable. You are much too conceited to tear your hair, make scenes, blackmail me with emotion. Dishonor or not, with or without love, I want you."

"Mark, in China . . ."

"Even in China we can be together. Of course there will be bad times, but not forever. If we are married no one will hurt you, in your own country, or anywhere. I shall look after you. I want to. I want to take care of you, do you understand?"

He was somber with repressed fury. I was tired, bewildered, happy, wanting to believe. It would be wonderful to be in China and married to Mark. There was something else, something at the bottom of me. But I could not remember what it was. On our stone he said:

"I will not let you go by default."

Round and round go the squirrels of the Chinese animal market. In their small cages, they tread a tight eternal wheel, a spindle of bright wire, with intent, impassive look. Under the perpetual motion of their paws the spindle disappears. It is an invisible whirr of bright air which the squirrels turn without end.

Round and round we went in our thoughts. Exaltation shed, we lingered for three days in a world of practical difficulties, considering all our blind alleys. Unsparing, unkind.

"We could go to India. You could be my mistress in India. I hate the thought."

"I cannot go anywhere but to China. I have no passport."

"No passport?" said Mark, alarmed and incredulous.

"Chinese don't need passports from Hong Kong to China. Mine lapsed when I came from England to Hong Kong in February. I cannot get one now, except, of course, illegally. It's very expensive."

*"Pas de papiers,"* said Mark.

"Martha Monk would say that I'm trying to marry you for your *papiers,* Mark. Some Chinese girls do it, in these difficult days."

We laughed.

"I could give you up, of course."

"Of course."

We left it at that.

"I cannot just walk out. It would be cowardly. I must convince other people."

"Of course we cannot run away. But if ever you are not sure, you must not spare me."

"Neither must you. I would not forgive that."

Endlessly we paced the invisible wheel.

"I won't write until I've got something definite. It is too easy to escape into a dream of you."

"I won't write."

He bit his nails badly during those three days. My inside refused to work well; I could not swallow. We looked at each other, and I thought: "If he were mad or a leper, it wouldn't matter."

Round and round, treading the circle of our thoughts.

"What shall I do with your letters? It's such a temptation for me to read them. It would be too easy . . . I must throw them in the sea."

"If you do, don't forget to put a stone with them, Mark. They might float."

"Would they float?"

Round and round.

"The children. They'll always be my first consideration. But they don't see much of me now. I don't know whether children are better off in an unhappy marriage or a satisfactory divorce, do you?"

"No divorce is ever happy at first. Too many hurt feelings."

Round and round.

"I don't want to drift from one cheap casual coupling to another. I never want to be reminded of those things again. I was just on the point of drifting when I came to you."

"You won't drift. I did not know love was like this until I met you."

"Perhaps we could wait. The children would be grown up."

"We could. I could wait ten years for you."

"I could. But we must have a decision. I must make sure that I shall have you in ten years."

On and on, intent, impassive. Squirrels in a cage.

"Are you going to China next month?"

"I'm so muddled, I do not know."

"Could you wait? Wait till I'm back. It won't be very long, three months so so . . . but you must go if you want to."

"I'll wait. I'll fix myself another job. I've got friends. I shall get on all right. I'm a good fixer."

"Yes, I know you are a good fixer."

And so Mark left, and we went through it all over again.

On and on we went. In the next six months I was to go back to China, back to the missionaries, back and forth to so many people, trying to find a way, a guiding thread. Walking half blind, heartsick, accepting the effacement of reassurance; and every day our worlds of reality coming a little more apart.

We did not run away. It would have been too easy.

Round and round.

# CHAPTER XIII

# Starting Points

*Suchen*

In a few moments the gangplank would go up; Suchen and I would part. Already the trombone and the clarinets tuned incoherent Auld Lang Synes; the happy tearful voices of friends clashed in excited rise and fall; the high-pitched shrieks of whistles tore across the decks; the sampans, loud with clatter and bump, crowded backwards, backing away from the ship. Suchen prophesied a voyage-long seasickness for herself; Baby, a small Suchen with blue-black eyebrows and pink dimples, lay beatific and observant in the arms of a grinning Cantonese amah.

Amah was dressed in her best black silk trousers, white jacket and wide grin. There was something reassuring in the grin with its vistas of strong white teeth projecting haphazard as squatters' shacks from an overhanging upper jaw, and her widely spread, shining, patent-leather shoes with square toes and large steel buckles. Amah was happy. She was going to America.

Suchen was not a good fixer; her helplessness made it a pleasure to do things for her. Friends of her husband had wangled the passport, the visas, the amah. Her finances were re-established. Before his demise at the hands of the last government, for collaboration, her husband had laid up for Suchen and Baby treasure abroad. It had been gold bars and Japanese goods; but then, in Hongkong, did not some extensive and highly respected fortunes owe their solidity to black-market traffic in food to the inmates of the Japanese prison camps?

"What are you going to do, Suchen, in America?"

"Be happy."

"You'll never come back?"

"Never. I'm tired of terror and disease, hunger and misery, and always seeing poor people around me. Always the crowds, and their poverty. Many of our friends and the people we grew up with are now leaving China with no intention of ever coming back. You live in the stars, Suyin, who think otherwise. I never want to be insecure and frightened again."

Everyone wanted security. Security no longer a word, but a deity, a life-demanding god. I could not worship or dedicate myself to it; I could only hang in precarious balance between Mark and China.

"I want to be comfortable, and I want for Baby the best there is in the world. America is wonderful, Suyin. You ought to come to America. Hong Kong is not safe. It's the overhanging rock poised above the abyss. Weren't you offered a scholarship to a New York hospital a little while ago? What a fool you were to refuse it. Think of Mei, your daughter. Her future, her security, and yours."

Security. Other people went to it, for their life had changed unbearably, had become a serial terror. A piece had been left out of me, as it had been left out of Mark. I could not run away. If I tried, I had to come back.

It was right to run away from danger. Security was right. I, too, was afraid in my heart. But it was my fault that I found people smaller and meaner, shrunk in a fixed search for security. Deep buried in this word lay the talent of the slothful servant, unadventured on the dangerous seas of life. For this strange end, men planned, with singlehearted passion, pensions and retirement; at twenty dreaming of sixty-five; in youth aspiring to safe senility. For the security of death, they forsook living. Security armed and rearmed the nations groaning under armaments and yet devising ever more efficient ways of killing their own kind.

Of course we could go to America, Mei and I. Friends would lend money. Passports could be bought. Ways out could be fixed. America was a wonderful place. I loved my American friends, so generous, warmhearted and sincere.

But I could not go away. I could not think of going from this land where Mei's father, and I, and Mei, had our long deep roots. I could not think of her as a "White Chinese," uprooted, alien in a strange land, heart turned forever towards the country left behind. We would not go away until we were pushed out altogether.

Shaking my head dumbly, I said to Suchen what I always say when I have no intention of doing anything at all:

"Perhaps you're right, Suchen. I'll think about it."

## Oh-no

She was now an inmate of the Po Leung Kuk, the Institution for the Protection of Virtue. It shelters lost children, ill-used slave girls, and girls who have been kidnapped for immoral purposes. The Secretary for Chinese Affairs of the Colony looks after it. The girls learn sewing, handicraft, a little reading and writing.

"She is very intelligent," said the Matron. "She is most eager to learn. You must bring her some books next time you come to see her."

Oh-no was doing cross-stitch with the same relentless passivity on her froglike face that she wore while I examined her in the Casualty Ward of the Hospital. The power of her silence was overwhelming. I clung to her mentally, as if she could save me from inner disaster; she, a slave girl who, in the eyes of her race, had lost her only asset: her virginity. For even now the Chinese make a fetish of virginity for maidens and chastity for widows. Many a young girl is still brought to me to be examined before marriage. Many times a week I write a certificate beginning: "I . . . certify this girl to be a virgin." Few Chinese men will marry a girl who has been touched by another man. That is in Hong Kong, in 1950.

"Oh-no."

"Doctor." Oh-no answered me in the prescribed polite manner, standing up and bowing to me.

"Who gave you that name, Oh-no? It is not a name."

It was a year before Oh-no began to smile. She said, in that matter-of-fact manner so terrible to see:

"When I was brought into the Hsu family, I was a baby, crying all the time. I said 'Oh no, please, oh please, no,' and nothing else. Old Mother Ching told me it was because I had been so ill-treated by the merchant who sold me to the family. She called me Oh-no."

"Why did you run to the police? Who told you about the police in Hong Kong? In China everyone was so frightened of the police."

With that patience which made of her answer the most obvious thing in the world, Oh-no replied: "It came from looking at the sea. I did not go to the police. I ran to the sea. Every day I looked at the sea, lying between two hills, talking to herself, as I talked to myself. I ran to the sea when Old Master tried again. A policeman on the road stopped me and took me to the police station. A foreign devil was there, and he asked me why I ran. That is how it happened."

Often in the months that followed I heard her voice, not light and clear as Mei's is, but deep, and a little rough: "It came from looking at the sea."

### The Goldfish

Adeline Palmer-Jones had her sycophants. Ernest Watts had his disciples. Blue-eyed in a dove-gray Chinese gown, he raised a slow finger towards heaven as I entered his flat. Affixed to the door a white piece of paper proclaimed: "To live alone Man must be either Beast or God."

Depending from the ceiling a samurai sword and scabbard hung by a fine red string, revolving slowly on a small axis.

The visitor's chair was capacious and low, in the tradition of perennial psychology. It induced the required abasement in the presence of a superior being.

I needed a sage, a saint or a god. I was muddled, in search of an oracle.

Ernest Watts had been a long time in the East. He was the Goldfish, rare and well read. Philosophy was his handmaid. Did he not exult in magnificent words? Was he not disliked by the humbug and the idiot, the wordmongering and the thoughtless, as is the rule for sages? He had talked to me one day when I met him pacing the draughty Hospital corridor while a storm wracked the windowpanes, howling desolation round the gray walls. Had I read Sartre? I confessed that Existentialism was a name to me. Had I read . . . I shook my head, backed away faint with awe. Alas, my printed loves so few. I did not keep abreast with modern lore, for I had not opened a novel in the last ten years.

Ernest Watts had his disciples. Besides that eternal Peter Pan, John Tam, I had met other young men eager for his knowledge and the acerbity of his wit. What mattered if some appeared to me unbalanced? They were young; I was thirty-two. They shunned contact with the uncouth and the imbecile; I, plunged into humanity at its bleating, stinking best, felt acutely inferior when confronted with them. Ernest Watts possessed knowledge and wisdom. Mark liked him. "I like that kind of precious conversation. I like people who do things well: Watts, and you."

I took my question to the shrine of Ernest Watts, and sat before him, geared to a resolve not to evade the brutal truth.

"Mr. Watts, I am sorry to bother you. I need someone to tell me the truth. I am so muddled."

A half smile encouraged me.

"Mr. Watts, I am in love."

The impassive, inscrutable, reserved Oriental is another myth. There is no people less reticent, more eager to discuss their physical ailments and their mental interiors, than the Chinese. In China one always knows everything about everyone else. Where, at a certain stage, Europeans withhold part of the facts, draw a modest veil upon further events, the Chinese carry on, undismayed and unfaltering. There are no unmentionables in China.

"I love Mark Elliott."

"And where, pray," said Ernest Watts, "do you think your unrequited love for Mark Elliott will lead you?"

Heedless of the adjective, my eyes on my hands, I replied:

"It is not unrequited; I think he wants to marry me. And you see, it's all so worrying. . . ."

I did not go on. His body had become rigid. His eyes were fixed. He was listening, but not to me. Attentive to something else, something within himself.

"Do you think you are more unselfish than others?"

"I think that I am normally selfish, like everyone else."

"Yes," said Watts, dismissing me with a wave of his hand. "I think you are."

I rose and left. Oracles are like kittens. You take them home in a covered basket, keeping the lid tight shut that they may not escape.

I had not said what I wanted to say. There was something else at the bottom of me. But I had no words for it. I shook my head as a puppy out of the sea shakes the water out of its ears, and wrote a little note to Ernest Watts: "Thank you for turning my mountains into molehills."

I was being courteous, Chinese fashion.

Two days later, suddenly, I knew what was wrong. I had treated Watts as a Chinese, and he was a foreigner. Knowledge he had, and wisdom perhaps — all of the mind, none of the heart. The understanding heart was not his; he could not hear the silence.

I had wanted to speak about China, and instead I had spoken about love.

"Well, that finishes the Goldfish," I thought.

But Ernest Watts had not finished with me.


*Mr. Franklin*

Why, in Chungking, had I disliked Mr. Franklin so much?

In Hong Kong, he was just another Englishman; prosperous, well fed, benevolent on the background of the stolid Victorian edifices;

wiping his face with a semiharassed, cheerful smile, ordering another drink in pidgin English. "Boy, can do one piecee drink?" In the elevator he had said with commendable good will: "Boy, can do another piecee man?" The old attendant had looked at him with blank impersonal eyes.

Mr. Franklin had left Chungking after the liberation. He was happy to be out of China, mournful to be going home. He regretted his cat. He thought the Red soldiers very efficient, very smart. They behaved with great dignity. They paid for everything. There were far too many parades and processions, too many meetings. He thought that China would soon be her old self again. "This sort of thing won't last. I've never known a Chinaman yet who wasn't crooked one way or the other. Soon, they'll be at their old tricks again, and life will be just fine."

Like many another old China-hand, Mr. Franklin thought that only Westerners were masters of machines. "Shanghai is in a terrible state. The Chinese have never been able to run anything themselves, and they never will."

Neither Sen nor I protested. I had brought Sen to tea with Mr. Franklin, liking the contrast; Sen had such wonderful English manners. Sen looked at Mr. Franklin with carefully amused eyes. Here in Hong Kong, in that half-unconscious resentment of the whites which is the unspoken atmosphere of many a Chinese gathering, I expected Mr. Franklin to say these things. Mr. Franklin was part of the Old Order; by himself, he did not mean anything.

Mr. Franklin had been to the University, where he had old friends. He had walked round the buildings, still dilapidated after the last war. "The students here are quiet, not rowdy and Red as in China. In Chungking they're refusing to take their examinations in order to attend parades to save the country. Those here seem well off. Many of them have their own cars."

"Yes," said Sen. "Many sons and daughters of prosperous Chinese families from Malaya and Indo-China and Southeast Asia and Hong Kong attend Hong Kong University."

Mr. Franklin was in two minds about the value of higher education, Western style, for Asiatics. "You were much happier in the old days, when you had your own culture. We've spoiled you with Western ideas which you cannot handle. Didn't Sun Yat-sen, who overthrew the Chinese empire and made the revolution forty years ago, study at Hong Kong University? There you are, that comes from teaching democracy to you people. It breeds revolution."

Sen reassured him. "Hong Kong University does not try to teach democracy. It may teach medicine, economics, literature, but it does not teach democracy, since, like every other colonial institution, it maintains a double standard. It may have bred one revolutionary by irritation, but it does not train many democrats by example."

"Well, I hope you're right."

"Hong Kong, Mr. Franklin, is an island of Private Property. The University is mainly a rich man's university. Good wealthy families, steady jobs, well-established practices after graduation; banks, lawyers' offices, and private medical enterprise, raking in their thousands every month. They are not hungry, either for rice, or for ideals. Security is what they want, and what they get. There is no communism in Hong Kong University."


*Anne Richards*

"The writer today is in a morass," said Anne, flinging down palette and brush. "The painter still lives in a privileged world, building a vision of his own without wasting effort to please. The writer lives in everyone else's world, and now everyone reads, and nearly everyone writes. I, a painter by nature, who understand only objects and people, have been asked to pass judgments, and to discuss ideas."

Anne was back from Southeast Asia. She was unhappy about it, as so many Americans were unhappy. Unhappy about colonialism manifest, for Americans love the idea of freedom and equality for all peoples. The double standard unabashedly maintained, a perpetual source of resentment between the races, dismayed and revolted Americans.

"*C'est un scandale, c'est un scandale,*" shouted Anne, dancing her ninety pounds round three bulky guardians of the law kicking a native prostrate on the ground. In another country, Anne had been assailed with requests for financial help. "Oh, I'm an anticommunist, so please may I have gold dollars," was a chant, the refrain Americans heard so often. It confused them, made them suspect their own idealism. Too well did they know that gold dollars bolstered anticommunism; too many anticommunists were bought with gold dollars.

Anne's unhappiness expressed itself in floods of color. She was trying to fix the gaudy sunset on canvas, and more than succeeding.

"All I want is to go back to Peking. And now China is so very much against us. It hurts, Suyin. We've tried to help, we've really tried, and now it's all gone sour. The teeth of the children are set on edge."

"You'll never get away from the idea of China, Anne. It's your inner climate. You've been bitten, just as Mark has."

We were depressed, Anne and I. The news was so gloomy. Rearmament; war round the corner; senators hopping about; my own country, inflated with success, proclaiming that America was only a "paper tiger"; better bombs invented; spy rings unearthed; Japan selling mightily to the northern Chinese ports; Hong Kong precarious, strikes and factories closing. All the doves wore wreaths of bayonets and clutched sticks of atom bombs between their claws.

"I wonder," said Anne, "what it must be like for you, Suyin, at this moment. You who belong to both worlds, who read and write and speak and think both ways. You who can always explain the meaning beyond the words we hear. You must be absolutely torn in two. And loving Mark does not make it better, does it?"

"I am torn all the time. And loving Mark makes it terrible."

"I hope," said Anne, "that the day will never come when your country and mine will be at war, Suyin. When we shall call your people the yellow bellies, the subhuman, and our late enemies fine fellows and democrats. I was just wondering whether one day you would call me a ferocious beast, a viper, and a spy, Suyin."

"It has already begun," I smiled with pain. "Name-calling has already begun, Anne, you know that."

"We the Americans have always looked upon China with special love," said Anne. "I hope it will not make our hatred worse. I think we shall always make a distinction between your people and your rulers."

"That won't make any difference at all, Anne. It's the people who get killed."

"You'll always write to me, won't you? You won't forget me. We're friends, Suyin. We're friends. Nothing will make any difference, will it?"

I stared at Anne. Would there come a day when I would not be her friend? And Mark . . . would I hate him, because he was one *ist* and I was another *ist?* Would it happen? "I think I shall always be your friend, Anne," I said.

"I couldn't bear it if you, too, learned to hate us," said Anne.


*Suzanne*

Suzanne looked worried, teetering on her chair, twisting her hands, the only restless thing in her charming flat.

"What is the matter, Suzanne?"

"It's my friend. He wants to marry me." There was mirth, consternation and anxiety in her voice.

"Oh, how nice, Suzanne!"

"It's not nice, it's annoying. His digestion is now upset. I am afraid it is the liver."

"But it will be all right, Suzanne."

"It won't. You don't know women. They always dig their toes in when their property is in danger. I hope his wife doesn't find out I've got Chinese blood in me. It would make it much worse for him."

"Suzanne, how stupid you are."

"I'm not. It is you who don't understand, Suyin. There's still so much prejudice about. It may be all right for you. You look Chinese, and you want to be. But I pass as white. If *she* knew, it would give her a handle . . . don't you see?"

"I don't. You're stupid; you're twenty years behind the times. All over Asia I've met people, doctors, professors, writers, prouder of Chinese blood in them than of anything else. We are just as good, if not better, than anyone else. Why do you want to measure yourself against a false white standard? This is our world, Suzanne."

"Not in Hong Kong, Suyin. Nor in Singapore, you know."

"Even in Hong Kong. The fault is ours. We carry chips on our shoulders, waste time in resentment, expect to be looked down upon. We make it an excuse for unsuccess. 'It's because I'm Eurasian, that's why,' we say. We turn ourselves into relics of the concessions, the good old days of white domineering; we ape the low white trash and their bad manners. It is our fault, Suzanne."

"You can talk, can't you?" said Suzanne. "But I live in this world, not in the stars. I know how much Eurasians have to put up with, and you know it, too, though you raise your nose and pretend you're better than anyone around you. I look white, and until now I've passed. It's made life easier — a bigger salary, my flat paid for. I wouldn't get these privileges if I were only a Eurasian, or a Chinese. You know that well enough, Suyin."

I said with all the arrogance and the pride of China in my voice: "Being Eurasian is not being born of East and of West. It is a state of mind. A state of mind created by false values, prejudice, ignorance. We must get rid of that state of mind. We must carry ourselves with colossal assurance and say: 'Look at us, the Eurasians! Just look. How beautiful we are, more beautiful than either race alone. More clever, more hardy. The meeting of both cultures, the fusion of all that can become a world civilization. Look at us, and envy us, you poor, one-world people, riveted to your limitations. We are the future of the world. Look at us.'"

"Goodness," said Suzanne. "Goodness. How you talk, Suyin. Is it true, what you say?"

"It is true. If only we will it hard enough, it will be true. We could save the world, Suzanne, if only we were not afraid. If we would just be ourselves."

Suzanne did not reply, and we spoke of something else.

*William Monk, and perhaps Martha*

"Want a lift?" said William Monk.

I was walking back from Mei's school, and did not want a lift. But already Monk was out of his car and shoving me in, jocularly. "There, all nice and cosy, eh?"

We drove off. "Mr. Monk, I'm going to the Hospital."

"No hurry. It's a beautiful evening. Fresh air will do you good. Let's have a little spin."

"I get plenty of fresh air at the Hospital. It's very healthy up there."

"Tut, tut, lass," said he archly. "That's what's so attractive about you Chinese women — that mixture of reserve and seductiveness. . . . Chinese girls," he went on at great and lyric length, "are the most beautiful women in the world. Lovely supple figures, dainty hands and feet, and skins . . . no wonder once you've had a Chinese woman, you're off anything else. Ours don't come anywhere near . . ."

"Mr. Monk," I said, "I am Eurasian."

"Are you? I wouldn't have thought it. Well, that's even more interesting, isn't it? Eurasians are more . . . passionate." (Here he tittered.) "I can see you've got absolutely everything to make a man fall . . . face like a mystery . . . your profile. . . ."

"Mr. Monk, where is your wife?"

"She's gone to Macao for a week. As I was saying . . ."

"Mr. Monk, mind the traffic."

Suddenly his hand shot out and squeezed my side with, I presume, the grip of passion. It hurt. "You're beautiful . . . do you know that?"

"Mind," I said sharply. "Heavens, you fool, you nearly ran over him." We'd nearly hit one of Hong Kong's innumerable jaywalkers. William Monk drove so badly. Either he leapt forward in spurts, or he went slow as a snail. The interruption made him bad-tempered. We shot ahead and arrived at the Hospital without talking about anything but golf, and swimming, and the Saturday races. I kept him to these topics all the way.

*Diana Kilton*
Diana is a member of the nursing profession.

James Manton once said: "Nurses so often marry police officers here. I am glad the force keeps a steady supply of nice young men on tap for these attractive girls to marry."

"How is Alfred?" I rushed into Diana's office, noticing the letter in her hand. It was good manners to inquire about her friend.

Diana frowned. "When will you learn to be discreet? Someone might hear you." She gazed round the otherwise empty office.

"I'm sorry, Diana."

Diana and I have known each other a long time. We met in England.

"There are things you won't understand even if you live to be a thousand. You're so wrapped up in Mark you don't know what goes on around you."

"Oh, but I know; I hear everything that's said about everyone, and all about myself too. It amuses me."

"Well, I don't want people to go round snooping into my private affairs. I'm not going to ruin my chances of getting something better if I can."

"I thought you were in love."

"He loves me all right. He's a good dancer, he's got a car. An M-G. He couldn't afford that back home. I like him all right."

"Oh, Diana, how I love you. You're so sensible."

"I don't put all my eggs in one basket, as you do. And yours is a leaky one. Still no letters?"

"No. But he said he would not write. It's . . . suffocating."

Her eyes clear, flecked with bright cruelty. "Well, what can you expect? He's gone home, hasn't he?"

"Oh, it isn't so, Diana."

"My dear, do be sensible. If you think your little public school boy will remain true to you . . . after all, it's jolly difficult for him, and your being Chinese doesn't make it any easier."

That night I sobbed so loudly that I woke myself up.


*Eileen Cheng*

"You talk too much," said Lucy Koo in mournful tones. "You talk far too much. Chinese people in Hong Kong don't talk."

Lucy Koo and I stood at the entrance to the King's Theatre, watching the taxis and the cars disgorge, Chinese fashion, incredibly large parties of adults and children. We waited for Mrs. Cheng and Eileen.

(Humpbacked, my winter days, a file of loaded refugees in the rain, dragging past a frontier post. No word from Mark.)

"Here they are," said Lucy. "They've come in a taxi."

Wrapped in glistening plastic raincoats, Mrs. Cheng and Eileen ran towards us across the wet pavement, and we all went upstairs to the dress circle.

"As I was saying," pursued Lucy, once inserted in her seat, "you must be more careful. At Church Guest House the missionaries call you the Red Doctor. It's not safe to talk in Hong Kong. Not if you are Chinese. You'll lose your job."

"I'm losing my job anyway in a week. You're talking nonsense, Lucy." Too often I had encountered this pusillanimous attitude among the Chinese in Hong Kong, this made-up fear. "We are not allowed to talk," they said, half exulting in the fact that they were not free.

"Listen," I said to Lucy, "you don't understand the English. They like courage. They are fair, nearly all the time, though not so much in the colonies as they are at home. The English do believe in freedom. The trouble is with ourselves, Lucy, that we do not talk openly enough. If we stood up, and said what we thought; if we helped them in their good schemes, and openly criticized their faults; if we asked for representation and for votes; we'd get what we want. Slowly, grudgingly, but we would get it. The trouble is that we want to be frightened. We like to pretend that we are victimized all the time, instead of only some of the time."

Lucy was not at all convinced. "You are talking of the English in England. In England there may be freedom, but out here you are in a colony. Here you are not equal, you are Chinese. There are two kinds of everything: houses, salaries, privileges and freedom. The white, and the other."

"It is our fault too," I said. "We are lazy, we leave it to the whites to run us. We just sit back and criticize. I will talk, and nothing will happen to me. Only the second-rate and the stupid will criticize. Those who matter will understand. You'll see."

After the film Mrs. Cheng said to me as we went whisking through the rain in a taxi which was dropping me at the Hospital, and taking the Chengs back to Repulse Bay:

"I am glad, of course, that Eileen will be going to the States. She is artistic, and she needs self-expression. But I am a little worried too. She may fall in love with a foreigner, and marry him. It would be a disgrace for our family."

"Oh no," I said. "Not in this modern age, Mrs. Cheng. Not if she marries a nice man, a well-educated foreigner."

Mrs. Cheng went on without any regard for Eileen in the front seat. "Of course Eileen is now a divorcée, which makes it difficult for her to marry a Chinese of good family . . . it may have to be a foreigner after all. But her father and I are old-fashioned, you know, and we shall still feel that it is a small disgrace for our family."

And there it was. On both sides. My people as bad as the English, erecting just as many barriers, foolish and useless. Something was needed to sweep away those prejudices, so that people would look upon each other as people, and help each other to better living. Something was needed. Perhaps New China was one of the ways of doing it. I'd have to find out.

*Maya Wong*

"Maya."

I had not seen Maya for over six weeks. November, the sunny, the most beautiful month of the year in Hong Kong, had been for Mark alone. We had had four Sundays, an autumn gathered whole; four days of love and sunlight to last us all our lives.

"Maya."

She had always been thin, and now she was gaunt. Her cheeks were flushed and drawn over the fine bones, her eyes luminous, her red lips finely wrinkled, like parched silk paper. In her neck, above the high Chinese collar, the fine quick throb of pulse went up and down, tumultuous and uneven. Even as I knew her disease, once again the awareness of her beauty, as she sat, hands together, gazing past me — once again her beauty diminished any horror that could be. And then I was stunned by the horror, and wept in front of her, knowing that she would die.

Maya sat looking on, a fine-drawn smile upon dried lips, a smile beyond laughter, mocking itself steadily. Her hands were a little moist as she turned the palms outwards, in consolation of my bitterness.

"How long have you known, Maya?"

"I spat blood two weeks ago."

"I should have guessed. Those colds . . ."

I should have known. If the eyes and ears of my heart had not been stopped up with greedy passion for one only, I would have known. For a moment I hated Mark, and that consuming intent which had crippled me for everyone else. I had not seen my best friend dying near me. More than blind, because of Mark. Blind, two months ago, when Maya and I lay together in the grass, talking of Mark, and she was thin and dark under the cheekbones and the eyes all day, her slimness too sharp, and shadows upon her in the sun. I had not seen. All of me turned to Mark only. Blind. Foolish and blind.

"My husband died of tuberculosis," said Maya. "It is fate. Do not grieve, my friend."

In a frenzy, and with contempt for the zeal it engendered, I moved. Maya was not a government servant. No priority for a bed. Waiting lists years long for the very few sanatoria. Two hundred fresh cases of tuberculosis notified each week, in a population of two millions. Deaths steady around seventy a week. Maya had three children.

"If I do not work, I starve, and the children," she said, laughing a little, puzzled that it had come to this.

I had let the world go moldering in my hands each hour. For six unsavable weeks. Now Maya was bright with fever and diseased in both lungs. I ran around in circles, completely helpless, seeking aid. An emotion of little amplitude, dryly bitter. For Mark engrossed me; such full sweet pain, his thought, that nothing was left for others but the bones of bitterness, and remorse.

Nora and Robert Hung would take the children. Already they had my daughter Mei, happy with them, happier than in my room at the Hospital. Nora and Robert said to Maya: "But we are all one family, for we are all Chinese together. Your three, our four, and Suyin's little one . . . all together one family. We are so pleased." And looked delighted.

But Nora and Robert had much family to look after — relatives, and friends, and friends of friends still coming out of China, squeezed reluctantly out, dribbling as flour dribbles between grindstones, coming to Hong Kong bewildered. "There is no way. We have tried. We could not stand it. . . ." And they would have to be fed, they would have to get jobs, they would try to buy passports, or even to get them legally. They would go: to the Philippines, to Australia, to South America, to Indonesia, to New York, to San Francisco. Passed on from house to house, from friend to friend.

So it was Anne Richards who paid for Maya. Anne sat at her typewriter and pounded ideas and passed judgments, and told the public what they wanted to hear. It sold. Often at night, she would read out to me what she called her "yellow journalism"; and the money went to pay the expensive fees of a private hospital for Maya.

Maya was lucky. She thought I had wangled it. She thought the hospital was free. Anne would not let her know. "You Chinese are now a bit sensitive about American dollars. Of course you are. So much money has gone to the wrong things. It's better if Maya doesn't know."

## Adeline Palmer-Jones

For the second time, Adeline Palmer-Jones bore down on me. Suddenly I realized why Mark disliked her. "Those thin lips set in the rigid lines of authority. How small and hard the still small soul, embedded in those vast, deceptively soft mounds of flesh."

"I saw your application for membership in our Association," said Adeline without preamble. "I didn't think you'd be really interested, I told them not to take any notice. You're going to Peking, aren't you?"

I swallowed. It was my pride I swallowed. "I've decided to wait a bit in Hong Kong, Mrs. Jones."

"Really." Her small eyes looked at me. "Well, of course, we are only interested in keeping the best people in our educational institutions. The rest can always go into government service."

In Hong Kong, it is the fashion in some circles to look down upon government service.

"I understand Mr. Elliott has left Hong Kong," she continued in a bright chatty voice. "Such a pity; I had asked him and Miss Kilton to dinner with us. He didn't turn up; he had already left, Miss Kilton told me."

Already it had started. At a dance one night the Monks had walked up to Mark, and asked him and Diana, who sat with us, to dinner. And others. Scrupulously they took care to let me know. Always they left me out.

There was nothing I could reply to Adeline. I was so tired. I looked at my shoes, feeling inferior, feeling guilty.

Mark was gone. Gone back to his world, to the reality that was also part of him. One day, from that vantage point, he would know how impossible our dream was. One day he would write, saying how sorry he was, that it was all a dream.

Here, in front of Adeline, dominated by her stare, in my tacit acceptance of her disapproval, I knew how impossible it all was. For Adeline was reality. And Adeline was right. Reality always won.

And oh, the pity of our bright foolish dream!

*Ernest Watts*

The hibiscus hedge swung its yellow-spired flowers. Deep pink against the bright green leaves, they framed a silken sea stretched tight across the gap in the hedge. I sat in the sun, facing the gap, turned seawards, coddling my pain. To sit on earth, let the sun lull my pain to sleep, as a mother her child. The dark pink hibiscus swung its golden spires on and on along the path, towards the House of Wisdom, in the sun.

Along the path came Ernest Watts with John Tam. John eager, enthusiastic, his words tumbling out in his excitement. I rose, heavy, full of the void that was the silence of Mark.

Ernest Watts struck. Six inches from me, sure that I heard every word, giving me his profile to see, he said clearly, slowly, to John Tam:

"Don't forget our dinner tonight. Archie Cuff is coming. You'll like him; he's a great friend of Mark Elliott. He'll be able to give us news of Mark, he's seen him in Bangkok only two days ago."

*Sen*

And so it was that muddled with pain, intricate with conflict, haunted by the knowledge of Mark, I went to Sen.

"Sen, next time you go back to China, I go with you."

"In a week," said Sen, "I go back. Are you taking your child? Is it for good?"

"No. I promised Mark Elliott that I would wait for his return, or for his letter, in Hong Kong."

"The eternal dilettante, Han. When will you give all of yourself to the greatest cause in the world?"

"I don't understand causes. And I must come back. There are more questions than the one of duty which I must settle."

"Is this Englishman worth all the effort, Han, and all the pain? Don't you think it is a waste of your fine energy? He may be a good man, but politically, Han . . ."

"I don't know, I don't know. I don't know what is important, and what is not. I must find out whether I won't destroy him, I must find out, I must be sure. I am in love, Sen, and a woman. I don't understand duty well, as you do."

"Duty," said Sen, "is absolute."

# PART THREE

# Crisis

# CHAPTER I

# Let the Sea Roar

Feet, dust, dust, feet, feet, flags, the shouting and so many
    banners!
The dragons, the crackers; the banners and the flags.
And the people.
The people and the soldiers. So many people.
The rifles and the sandals, straw marching in the dust.
The soldiers and the flags.
Winter blue sky filled with sun, over China.
We know ourselves no longer. This is not our people,
This transfiguration.
Outside the town the fields, jade green the small young rice.
Dark blue the hills, and people on the paths like streams,
Carrying their children.
Sky, sunlight, brown earth and faces,
Straw sandals in the dust.


Here they come, here they are: five-starred the flags whipping the
    sunlight.
At last, at last. The soldiers. The people unafraid.
(Why should we fear? This is the People's Army. This is Our
    People).
The speeches.
The shouting.
The ecstasy of shouting.
Shout. Shout. Shout. Ten thousand shout as one.
On and on. On and on. Clamor in the sunlight.
The children are marching.
The women are marching.

The students, the seamen, the soldiers,
The merchants, the craftsmen, the tailors,
All marching with banners,
Shouting under the stars.


The drums. The drums. The drums.
(Boom — boom — boom boom boom. Boom — boom — boom boom
    boom.)
The drums of the Dance.
The Yangko. The Yangko. The Yangko.
Dance out of the past, past present and future. The Dance.
Among the soldiers and the people, the dancers.
Red and gold dancers, and the drums.
Men stamping, shouting swift exultation. The Dance.
Women and men ecstatic unafraid. The drums.
Children laughing in the sun.
Faith. Dancing the Yangko.
Hope. Dancing.
Resurrection. Shout, beat the drums, dance, O people,
For it is come, it is here, is it not?
The drums. The drums. The drums.
(Boom — boom — boom boom boom. Boom — boom — boom boom
    boom.)


The speeches. The speeches. The speeches.
Words words words words words. Clamor of words in the
    sunlight.
There are four hundred and seventy-five million people in our
    Country.
Our Country has more people than any country in the world.
Our Country will be the most powerful country in the world.
Our Country will save the world.
We can beat anyone: we have so many people.
Tremble. This is the Future. Marching straw sandals in the dust.
Quake. We shake the earth in our march.
Our soldiers, our people. The banners and the flags.
The people our people. So many people.
Carrying their children. So many children.
So many.

THE FIRST AND THE LAST THING I KNEW WAS THE DRUMS. Their untiring, endless insistence encompassed the town and the fields of green young rice between blue hills, golden rape and pink beans in flower. Not sound but shimmer, quiver of air, arrows of light on the sea's face, light on sea water beating down forever. Harmony perceived with the body, swinging us in a dream more alive than any waking. To and fro went my half-born thoughts, back and forth on wings of sound, a rhythm emergent from within. A five-beat pulse, whorl of vibration eddying towards the hills, towards the covering sky, until all the world rose tremulous and alive, alive as a body in love. Our words and our actions a sensuous perception commanded by this beat, and we moving enchanted in throbbing aliveness.

Boom — boom — boom boom boom.

In the darkness I woke because the drums had stopped. Silence woke me and those around me at the Young Women's Christian Association. Stretched on iron beds, sleepers too suddenly bereft of sleep, we lay and held our breaths for fear of waking others already awake. Brusque silence broke the lovely insistence, cast us loose from the beautiful compelling holding us close. Aware in the night of our isolation, suddenly forlorn, desolate and outcast, we woke.

The drums would beat again, and lullaby-soothed, spellbound in togetherness within the night-cradled land stretched vastly around us, we would turn back; the in-and-out song of the drums wrapping us safe from small individual solitude, we would turn back to sleep.

Parades and processions. Meetings and speeches and slogans. Torchlight and sunlight parades: of housewives, with banners: *Freedom and equality for women.* Of Young Men and Women Christian Associations: *True Religion, free from imperialist exploitation.* Of Young Communists: *Death to enemies of the New Democratic Dictatorship; death to saboteurs, spies, running dogs of imperialism, and reactionaries.* Parades of craftsmen and engineers, Christian communities and merchants, peasants and factory hands, with banners and dragons and firecrackers and flags and speeches and slogans. It was an extended self, larger than self, that sat on one's heart all day in this enormous amplification of self which is a crowd. The people I, and I the people, and what was love of one man in front of this immense exaltation, this becoming a multitude?

My name is Legion.

Trance. Fixed enchantment of the many. A pall of happiness pressed thick from Heaven upon us. March, shout, dance, speech. Wave the banners. And sing. A nation singing.

My body left me. In abrupt hypnosis, seized by all-enveloping passion, individual love dwarfed and sweetness drained out of the beloved name. Another delight, another gooseflesh, and the intoxication of giving up, giving up the individual scrutiny, the tinily poised detachment; shrunk to a querulous pigmy the protesting control, insignificant and easily stifled within.

Trance. The dancing, the sinuous indulating Yangko, a river of people, in rhythmic motion, treading the earth with the power and the will of man; relentless as the flow of a river. Thus had I seen the Great River some months ago, moving its stream onwards in and out among the dark, impassive hills of West China. Thus did I now see the dancers, in red and gold with blue and scarlet and green sashes streaming behind them with the dance, weaving steadily in and out among the people, treading the earth to the sound of the drums. The trance of a river.

Three months after the liberation of the town the drums were still beating. Sometimes from the grounds of the Technical College; or from the Mission School at the East Gate; often from the soldiers' camp outside the South Wall. When I left they were beating. They beat today still as through the main street the open lorries roll slow, bringing the enemies of the people to swift death, while the crowds hiss and roar and thunder hatred and applause, and the cheerleaders raise their high-pitched voices in the shriek of slogans, and firecrackers are let off as for a festival, and the dancers, the dancers dance, dance, dance.

"I wonder, Sen, whether Master Confucius heard this five-beat harmony, and deemed it a fit measure to regulate the emotions of mankind. I wonder whether eight hundred years before that gentle Jew, the Christ, was born, our ancestors held their Spring Festival and their Fertility Rites to this dancing and this beat. It is from deep within our people, this bewitchment of drum and body. I feel it surge up from my belly, where all true feeling lies; strong and compelling as love, as if the marrow of my bones had heard it millions of days before this day."

"You always step back to feudalist and bourgeois conceptions, Han. When will you stop embroidering solid reality with fantastical dreaming? This is the democratic expression of happiness of our nation, liberated from imperialist oppression and the tyranny of corrupt officials. The song of the Great New World, the People's Democratic Dictatorship."

But to me a rhythm old as the earth around us. For can a framework of words alter the nature of essential man, and divest it of its unconscious, unescaped past? What has been is part of our body, tenacious as the protozoic slime of our cells, and what we are, which is the body, is implacable in its unwritten laws. Alas for our self-deluding, matter-snared soul, in arrogant foolishness claiming supremacy, claiming detachment and triumph over the sweet merciless body; for in denial, in repulsion, in rebellion, our soul obeys the unworded laws and the infinite changefulness of the changing body; in sickness and health, and in hunger that swallows thought, in terror that drives to cruelty. So much of our instant benevolence fashioned by our last meal, and the beauty of the world enhanced by our digestion.

Humility, then, so necessary, the only humility, which is living with one's own body, knowing deeply its cycles, its betrayals, its lusts, its decay. So difficult, to accept the insignificance of mortality. So necessary, to cherish illusion as part of the substance of reality; to choose to dream, mightily and always, knowing that splendid dreams are part of this our body, true as the solid reality of one's hand.

And perhaps because of this awareness, I think that I discern, in much that is claimed as new revelation and world-saving truths, only refurbished formulae, or the same wants and instincts, cravings and atavisms, ours in all their brutality since the beginning of our kind. Need, terror, hunger, cruelty, power, that yearning for more than bread alone which pushes man to sainthood and to bestiality. Poor man, wistful compromise between flower and dung, interval between birth and death, a partiality of perception and sleep. Man wants eternity and perpetuation in time and in space, fashions invincible images of himself for his worship, and forgets that he is beast of prey and angelic spirit coupled together in eternal mortality.

Ancestral and familiar gods of man, these urges within him, deified and adorned with words, old gods with occasional new paint upon their faces.

"Sen, do not delude yourself with visions of a scientific Heaven spotless as your laboratory, upon this earth. Perfection is a dangerous ideal. Certainly for the first time in five centuries we have a government that will care for its own people. We shall have honesty, hard work, an able, uncorrupt administration. But we may overreach ourselves. I am frightened of these emotions on the rampage. Emotions are older than the words which rouse them, and uncontrollable. We may become too fanatical in this our Only Truth. I am afraid."

"How can you be frightened of so much good? Look at our people, standing up, men and women, in the affirmation of their dignity as human beings; new people, once the destitute, the submissive, the uncomplaining born to labor without lifting their faces; their faces once meaningless as stones and the wayside grass, and now made alive, not by a God, but by man himself. Look at the work we have done already, abolishing graft, corruption, injustice, building new roads, sharing the land justly. And though we are poor, it is because no longer do we depend on money from abroad; we have food enough to eat. Food is cheap, and money is stable. New industries are springing up everywhere. Just look at what we have achieved in a very short time. Does it not prove that communists everywhere in the world are more competent than the bourgeoisie?"

"I do not know. When I am one of the many toiling in this upsurge of honesty, enthusiasm and faith, I am happy. Many of us are larger beings than we were, because now there is purpose to our living. Each one of us consecrated to rebuilding China. But sometimes, I am afraid."

Afraid. Afraid of this persistent and pernicious obsession of man for the exaltation of Sacrifice. To sacrifice flesh and blood, the joy of the heart, the mystery and the pleasure of the body to the hungry amoral flame of a spiritual tyranny. Once it was a pyramidal God ranting among thunder clouds; and now it is the State shrieking through microphones. But always this urge to become bigger than self, dedicated to divinity; a supremacy all-demanding, wrathful and for ever unappeased.

Religious emotion; Faith in Man. Like all new-roused faiths, intolerant and fanatical. Come to clothe the poor, feed the hungry, do justice to the downtrodden. With its zealots, its saints, its soldiers. Rousing the lovely things in the soul of man: ardor, craving for purity, single-mindedness and self-abnegation. But also overreaching itself, working itself up into frenzies of hatred for those that did not conform; denouncing and suspecting heretics everywhere, imposing terror in the name of justice, and forgetting mercy; on and on, driven to purification by death, public execution and Holy War; nothing that other revolutions and other religions had not done, on a bigger or a smaller scale; inescapable, the pattern it would follow.

For man would always strive to conquer the world, to establish the will of man in the name of his God. With banners and shouting, legions and crosses, eagles and suns, with slogans and with blood. Feet in the dust, head among the stars.

Old gods with new, wet paint upon their faces.

# CHAPTER II

# The Little Town

In the change from the old confusion to the new discipline, came an awareness I had not had of those things in the old world which make the new seem inevitable.

These antagonists seemingly pitted in unrelenting opposition appear to me now not as antitheses, but as complements to each other. Twin aspects of the same needs, desires, cruelties and aspirations of mankind, inseparable as night and day, influencing each other all the time, bolstered by slogans and catchwords equally absurd, reinforced with economic theories founded, on the one side in waste and inefficiency, and on the other on faith in an impalpable continent of time, never to be reached, called the Future. What would communism do without an enemy? And what might spur the democracies to clean up their own houses, but the danger of losing their all?

Here the tentacular past reached forth and corrupted the present. The vices, neglects, omissions and injustices of the world called free reaped a terrible revenge in a world where the word meant something entirely different.

At every step some iniquity on the one side was invoked to justify a new violence which was to banish it from the face of the earth. And as the past polluted the present, so was the present sacrificed to the future, and the future was a monstrous delusion which had conquered the reason of man.

Perhaps it was in the little town that I began to understand the meaning of freedom; now that discipline was to mold our every thought, men and women found deep within themselves a tender strength, reserves of understanding, charity, patience and courage, a clearness and a steadiness which preserve the freedom of the human spirit. It is in bondage that freedom comes.

One thing I knew. That whether we liked it or not, there was no going back. This was the present, the moment now. And the future, in spite of all predictions, all threats, all plans, the future everywhere still remained completely unknown.

"Sen, everything is the same, and yet completely different. It is like standing in front of a mirror, looking closely at oneself for the first time, and left is right and right is left."

"You must learn to see things differently. It is easy, once you *see* correctly. You are now hampered by your feudal, reactionary interpretations of facts, which are incorrect, Han."

It was true. There were so many ways of looking at one thing; and some called it good and others called it shocking. I knew it so well, with Mark. But Sen said:

"There is only One Correct Way, and you must learn it."

We ambled across the main road from the Y.W.C.A. Between yesterday's procession ruts, icing-sugar frost was thinly spilled, soon banished by the unstinted sun poured upon gray roofs, stripped willows, and man-high anthills of gray ooze dug out from the sewers. Fragrance of plums and magnolia reach our cautious nostrils between whiffs of the throat-rasping stink from the opened sewers.

It was the first time since the little town had sewers that they were being cleaned. Not by coolies, but by the sons and daughters of the citizens, the students of the Technical College, the High School, the Middle Schools. They toiled six weeks, then the sewers were clean.

The Young Communist Group members went about encouraging the students, kept them to their task: "You must not do this only in a burst of enthusiasm, for a few hours, a few days. This is no make-believe, as in the last regime. In those days they drew up magnificent blueprints, launched vast projects which required millions of American dollars. But nothing was done except a great deal of graft. In those days the students of this little town started to build a road, but they soon gave it up, and a gang of coolies were hired to finish the work. This time we have a program. We shall carry it out. We mean every word we say."

Walking in battalions with picks and shovels upon their shoulders, the students went in the morning to the sewers, singing the new marching songs. Here and there the citizens of the town watched them in wondering, skeptical groups — women with bared bosoms suckling babies; shopkeepers tapping long bamboo pipes against the corner stone and sheltering their hooded eyes from the morning sun beneath their black round skull caps. Sometimes a Miao came down from the hills with silver beads and buckles of copper and turquoise, and sometimes a Tibetan in yellow and sheepskin gown. There were still parades and processions and many meetings, but the drums now tapped for work, not play.

"We have had our holiday, and our rejoicing. Now we work. We have a program."

The river would be dredged. The fields must be drained. The dikes must be repaired. Trees must be planted on the bare slopes. It was the people's river, their fields, their hills; but there was no public spirit in the little town. For centuries, outside of the family clan, no man exerted himself; for centuries manual labor had been immensely degrading; for centuries the people had looked upon government as inherently oppressive and all its tasks forced labor.

The Youth cadres were admirable. Hour after hour, day after day, week after week they would go, up and down the countryside, explaining, patiently talking at the shut, sullen, resentful faces, the peasants intent on giving away as little as possible, intent on hoarding rice and defaulting at every turn; suspicious of anything from the outside; too often betrayed not to disbelieve. With relentless patience, the young communists taught and preached. And it was utterly moving to see the slow unfolding, the faces come alive, the mouths open and speak that had remained obstinately silent, and the whole man flower, conscious of his dignity as a man upon the earth. For this miracle, any sacrifice could have been made, and gladly. To see it happen once was enough to believe.

In the city, after the first flush of enthusiasm, there was the same recoil of suspicion, the same deep-grounded mistrust. There were only two ways to keep the people at work. One was to stimulate them to the utmost pitch of enthusiasm with parades, and speeches, and meetings where everyone was not only allowed but compelled to speak, and the other was to tax and fine the wealthy families until they and their innumerable dependents had to work.

It was the Youth Group which organized torch parades at night, with the splendid starred flags bearing red and gold in the night wind, and the heart-lifting multitudinous roar of the people, and all the brown faces transfigured, ecstatic, jubilant in the torch glow. The Chinese are an emotional race, and with the songs, the speeches, the drums, there came outbursts of hysterical fervor, the release of desire to sacrifice, to pledge, to dedicate oneself. And so the multitudes pressed forward, their spirits conquered on the instant, volunteering for the dredging of the river, for the building of the dikes, for the spring planting. But next morning, sober and cold, they did not fulfill the promises of the evening before. The habits of a lifetime die hard.

The Youth cadres sometimes sent a member, boy or girl, to the houses of the defaulters. The young communist would arrive, and sit there, hour after hour, always polite, intolerably patient, ineffably firm, talking, persuading, preaching, teaching, arguing, questioning motives and intentions, appealing to unselfishness, talking of love of the ancestors' country, and the necessity of sacrifice. Unlike other human beings, the young communist did not need food, drink, or sleep; one day, two days, three days, and before these youths of steel and fire, the most bullying and swaggering merchant, the most astute and wily hoarder broke down, wept, beat his breast, joined a working group, and paid. Nothing can resist intense conviction except an equally strong conviction.

To the communist, each individual was a fortress to be taken by spiritual struggle alone. That the struggle involved sleepless nights and physical strain was added proof of spiritual superiority. They were out to conquer souls, and the bodies would follow.

For the absentee landlords, the idle rich, the warlords in retirement, there were fines, and buying of National War Bonds, and taxes until the family had nothing left to sell in the streets. The fiercest and richest ex-warlord of the little town was paying for the cost of a new road to the next city. "It is your contribution to your ancestors' country. You will pay."

The members of the Youth Group which had worked underground for the last two years in the little town were now in the open, organizing, planning, leading the citizens. They had seen many of their comrades imprisoned, tortured and shot by the Kuomintang in those nightly terror raids carried out in all the universities throughout the country. They were seasoned fighters and lived only for the Cause and the Party. Devoid of human weakness, absolutely pure, absolutely sincere and occasionally very naïve, they were respected by everyone, and many had caught from them some of their passion for work, their honesty and their altruism.

Two of these young people had tuberculosis, badly. That did not prevent them working sixteen hours a day. When they spoke they kept a hand upon their mouths, so as not to infect other people. They have since died. "Life does not matter. We gladly die, for we have seen the Revolution triumph. It is the most wonderful thing on earth, to die for one's Country and the Cause."

Martyrs and saints of the Kingdom of Man, they had their reward.

One of them, the political commissar of the little town, gave a speech in the Social Hall of the Technical College. With its wooden benches, cement floor and raised platform at one end with chair, table and a glass of tea pale as water, it held that air of musty innocence, of delicate decay found in many English public halls.

The Commissar, with ten years of civil war, and two bouts of torture behind him, spoke of the Great Brother, Jesus Christ:

"Jesus was a good man. He loved the poor, gave food to the hungry, and died for his beliefs. We must love each other, as Jesus loved. He was a good communist."

Several weeks later, in the same hall an ex-Christian, now communist, one of those opportunists to whom jargon comes easily, tore a picture of Jesus in two, shrieking that religion was the vehicle of cultural aggression and the opium of the people. He was arrested next day as a counter-revolutionary.

From Christianity, that revolutionary religion, froths forever the ferment of social conscience, resounds forever the terrible cry: "Woe to the rich, woe to the hypocrites."

Another meeting I remember, held under the auspices of the Technical College students, was on New Love.

Our emotions had to be reordered. We had to feel correctly, too. And love was a disturbing element in this discipline which was to make us efficient, militant instruments of the New Democracy. Love was a problem which had to be explained and organized, like every other. So many party members, said the speaker, found love a difficult question. Some looked upon it as a purely animal function, others said it upset their work. New Love was not to be subject to the vile lust which attended the prerevolutionary emotion. New Love was founded on respect and identical political ideals. It was impossible for individuals belonging to conflicting classes to love each other. It was impossible for people with feudal concepts to love in a progressive manner. Personal emotions were a function of class consciousness and political ideologies. Needless to say, the speaker went on (she was a cheerful, pink-cheeked, rotund mother of five, lecturing throughout the country on the New Feeling), love must never never interfere with work.

Afterwards many a young man and woman rose and gave it as their opinion that love interfered with work. "We have no time to take walks, to look at the sunset, to talk romantic nonsense. Time is precious. We must rebuild the country. Those of us who are dedicated must give up all personal entanglements, as we must give up our fathers and mothers. We must give up everything for the Country and the Cause."

I felt selfish, unprogressive. I wondered what Mark's political ideologies were. I could not think of a label to hang round his neck. Were we of conflicting concepts? In Hong Kong many an Englishwoman would consider that my race rendered me unfit to marry Mark. In China . . . I knew what Mark would be called in New China. Did we love each other? That was on another continent. I tossed and turned, universes away from him, very lost. And then reflected that human nature was human nature. In a few days, a few months, a few years, these young people would also love. The passionately convinced would still love the lukewarm, the good worker make up for the slacker, and the model political commissar buy his irreverent and inefficient lover a lipstick. Our blessed human weakness would take care of all this inhuman perfection.

There were many childish and naïve things that were being said and done; but this was a new heaven and a new earth, and wisdom and maturity take time to be achieved.

One thing which we suffered from, Sen and I, and many another Western returned Chinese, and also many a missionary in China, was our own conscience. Many of us now felt guilty, simply because we had not starved. We had not known the swords of hunger cleave flesh from bone, and also wither bone. What we meant by food and what the poor peasant meant had an essential, an animal difference which frightened and overwhelmed us with shame. I remembered, from the semiconscious depths of childhood, sitting in the dining car of a train going across the Northern plain from Peking to Hankow. My parents, my sister and I round the white tablecloth, and through the window was the plain, completely flooded, an ocean of brown water; here and there the top of a tree, here and there a roof. And on these roofs were people sitting. And then the waiters came, serving our first course, and all through the ample, many-coursed meal we sat and ate and looked out of the window, while the train ran on through the plain, and on the roofs, water-surrounded people waited to die.

This memory pursued me for many years. Now I was more conscious of it than ever. Untouched by religious or political ardors, with no urge to dedication, my weakness was the immediate personal need, the consciousness of hunger, suffering, and pain handled and seen and heard. And now I was stabbed with guilt, because of this memory.

I found that some missionaries in the little town were also troubled with conscience. It seemed to them that all their work had been on the wrong basis. They had only scratched the surface of things, never adapting themselves to the needs of the country they had come to enlighten. Their souls were dim with unease; they now understood another way of performance. Their rightness was no longer all right, neither was wrong entirely wrong. The problem of good and evil confused them greatly.

The Baillie school teachers were wholeheartedly in favor of the new order; their work flourished, and none of them was included in the campaign which was to assail the missionaries.

"The traders and the missionaries came together to China. Imperialistic and cultural exploitation, preaching and robbery, walked in, hand in hand. Together they must go."

The campaign was an ugly thing, and became steadily worse. The mixture of accuracy and falsehood in the attacks was bewildering; motives, intentions, facts and fancy were inextricably tangled with political issues. In some instances gross slander, with a strong flavor of the Boxer Rebellion about it, was used to stimulate hatred.

"The missionaries kill our children. Hundreds of babies' corpses were found in one grave."

"If you saw the dying condition of the babies they pick up, if you were a doctor, you would know these babies could not be saved. Why not accuse the parents, who threw the babies away on the streets, in the public cesspits, instead of the people who pick them up?"

Among the missionaries in the town, one man, under cover of research, had been doing intelligence work. It was true; no one could deny it. And because of this one man, all became suspect.

The Chinese Christian community meetings were a mixture of political study, religious revivalism, and spiritual somersaulting:

"New Christianity must support the Common Program. We are all Chinese together."

With open confession, repentance, and later, denunciation of traitors and counter-revolutionaries, the New Christians freed themselves from the heresies of cultural and religious aggression. "If the Communist Party had not opened our eyes," shouted an exalted Christian, "we would certainly be doomed victims of imperialistic religious exploitation."

I wondered whether the Reformation in England had produced similar crescendos of fervor, illumination and patriotic intensity. It was in this atmosphere of Oxford Group and Inquisition, with meetings that opened and closed with prayer, that a highly placed churchman of a certain denomination accused another one, in the little town, of counter-revolutionary ideas, harboring foreign newspapermen and spies, and theft of church funds.

Next day the papers reported: "The whole assembly heard with indignation the list of crimes against the people performed by this man since 1931. In righteous indignation Y [the accuser] turned to the audience and shouted: 'Don't you think a criminal like this ought to die?' And with one voice, good Christians all, they replied: 'He ought to die. Kill. Kill.'"

I wondered what would happen to the Chinese Catholics. They were few in the little town. Theirs was no elusive, expendable interpretation of the Bible. Theirs was a discipline and a conviction which would not let them yield. Among them was the deep courage, the fortitude and the conviction which earns respect and admiration, especially perhaps in China, where belief in virtue is unshakable.

It seemed to me then that whereas Catholicism asked its disciple to choose himself as his own accomplishment, his soul's salvation as the end and aim of living, communism demanded an utter renunciation of self, a total abnegation in a Great Plan whose achievement the self would never see.

I did not get on well with the Protestant Christian sect. When one of them, an earnest woman who had taken a fancy to me, came to me, I was hostile.

"Now," she beamed, "you have been with us, and seen our New Spirit. Are you going to become a Christian?"

If I told her that I was not anything, that I was nothing, and chose to remain so, she would try to convert me. So I replied politely: "No, I cannot be a Christian, I am a Catholic." She left me in my peace bought with a lie.

At one of our meetings we discussed the question: What has the Christian Church accomplished in society during the last two thousand years in comparison with what the Chinese communist party has achieved in Chinese society in a short period of thirty years?

It was clear that the party was the more efficient organ of spiritual and physical change. Doubt assailed me, that it might be so.

In that spring for the first time the little town had its elections. All circles were represented — the women, the schools, the Christians, the farmers, the shopkeepers. Many of the delegates had never been to a meeting before; some could hardly read and write, but all, after a while, became passionately interested in doing a good job.

"The people must learn to take an interest in things beyond their own families."

And here was the beginning and end of freedom. For many people, the small shopkeepers, the poor peasants, had never voiced their grievances, and now their advice and criticism was sought. Now they would have some control over their own future, as a group. For them, this was freedom, real freedom, within the orbit of their own community. A more concrete thing than the nebulous freedom to voice an opinion on subjects which did not concern them directly and which they would not understand entirely.

"This is disciplined freedom. The People's New Democracy."

The freedom *not* to participate was gone; the freedom to criticize on the basis of the new principles was given in exchange. Where general policy was concerned, there could not be disagreement. Where local, concrete questions were involved, public discussion was encouraged all the time.

It was not possible for anyone to remain aloof from events. No one could stay at home or stay silent. All must turn out for the parades and the processions. All must participate.

And that is why there were the People's Courts.

"This is the People's Justice. In the past injustice was bought and sold behind closed doors. But we do not fear the truth. The people will judge."

In many cases justice was rendered, and was fair and right. But in other cases it was not so. There was the case of the doctor who had caused the death of two patients through neglect. Now he was brought to judgment. The trial was conducted openly, and other doctors were summoned as expert witnesses. He was convicted and punished. It was most impressive. There was the case of the patient who had died from natural causes. But he had died in a mission hospital, and at that moment all was done to discredit the missionaries. The hospital was accused of neglect.

"That does not mean anything to us. He died of neglect," said the People's Court, when the medical experts provided medical evidence that the patient had died of an incurable disease.

"We don't understand these things. He died of neglect," they repeated when the slides of the pathologist were brought to prove that all had been done that could be done. The hospital was fined.

Rough justice under Heaven. Or was it only another kind of injustice? I have seen a few public executions in my life, mainly because in China executions are nearly always public. The first one happened when I was seven years old, in Peking. Our amah took my sister and me to see it, unknown to our parents. We went with her happily when she told us we were to see an execution outside the Heavenly Peace Gate.

"Do not tell your mother, though."

"Are they bad people, Amah?"

"Very bad." Amah shook her head, rolled her eyes. "They are wicked communists. They will be put to slow death."

Slow death it was, for they were being tortured, and I shall always remember the crowds roaring, the smell of sweat, and suddenly being sick and the sour taste of my vomit as they held up the man to be seen once more before they cut off his head.

And so from time to time existence was punctuated with executions. Communists, always communists and Red bandits, being put to death, all through the years; in Peking, in Nanking, in Chungking, everywhere. And now the wheel had come full circle.

"Blood must be paid in blood."

Rough justice under Heaven.

But now instead of being merely spectators — and we are Elizabethans still, where executions are concerned — we all became active, vocal participants. We were all involved.

As long as the processes of justice were unknown to the people, the people would always shake their heads and think: "There has not been enough money to save life." So deep ingrained is the habit of injustice. But now money would not buy life, but endanger it; money would not obtain a substitute victim, it was fatal to its owner. Three decades of civil war; much blood spilt, to be repaid in blood. Justice fulfilling many aims. Striking terror in the hearts of those who still went free, getting rid of undesirables, but also purging away the last elements of opposition to the new discipline, coercing all, under the spell of fear, to acquiescence, and creating a storm of denunciation until all personal loyalties were in doubt.

And since executions were symbolic, a people purging itself of evil, an expression of the "will of the people," no one was allowed to keep silent. All had to participate. The many opportunists who always flourish in the wake of a revolution did a great deal of harm. Not only in the villages where, because of lack of sufficient cadres, the government had to employ ill-trained new recruits to organize rice-collecting, but also in the cities. Eager for quick results, brutal with new power, these undid the good impression and the influence of the experienced cadres elsewhere, and were the source of endless denunciations, especially when the spy and counter-revolutionary campaigns set in.

"We are very careful. We shall only punish where guilt is proven." But in China it is so difficult to collect accurate evidence. It is very difficult to sift falsehood from truth. To be denounced was to be suspect, and to be suspect was dangerous. There was so much emotion on the rampage. And though only those who had spilt blood were to die, yet it was not always so.

And a crowd loves to roar "Kill, Kill," unthinkingly.

As a day in winter grows short, hemmed in by implacable night, so control tightened, discipline swung in, enthusiasm was consolidated with the spur of hate.

Some returned students, still wearing American shirts, jaunty ties, their luggage bright with labels, came back to the little town. They arrived in the middle of the hate campaign, and wrote articles in the newspaper denouncing the persecution they had suffered in America

"What about your friends, over there? They won't like it."

"I wrote against the system, not the people. I was not disloyal to my friends. We are against imperialism. This is our country, and it was necessary."

One medical student had left the little town but now returned to it

"Why did you go away?"

"Because I had to write a political thesis in order to get my degree No one is allowed to keep silent. I went away."

"You are back."

"I am back. The outside world is hard. There are hundreds of doctors out of work in Hong Kong because their degree is not recognized. My family is here, this is my country. A lot of new hospital are being built; the medical course is being cut short to train more doctors. I am a doctor, only the people matter. Politics go, people remain."

He wrote his thesis, got his degree, and later volunteered for Korea.

Sen and I watched the army parade. The People's Liberation Armie were so different from the Kuomintang, it was still a source of pleased astonishment to the citizens of the little town and the peasants that there was no looting, no raping, no beating, no burning. The people cheered and cheered as the army went by.

"This is the People's Army. This is our People."

A career in the army was popular. Even intellectuals, always averse to personal danger, were volunteering for the army now.

"Let anyone dare to attack us, we shall defeat them."

On and on they went, faces alive and proud, doomed by their virtue and their devotion as others are by their crimes.

"We know what we are fighting for. A better world. For the Country, for the People."

Perhaps it is so, that men must be given something to die for, to believe that their lives have not been in vain.

On and on. Sen's eyes glowed with enthusiasm. It was a wonderful sight. "We have so many people. What does it matter if we lack equipment? Individual courage alone counts. Man-courage versus machine power. We can always drown a sea of fire with a sea of men." Sen knew what he was saying.

For later, in Korea, it was so. Convinced that China was threatened, with fine impatience to help another Asiatic land invaded (as we saw it) by white imperialism, the ancestors' country went into war. And though all the soldiers were not volunteers, yet there were many many volunteers. Many people in the little town went. The Korean War was popular. It consolidated the power of the New Order. To the citizens of the little town, it is a Victory.

"This is what the determination of a people can do. We have beaten the largest power in the world to a stalemate. We, a peaceful people, have stopped the warmongering imperialists."

We watched them, Sen and I, and I was sad. Because I do not understand why men should want to die. Because so many of them would die. But Sen was pleased and proud.

"You are going back to Hong Kong."

"Yes."

"I suppose," said Sen, "that you will end up like so many running dogs of imperialism. In America."

"I don't think so. I cannot run away. But now I must go back to Hong Kong."

"Really, Han, you are so selfish, so emotional. All because of a romantic attachment to one man . . . and this man not of your country, not of your people, and not free."

It was not altogether so. But I could not explain to Sen. "I must see clear within myself. I am terribly muddled. But I will not run away. And one day, I shall come back. When I am clear within myself."

Sen tried to persuade me. He said wise and sensible things. He made me feel small, and selfish, and ashamed. For all men want to be good, to be noble, to be unselfish. And I am not good, I do not want to be unselfish, I want to be myself.

"You are completely feudal in your personal, subjective approach to life. A reactionary, Han."

"But on the other hand, Sen, in Hong Kong, many call me a communist, because I love my country."

And so I left.

# CHAPTER III

# *Between Sea and Land*

$S$PEAK. WHAT SHALL I SAY? LET THE SEA ROAR. TODAY THE peoples speak, the multitudes clamor with megaphonic voice. Owners of the future redeemed by the large liberties of hunger and of want, those once anonymous as the wayside grass are now anonymous and relentless as the ocean's thunder in the affirmation of themselves and of their class power to destroy the Old Order.

Let the sea roar. Why should I raise a desperate small voice, I who stand precarious between unsolid land and confounding water, refusing both? My words are thrown back at me in the wind of the sea.

Asians like myself, belonging to a small "upper class," are intellectual Eurasians. We are all brought up between two worlds.

Racial Eurasianism is not worth talking or writing about. It is a small, negligible prejudice, kept up in outposts of empire where it remains a topic of unhealthy speculation and vicious gossip for bridge-bored white women: an offensive, harmless mania. If some racial Eurasians carry chips on their shoulders, resent the whites, grumble at inequality, it is because they ape white ways of living and white injustices. There is no problem for Eurasians who accept their Asiatic side.

But intellectual Eurasianism afflicts many young Asians and has nothing to do with race.

Emotionally held to our own land by sound and warmth of child-

hood, by sensuous unworded memories as background to adult feelings, young Asians are then sent on to mission universities, and from
there to Cambridge or to Columbia, to Paris or to Geneva, to be
modernized and to be Westernized.

From those comely garden plots of Western Europe and North
America, from well-ordered living unhampered by need for corruption, where intellect is charmed with discussion and stimulated by
ingeniosity, we go back.

Back to our own worlds of hunger, of unspeakable need, of flagrant
corruption and blatant injustice, begging hands and hideous sores.
From the academic abstractions of the West to the stark wants of the
East.

Abroad, we are favored students, endowed with scholarships,
wrapped in the fictitious glamour of "old cultures." We return to be
"kept in our place" in colonial lands. We come home to fit ourselves —
and most of us fail to do it — into an inferior standard of living. Meanwhile we have become unable to stand dirt, to disregard spitting. We
suffer from smells; we notice flies; we are addicted to the pull chain of
the hygienic water-closet while the peasant our brother wades thigh
deep in human manure. Small things, digging a large gap between
ourselves and our people.

We acquire split, two-layered souls. Underneath are deep emotions,
taboos and compulsions, repulsions and loves unexplained and dark.
Above, a glut of glib words, theories whose meaning disappears in
the presence of limitless want, ideas intellectually acknowledged and
emotionally impotent, behavior rational but suddenly forgotten when
the sea begins to roar.

Split. In our work, efficient replicas of scientists and scholars of the
West. In private, keeping loves and friendships safely dark, hatreds
low and deep, a safe somber house for the ungrown child in us, free
from encroachment, a refuge from the prying intellect of our Western
sojourns.

And thus, in facing different questions, we exhibit different characters. Capable of sudden brusque turnovers, of lightning contrasts in

reasoning and thought, without ourselves appearing conscious of the change.

Much of our lives is lived within this division. We know sudden transpositions, baffling to ourselves, in the meaning of words. We find no collateral concept in one language to express what is clear to us in another. We endure alterations of emotion which negate our reasoned convictions. We attach different values to the same words in different situations.

Habitual schizophrenes, divided within ourselves. And resentful of this division. A resentment which may flare up into hostility, may turn us in hatred against what we have loved, and has made us unwhole for life. We feel that others have lied to us, because our life is a perpetual lie unto ourselves.

We are laden with historical memories, which our traditional, monstrous, arrogant pride, the unabated pride of the Chinese scholar class, keeps alive and rankling. And even gratitude for the philanthropy bestowed upon us carries within itself those seeds of bitterness and resentment.

It is in Asia that we have seen the Western world undone, that world which we admire for its technical felicity, and at the same time resent. It is here that we have seen it undone by itself; its unfulfilled promises, its generosity with many strings, its convenient high-sounding absurdities; its reluctance to let go, its parsimonious philanthropy. Of all the evil done in the past, we in Asia enjoy the fruit, rotten or ripe.

When the New Order came in with benevolence and marvelous flags, with heart-stirring words and unity, with coherence and love of country — giving purpose to living, making death negligible, dazzling Today with the song of glorious Tomorrows — we had to choose.

It is not easy to cut out great pieces of oneself. For whatever the West had done, some of us had loved it for one thing: that delicate reality, frail and hard to handle, gentle, and strong in tenderness — spiritual liberty.

And although even in the West spiritual liberty was fast waning under the frenzied compulsion of fear, yet it was there that we had known it.

It is not easy to choose between two worlds of the mind. But one of them had become, for many among us, elusive. The value of noble pronouncements destroyed by unwholesome facts, the meaning drained out of abstract words such as freedom and democracy by the peculiar systems authorized under their names. Words much bandied about, these, too often bolstering up old and inefficient inequalities, worn out puppet shows. And so in our minds the suspicion, a suspicion which was to grow until we learned to suspect everything and everyone.

And thus many of the best, the more honest among the Westernized intellectuals of China, chose. They forsook individual, personal freedom for a larger self than their own, although it meant a control and a discipline stern and repugnant to a part of them. They chose what might overwhelm them, not through cowardice, nor through opportunism, but because they had a social conscience, they loved their people, and they had a deep need to be whole again, unfrustrated in service to a land so much in need of them.

They chose against themselves, renouncing the small liberty of one, so insignificant-seeming when faced with the spiritual challenge of communism in lands where freedom from hunger has never been known. They relinquished a difference which had made them alien among their own people for an oppression which would free their energies for the good of mankind.

Christian missionary influence — so strong in the lives of many foreign returned intellectuals — only helped to achieve this abnegation with more pleasure.

Had we not been taught that service to others was the purpose of life? Imbued with the ideal of social justice, could we now retain a creed of personal freedom, a creed suddenly become a vicious, selfish error, running away from devotion to our fellow man? Was not sacrifice of self Christian excellence? Many could not refuse the challenge of spiritual heroism, resist that deep passionate urge which transcends the narrow bounds of individual living; to work with man, for man, in a great, a breathtaking enterprise: the Kingdom of Man upon earth.

Our ardent nationalism, that foundation stone of the New Order everywhere in Asia, stimulated and irritated by contact with the West, pushed us headlong, making many of us choose, not a political creed, but our own land, China.

And that is what must be said; in spite of the sea's roar, in spite of the land's heave. A sober truth which no one will like, and all alike will condemn. But it must be said, for the time will come when those who chose against themselves may suffer from their self-abegnation, from a consecration fervent, passionate and wholehearted.

In dreadful irony, they may see their words twisted, their devotion warped, and their best intentions serve ends which they had not conceived. But now that it seems so right to hail as heroes those that flee persecution to freedom, and that it is so wrong to say a word for those who chose not freedom, I must say it.

They remained to serve their people. They believed beyond political creeds, beyond wars and balances of power. They did not join their voices to the small indignant chorus of those who pollute the word of freedom with hope for a third world war to re-establish an order dead long ago.

They wanted to be whole again, wholehearted among their own people. Some of them were the best and the most honest among us. They are in China.

The question which I had thought mine alone, a personal choice, a settlement of fate for myself, I found not mine only but that of many another Chinese, many another Westernized Asian brought up between two worlds, split and two-layered.

And the choosing, with its vivid dismemberment, its gnawing suffering, a tragic irresolution, a Hamletian situation to be ended abruptly with a knife stroke, was the same for us all.

In the little town in China, later through the young lovely spring in Hong Kong, while my two worlds rushed away from each other with desperate speed and irrevocable determination, I knew that I would choose between Mark and China.

Never would Mark live and work in this New China. He might try, if allowed in, which was doubtful. He would be suspect, followed, censored; he would have to go out again. Frustrated, as so many Europeans were in Hong Kong, who could not dream of life without China. And now China had thrown them out.

Without Mark, I might perhaps fit myself into a new hard pattern, although I would never understand political passion and hatred. Setting my teeth, turning my back on things I had loved, going back to the smells and sound of childhood and to people, my friends, to comfort me in my bereavement of half myself.

With Mark, I would have to go away. Pulling up those tenacious roots, following him and serving him. Would I be generous enough to accept my own sacrifice, would I not be disloyal to him in the very marrow of my Chinese bones? I might destroy him.

For in the end it was not a question of love between two people who loved each other. In the end it was not Mark as a man and a lover who stood between me and China, but what he represented and what he meant. The world that he was.

I knew now why, in my room at the Hospital, two months before, I had said to Mark: "What is love? Should you be free to marry me now, I would hesitate. For something in me wants something else . . . China perhaps. I do not understand."

Caught up, like many others, in immense happenings which twisted and warped our intimate lives.

Split, rent from top to bottom. Physical duality nothing, race no barrier, education a bond between us; but spiritual division mine and that of all who now suffered with me.

One part of me would never belong to Mark; another part of me would never go back to China now.

I knew why I kept on traveling back and forth, back and forth in spirit and body between Hong Kong and China. Between Mark and China. And now I would go back to Hong Kong.

Hong Kong, excrescence off the coast of China, entrepôt of commerce and social anachronism, island of monopolies, where destitution is a punishable offense and refugee camps bloomed; Hong Kong poised between land and sea, dependent on China for its birth and the existence of its sumptuous capitalist enterprise; Hong Kong the haven of many like myself, waiting to make up their minds; waiting to let the dust settle, waiting to choose.

Only in Hong Kong was it still possible to sit down, and to choose. Only in Hong Kong was it possible for Mark and for myself to love, and for a short while to dream. Only in Hong Kong did our love exist; there was no time and no place for us anywhere else in the world.

Hong Kong, a little gap, a slip of comet, small interstice stretched between fixed stars, come-and-go rock where I might sit, a few weeks, a few months — enough time perhaps to find a way out. Enough to make Mark safe from hurt. For whichever way I chose, I might destroy him.

Hong Kong, island of high robbers and low ones, where I would steal from life a little sweetness before everything overtook us. I was immensely grateful.

And so between sea and land, raising a small defiant voice against the sea's roar, against the howling land wind, I stood, and not alone. Many stood with me. So many, silent but for the beat of their pondering hearts.

I went back to Hong Kong, and with every hour on the train the knowledge of Mark grew in me until it drowned all else; until again I walked enchanted, every particle of my blood possessed, and Hong Kong without Mark was still a world full of him.

Back I went to my old new passion, my quirk, and my condemnation, and to a cable from Mark.

A cable. I loathed telegrams. I could not open the envelope. I fingered and turned and twisted it; two hours of sordid agony before I tore it apart and read what Mark said:

"I have stopped biting my nails."

# CHAPTER IV

# A Realm Dismantled

BACK TO HONG KONG. BACK THROUGH THE BORDER WITH ITS wood barrier, its black-trousered women with baskets of eggs, hens, and cabbages; its little trains crammed with travelers; its coolie gangs loading and unloading lorries; and the strolling belted police gazing at the gray soldiers, their countrymen on the other side of the Border, with hermetic indifferent eyes.

I was to see the Border again; to note, heart tight as water over sea-bottom dread, the relentless change. More fences, barbed wire, police, plain-clothes men in loose black waterproof silk concealing their hip revolvers; the straggled, weary, queueing crowds, submissive mockery of order which comes from herding people for long hours together; searches, proddings, stamping and flourish of passes. And the happy corruption. For when the Colonial government decided that only Cantonese-speaking Chinese should be allowed over the Border, a thoughtful ordinance at the same time left passage to be effected "at the discretion of the police." Affable and wise provision; discretion so cheap, fifty Hong Kong dollars a life, and so many grateful lives. A whiff of benign corruption makes fragrant a barrel load of law.

Back to Hong Kong with its shop-window glamour and its factories closing at a moment's notice; with its enormous gleaming American cars, its ostentatious hill castles, its squatter camps. One camp sheltered six thousand registered and eight thousand unknown refugees; twenty new babies were born in it each week. Hong Kong with its great houses of trade and their monopolies controlling two-thirds of its area and three-fifths of its wealth; with its idealistic social welfare always too short of funds; with its food relief queues, its overworked clinics where patients queue at four in the morning to be seen at three in the afternoon; its tenements where squalor, disease and crime breed faster than relief, hospital or courts of law can mitigate; with its overflowing prisons, its savage sentences for the poor, its flourishing rackets, so numerous that it seems impossible to live without one.

Rackets. The woman racket, its latest refinement being the export of young Chinese women as temporary G.I. brides to the cities of America north and south. The gold racket, with bars stored in many a respected company's safe; an operation sanctified by abuse into "good business." The private medicine racket, thriving on a public riddled with ignorance and tuberculosis; the fish racket, the housing racket. The visa racket, the passport racket. Everywhere pollution nestled sweet at the heart of social endeavor, as sorrow dwells at the root of joy; corruption linked forever to the honest effort as a shadow trails a body in the sun.

Back to Hong Kong from the stern paradise of China; from the pursuit of Heaven upon earth to the pursuit of money; from the crusading intolerance, the forgetfulness of self, to the creatures of the cold constricted heart, the selfish averted eyes, the measured publicized donation. From a vision deluded to cynicism; from triumph, hatred and exaltation to the death in life; from merciless purges to unconcerned slow-killing neglect. Back from the nightmare of political heresy to the terror of losing one's job.

Back to Hong Kong, armed with unbelief, shaken in all but in love, with little laughter and no humor left.

Church Guest House was tight with missionaries. Was it only a year ago that I had lived here for three months? I was now back for an evening with Mary Fairfield, out of China for the last time — Mary Fairfield, with her New England accent, her quiet face, her nebulous knitting, who had turned back to China with her three children a year ago in obedience to the Will of God, a direct answer to her deep faith.

In the homes of the Chinese wealthy class of Hong Kong, the raw light of popular neon splashes on sleek hair shining as kingfisher back, bounces on scarlet nails and glistening teeth, deflects solidly from sparkling spectacles and gold wrist watches, spreads in creamy satisfaction upon smooth-skinned women's faces. We love light as we love noise, a great deal of it at a time.

But in the basement dining room of Church Guest House, the ceiling tubes shed harsh blue haze upon four hedges of physical discouragement hemming two narrow, white-clothed tables. Next to me twisted a red-chinned girl, her sharp elbows and wrists swung between them a pendant curve of flesh, sagging precursor of the years. Opposite sat many furrowed and plicated necks, indecent to an eye trained to the high Chinese collar and the buttoned Young Communist jackets. There was much dandruff on some shoulders. At one table a Methodist spinster in scarlet chattered, hardly pausing to breathe lest the advantage be wrested from her. Bridling, alert, all purpose lost for talk, and life a flux of words because she could not go back to China. We drank stiff white soup, and behind the ugliness I began to see the quiet sad eyes of those who sat mute under the neon light. People who had suffered uprooting.

On and on went the scarlet-clad Methodist, stringing the bad news out of China, gloomy predictions and immediate disasters, a woman stringing pearls on a thread of bitterness. Her ocherous desiccated features, the restless motion of her tongue, dominated the table, but her heart was deep in China, where she would not go again.

Missionaries out from China, greater in their hour of trial than in their days of strength. A few bitter, many grieved, most uncomplaining. Behind those faces, garrulous or pensive, the apprehension of the narrowed life, a future divested of the length and breadth and immense vitality of China for them to roam in; stranded in a world tight and small, now that China, their China, was no longer theirs.

After dinner we sat in the drawing room, seeing through the windows the harbor, orange and ship-studded, the hills night-dark towards China. A fair young man thumbed an English newspaper under a table lamp. Mary Fairfield's cold soft whisper was in my ear. "He's been fifty-nine days in prison in China; suspected of spying. The district he was in was difficult. It depends where you are, some are worse than others. He's going back to the States now. He did a year and a day in prison there. Conscientious objector. If there's another war he'll go to prison again. He's the draft age."

The Methodist in scarlet sat on a sofa with a large bald man holding thick veined hands in his lap, his long yellow teeth between his lips. "The China Inland Mission are all coming out . . . after all we did for China, look what it's doing to us."

Her eyes darted, expectant arrows poised in air, thrust their inquisition at me. Later she might say "That was the Red doctor . . . and have you heard about her affair?" She collected information and kept none of it to herself.

Mary Fairfield did not utter judgment. Her gentleness, her forbearance, wrung me with shame.

"I was so glad I went back. I began to understand so many things. Why your people dislike us, our presumption, our arrogance. We should have left years ago, but Westerners can never let go easily. Acquisition is our weakness."

She began to knit.

"I was glad to leave. We were an embarrassment to our Chinese friends. Knowing us meant trouble. Yet I have never felt so close, so near, so equal to your people. And they were kind. Now that we no longer had any privileges, they bore no ill-feeling towards us. But we were imperialists and aggressors and spies, and so we had to go. I was glad to go."

"The Roman Catholics won't be able to stick it," said the scarlet Methodist. "This is only the beginning. Things will be much, much worse." And she nodded with sad satisfaction.

In this room were the remains of a hundred years of missionary work in China. A hundred years of devotion, sacrifice and good works. For the glory of their God, in unselfish zeal, men and women of twenty-nine denominations had gone to baptize the heathen, teach their variety of the Only Truth, heal the sick, feed the hungry, fulfill themselves and the will of their God. Days of strength. Shining, glorious days of devotion and of strength.

In this room were the people who had worn down our traditions, broken our selfishness, awakened our social conscience, armed us with ideals, dragged our scholars from their poetic torpor and our peasants' superfluous babies from the cesspits, built our universities, our hospitals, and our puritanism.

They also had made New China. Although now we cast them out as instruments of foreign aggression, they had also made us. We were part of each other.

Sitting with the missionaries, listening to Mary Fairfield with one ear and to the scarlet woman with the other, I thought that I saw what place missionary effort would hold in my country. And I was ashamed of my people.

I was not ashamed of getting the missionaries out. Perhaps it was time they went; but I was ashamed of the way it was done. I writhed to hear the political twist ascribed to all intentions; the name-calling, the spite, the hatred, the enforced humiliation; the need to destroy so much, that extravagance of fear, suspicion and denunciation let loose like a typhoon over China. A violence unworthy of a great people.

"We shall see now whether the seed of the Christianity we planted will thrive, without subsidy or dependence, on Chinese soil. This is the test, the greatest challenge to the vitality of Religion. God's ways are not ours, and perhaps this will be good for us in the end. We had become smug, too comfortable, with our servants and our furloughs, our missionary compounds away from the Chinese people. We dabbled in power, especially us Methodists, we had so much influence with the last government. . . . The Chinese Church must now carry on Christianity. I have faith in God and in your people." Thus Mary Fairfield, a child of God.

The scarlet woman talked and talked. "He was such a good Christian, we thought of him as our next Chinese bishop . . . sent twice to the States, so keen on Moral Rearmament . . . just like one of us . . . and now he's turned right round, and denounced us all. . . ."

I did not get my old job back, because Mrs. Palmer-Jones saw to that. So did William Monk.

I got another job. I typed records.

A secretary would have done better, but in this University department the budget provided for a doctor, not for a typist. A doctor it had to be; it looked well on the staff annual photograph; the salary of a doctor was only very little higher than a secretary.

There were the records, in terrible medical handwriting, in dusty boxes going back two years. They had to be typed. So I typed records.

I needed this pause, this taut interval of life disbodied, mechanical motion freeing the mind to suffer the hard-pressed assault of words, to be mangled by sentences riding straight through consciousness as rocks are hurled through air by an avalanche; to be driven to the cruel extreme of indecision; to escape none of the morseled agony meted out during the spring.

While my fingers copied, I, thought-riddled, turned inwards. Evenings and nights found me wandering, unconscious of time and flesh, walking miles and miles of streets, staring, searching, discovering, learning — learning what I shall never know.

And I waited for Mark, knowing he would come back; knowing our days numbered with care, our love weighed out to us by scruple, however dense and driven, compact sweet fire suddenly engendered and not soon to go out.

I was grateful for the job.

Back to find a place to live.

Mei, happy with the joyfulness of children, living in Robert and Nora Hung's house, had not grieved at my absence, but now she wanted to be with me. The Hungs had many friends to shelter, I could not stay with them.

The Chinese Y.W.C.A. was crowded, and children were not admitted. The Helena May Institute, and the European Y.W.C.A. were for whites. Everything else was too expensive; the rent of a small room was as much as my month's salary.

"Why," said James Manton whom I met in his little Rover in front of the bombax trees vaulting their fresh orange and scarlet crackers up the University Drive, "come and stay with us."

"Oh, I couldn't."

"Of course you can. We've got a guest room. Come and stay a few weeks. You look thin and tired."

I had dinner with James and Fiona that night. The room. The shaded lights with their wall aureoles; the pink and the green chairs, over there the striped one in which Mark had sat, crossing the blossom-laden carpets, smiling and coming to me so easily, so easily; and now I was filled with this one man as I sat, sipped my coffee, and held back tears.

"When can you and Mei come to us?" asked Fiona, disengaging her handkerchief from the small teeth of Lotus of the Congo, otherwise Lolo, a Bassenjee playful as a kitten, with paws soft as lilies and more deft than human hands.

"Oh, Fiona." Tattybogle sprawled on his settee in happy postprandial coma, posturally very indecent. He opened one eye and looked at me.

"We'd love to have you. I've always wanted to have more Chinese friends," said Fiona.

In a rush I saw Adeline Palmer-Jones and the illiberal compression of her lips. I felt William Monk's predatory brutal hands. Ernest Watts's contemptuous profile hovered over my shoulder. I must warn Fiona.

"You're sure it's all right for me to come, Fiona?"

"Of course, Suyin."

"I'm Eurasian, Fiona." I sounded impossibly tragic. Tattybogle closed both eyes.

"Good heavens," said Fiona.

"You see," I said, already hopeless.

"Suyin," said Fiona, "what on earth does it matter whether you are Chinese, English, or Eurasian? I always knew you were Eurasian, you told me so, don't you remember? But why should that make any difference? Hong Kong is full of Eurasians, they are our best citizens. James and I just like people as people. You ought to know better."

I wept. I was very tired.

"You're upset and worn out. You're talking nonsense. You've been listening and taking seriously the small mean things that small mean people say over here to bolster up their inferiority complex. James and I are just thrilled to have you stay with us. What's the use of being a democracy," said Fiona, "if we don't treat people as people?"

And so it was with James and Fiona that my last shred of feeling about race disappeared. They looked after me, fed me, took me out, made me laugh. I learned to laugh again at the petty cruelties which small sadistic humans do, more vicious and hurtful than large sins which require courage to perform.

With them I learned to believe in freedom of the spirit, an understanding and a release springing from within oneself. I saw that the thing called democracy was possible, although everyone in a democracy is not a democrat.

With James and Fiona I gathered strength and courage for the harvest coming, and when the time was ripe they helped me to reap the full sheaves of my joy and my sorrow.

Mei and I were to stay a few weeks. We stayed eight months.

It was not well with Maya.

The disease that charged her flesh filled her with a torment of agitation. She had lived gently, bearing life in soft hands of daydream, and now rebelled against the discipline of the bed. Twice she wandered away from the nursing home. We hunted her, Anne Richards and I, in Fiona's car, and found her walking along the seashore miles away, she who had never walked for pleasure before.

As life was reft from her she clung to every rooted thing, to the motion of clouds and planets, to the solemnity of mountains. She who contrived a subtle Chinese passion for small detail, filigree harmony

of leaf and petal, now that the boundaries of her life extended into the
darkness of dust and oblivion, began to encompass vague, vast hori-
zons. With bright dilated eyes she fixed the brown rim of sundown,
distances once merely a length of miles to her, and her lips and fingers
carried, in their unmeasured clutch for the unsubstantial, the impatience of her agony.

One day I found her sitting at my desk in the office, having fled her
bed again, and as if it were the most natural thing in the world, she
began to tell me about the tree.

"As I walked here," said she, "something which had not happened
before occurred to me. Halfway up the road I sat under a tree to rest,
under a candlenut tree. Facing it, looking at the straight gray silver
trunk, ringed and speckled with a frolic of young days, at the dappled
white-flecked leaves, plumage-mottled birds poised for the gust of
flight, under the cool green shadows spread over me, and the slanting
sunlight falling upon my hand, I became that tree.

"Insidious and bone-deep the transubstantiation; an enchanted dupe
I sat, my heart the tree heart, coursing sweet green sap, sweet fire
within my veins. I knew its secret name, its drift of years; I felt my
thick mindless roots clutch the live earth, digging through earth and
stone groping for water. I heard each leaf grow out, an unfurling pen-
nant in strong search of that other rain, the light. I strained my
branches, insinuating into emptiness the flourish of my life. I knew
the self-absorption of the tree, the peace acquired at last, its contemplation of the day. I sat on without motion, tree basking in sun, and all
previous awareness a half-remembered dream.

"Suddenly there was a wrench, I coughed, and the division fell between the substance of the tree and myself. I was I and the candlenut
tree stood above, green and dappled with flakes of sun, remote, unknown. I came here."

"Maya," I said, "you and I were always Taoists, and a little mad,
and now you have beaten me, for you have become an Immortal."
Then I bit my lips for saying what would so soon be true.

Maya smiled, it was shocking to see the glory and exultation of her smile. "Call it what you wish. Death is only an accident, what matters is life. I love life so, I care not that I die."

She left, humming a frivolous ditty, ten centuries old:

> Oh loveless hearts are blithe and strong
> But she that loves must moan.
> Grief that was once a wisp is grown
> Ten thousand fathoms long.
>
> The farthest depths of earth below
> And the sky's widest range,
> Space will confine, and seasons change,
> But my love is not so.

In a few weeks it was over. Maya had no resistance at all to tuberculosis. She became blind, raved gently the whole long day, and died at night when no one was about, her pupils enormous, her cheekbones like ivory twigs. She was filled with disease, lungs and bowels and brain; and with nodules even in her eyes.

# CHAPTER V

## Spring Is Come Home

> Again the spring's half here,
> Anguish alone I meet.
> Plum blossoms whirl their storm,
> Snow petals fall on me.
>
> The wild goose roams the sky,
> Hope's omen unfulfilled.
> The far roads lead my dream,
> On your eternal quest.
>
> Oh, smile at lovely sorrow,
> Fresh as the grass of spring.
> Wherever my feet wander,
> Still the young fields are green.

You AND YOUR SONG POEMS, SUYIN," SMILED NORA. "IT'S freezing. Chinese New Year ought to be cold, since it's only the first day of spring, but today even the grass shivers."

"This is the year of the Tiger in the old calendar," proclaimed Robert. "A bad year. A man-devouring year. There will be war this year."

"Mrs. Cheng has flown back to Formosa," said Nora. "The Kuomintang were suspicious of her long stay in Hong Kong. Hong Kong is a meeting place for everybody, on every side. They thought she might be negotiating a family turnover with the Reds here, and they threatened to shoot her husband, so she rushed back."

"There will be purges in China this year," said Robert, who was pessimistic. "Just wait. This benevolence won't last. It cannot. You cannot establish a revolution which overturns the world without a lot of bloodletting."

"Anyway, Eileen is now safely married to her American." Nora pursued her own topics. "Mrs. Cheng says she does not like it, because he is a foreigner, but secretly she is very pleased. Eileen is off her hands, and she won't have to buy a passport. They are getting so expensive."

"America is only a paper tiger," continued Robert, who had tigers on his mind, and was worried. "That's what the Peking government says, and I'm afraid it's true. The Americans are degenerate with good living. They've got too much money." He shook his head. Business was bad.

"Americans have the atom bomb, they can always knock Russia flat with it," said Nora.

"Russia also has the atom bomb," said Robert.

It was the third day of Chinese New Year, and by the European calendar near the end of February. Mei and I were at the Hungs, wishing them a Happy New Year.

Chinese New Year is the noisiest jollity of Hong Kong. Weeks before the day, the shops, open till midnight or later, are crowded with people and crammed with monstrous arrays of food. Oranges and bananas, litchi nuts, pears and apples and quince, carambolas and grapes, tangerines and persimmons, pummeloes, pineapples and mangoes; baskets smothered in paper roses embracing bottles of brandy, whisky, gin, vermouth, port, sherry, Cointreau, Kümmel, Bols and Benedictine, wines and liqueurs from all over the world. Enormous ribboned boxes of chocolates from Switzerland, tins of shortbread and biscuits from England, cartons of candy and Kraft relishes from America; swagbellied jars of candied orange peel, whole kumquats, pineapple chunks, ginger cubes, lotus buds, walnuts and almonds and coconut balls. Californian whole tinned chicken and Chinese dehydrated ducks flattened as waffles with billed heads looking out of their wicker envelopes; entire suckling pigs basted a delightful brown; speckled red

and white sausages in bouquets hanging from shop ceilings; the shouting which is the ordinary conversational tone of the Cantonese; the
perpetual click of wooden slippers clattering on the stone pavements;
the blare of radios going full blast on five thousand shop counters six
feet from each other; the cars honk-honk-honking their way through
the packed streets; the houses gaudy with scarlet paper on doors and
lintels and walls; the incense sticks smoking in handfuls at corner steps
and under tables to the earth and hearth gods; the children gay in shiny
bright satin clothes; the lovely sweet-scented enkianthus, bell flower of
New Year, swaying in tall vases; and rows and rows of plum and early
cherry blossom and narcissi at the Wanchai Flower Fair.

And the firecrackers — a threat to hearing and to health, to sleep and
sanity. The law limits their cannonade to a bare forty-eight hours, during which Englishmen plug their ears with cotton wool, swallow sleeping tablets, and shun the streets. In unrelenting, soul-smashing, ear-
pulverizing thunder, without stop during the light hours and the dark,
the firecrackers sizzle, roar, pop, burst, whoop, smack, thud and bang;
backfire behind and under cars; whizz from balconies and windows;
salvo at street crossings, detonate under empty tins. Suspended from
the roof of famous restaurants three storys high, and reaching down
to the tarmac road, they burst steadily for over half an hour at the
modest cost of a thousand dollars every six minutes. The streets are
rivers of red paper and cinders, everything smells of roast pork and
gunpowder. With lunatic joy we hear so much money vanish in fire
and sound, for thus a frugal race explodes in frenzied extravagance on
ritual occasions: funerals, the birth of sons, and the New Year.

Comparatively, in the Hung's house near the sea, the shouting of
eight children was nearly silence. We sat round the electric fire, ate
New Year cake made with glutinous sweet rice, and gossiped.

"Speaking of a wild goose," said Nora suddenly, "a letter came for
you this morning."

Wild geese, in Chinese poems, mean letters from a beloved.

Instantly the cake I was chewing stuck in my mouth, refusing to go
down. I could neither move nor talk while Nora put into my lap

a typewritten airmail envelope covered with Indo-Chinese stamps.

"Don't get upset, Suyin. Remember the cable that came for you? You lay two hours flat on your stomach, refusing to open it. Yet it was good news, was it not?"

"Yes, Nora, good news."

It was on the beach below this house, in the torrid milk-white July a few months ago, that Mark had said, smiling at me and mocking himself with that gentle, desperate unbelief which infected his living:

"When I stop biting my nails, I shall know that you have a hold on me which no one else has ever had."

"I want no hold on you." I heard my voice, hoarse with the valor of ignorance, proclaim its earnest faith in the immensity of a word I did not understand. A lie, and still the truth.

"Open the letter, Suyin," said Nora. "Don't sit there dreaming. Open it. He loves you and you love him."

"What is love, Nora?"

"You ask me that? How can you ask, Suyin? Nothing is better than the love between you two. When Mark and you are together, it is a glory and a splendor. You are always turned towards each other, and so beautiful together. You shine."

"Sometimes it seems to me that because of love, I cannot have him. Not in the normal way people talk of having."

"Don't be a fool," said Nora, irritated. "Don't give up for great reasons this lovely thing between you two. We live in this world, and in this world you must be selfish for his sake, and not for your ideas. Don't throw Mark away too easily."

"Nora, what is to have, and what is to give up?"

"Read his letter, you dreamer, and stop being a Taoist."

But I kept it tight in my hand, Mark's letter, my passport to destiny, unopened until I was back that afternoon in the house in Conduit Road, sitting, as that first time, next to the striped chair. And in the empty room with the phantom of Mark coming towards me with a smile like a flower, I opened the bulky envelope and I read.

* * *

O heart of man, dancer on a tightrope slung between despair and ecstasy, slender taut rope between the brutal fleeing earth and the immense and savage sky; strand across the abyss, threaded with pain and joy, hatred and faith, lust and courage, injustice, cruelty, tenderness and love. Heart of man, lord of life encompassed by the broad horizon of creation, walker stepping between emptiness and vacancy, watching his feet tread perilously the thin small cord of existence. Heart of man, stubborn actor doing his tightrope trick from nothingness to oblivion, not daring to flag, never daring to stop.

*My dear,* Mark wrote, *this is to tell you that I love you.*

And all the rest as nothing to me; that we would never marry, for he was held fast, someone else's property, not to be released despite the hollow years; that he would not go to China to work, for he was not of the right political color; in spite of recognition; that one of two ways only seemed pressed upon us: running away to live together, forcing a climax with defiant gestures in the name of love, or giving each other up, with equally histrionic, frustrating gestures, in the name of despair . . . and either course a defeat of ourselves.

*I don't want to drift. I want there to be someone I can be faithful to. Without you, without the thought of you, everything seems so meaningless. I had been running away, rushing about, busy, as you said, buying tickets to Cambodia or Timbuctoo, running from the emptiness within. I can never go back to emptiness.*

Through the consciously moderate words, beyond the charming anecdotes of his many journeys, his distress reached me unreduced by the lightness of his many-paged many-dated letter, "A Journal to Suyin."

Smothered in a garb of bland words, the suffering he had endured pricked sharper than my own.

*I came to Hong Kong to do as some of my colleagues do when they get to a new place — line up a woman for the satisfaction of their needs — and did not know that it was love itself that I would find. Strange that at thirty-six I should be so deeply, so contentedly in love, so absolutely convinced, as never during my more turbulent and younger years.*

Through the French windows I saw three blind soldiers in dirty gray uniforms come into the garden through the wide-open gate, with their sticks far-stretched in front of them. And I thought: "How strange! Even the one in front, who leads the others, is blind."

*And now I am no longer afraid, or worried, or unhappy. Suddenly I've stopped worrying. I've stopped biting my nails, I've stopped being frightened of airplanes (I am so often in them, it is against the laws of probability that I should not crash again, this time for good). I am filled with thankfulness, and there is no room for anything else but the happiness of loving you. God has been so good to me in allowing me to love you. There is nothing else.*

I cannot bear it, I thought, I cannot. Unbearable, suffocating. Let this cup pass from me.

*You are the door, the way to understanding, the light at the end of an endless corridor of darkness, the still center at the heart of the cyclone. And I am so happy, although we have probably no hope at all. I can never go back. There is no going back from life.*

Razors going through me. Physical agony, doubling me up with nausea and suffocation, mixture of desire and delight, blind surge of greedy joy and extravagant pain, pure prolonged flame of agony, burning, burning. And the earth I knew, the whole earth pageant of exaltation and misery, triumph and failure, joy and sorrow, scattered to pieces, falling about me, plummeting down, falling as a stone falls, scattered and hurling down. I shall die of this, I shall die of these simple, commonplace words of love.

"Mercy, mercy, have pity upon us."

The blind soldiers stood in the garden, their gray padded uniforms were filthy, the gray wadding came out at the corners. Ah Sun, the old servant twenty years with Fiona and James, shooed at them as a farmer shoos fowl. "Out, out. This is a white man's residence. Go out."

"Mercy, mercy, have pity, for we starve."

The blind soldiers were Northerners from the defeated armies drifting south, drifting to Hong Kong, and they did not understand Ah

Sun's Cantonese dialect, neither did he understand them. They raised their blind faces full under the wide cold sky, and chanted:

"Mercy, have pity, mercy upon us."

And so they went on, Ah Sun making impotent gestures, not touching them, defending his master's property with gesticulation, and the soldiers planted in their blindness on the path, holding out their sticks and their hands, and singing:

"Mercy, mercy, have pity, for we starve."

I shall die, I shall die. Shivering with sweat, and the earth roaring softly past, relentless, going away from me. Bereft and smitten, not knowing what I had known, not loving what I had loved. Rent in the moment of ecstasy, shattered in the instant of total possession, all that was real taken away, filled with emptiness and the splendor beyond all words.

"O Heaven," I whispered, "have mercy upon me."

And there it was.

Through the door into the garden. Up the mountain, up the shining magic mountain, up the mountain each one of us must climb some day or other, into the glory and the splendor, or else stay forever seeking, and finding not at all.

O numb exultant immensity of that without a name, which was from the beginning. Call it what you will, God, or Heaven, Tao, or ecstasy, giving life to heaven and to earth, mounting the furthest star and still not high, singing below the springs of death and still not deep. Timeless and filling space and the void between the passionate leaping stars. In the ant, and in the broken tile, in dung, in dust of dust. Unmeasured vacancy, naked and familiar, only a word away and forever unuttered. Immense desolation and overpowering happiness. A single moment all devouring, desperate flame scouring me, leaving me bereft of all I knew, smitten in all I loved, and with unutterable conviction that I had gone up my mountain, and there it was, never to be again. Such moments come only once.

"Have mercy."

Back from the mountain, back from the radiant summit, the miracle

achieved; breathless and broken. Back from the realm of nothing whatever, stunned and shivering, shaken with physical nausea; back to hear
the blind soldiers, triumphant in their blindness, intolerant with fabulous conviction, raising their voices:

"Have pity, mercy, for we starve."

And so at last I saw, and found, and finding thus, was lost; lost to
find forever, never to lose completely. And so at last I knew what love
was in its immensity, and how God had used us through this passion
strong as death to give each other life. And life has no end.

There was no end as in the enchanted tales, where they live happily
ever after; because now the normal was the unreal and the impermanent, and pushed beyond it, we could not go back. There was no going
back from life.

And for a little while I wept, sorrowful that the normal was not for
us; the man-woman comfort, the constant reassurance against human
loneliness of human loving; it would not be, alas, and it was such a pity.
I wept for myself, and for Mark.

For in the intolerable moment with that which has no name, I knew
at last that Mark did not love me. Not the me I knew as myself.

Mark loved the passionate flame, the singlehearted ecstasy, the eternal
quest. His eyes were fixed upon the mountain, and though the words
were written to me, the song was for the vision beyond. For all men
are thus made, and some more than others; all, all the world, was
hungry and thirsty for more than for bread alone. I had seen it
in China, in the little town bright with sun and exaltation, that
men clamor for food but die for something else. I had seen them
deny their own vision, and in the end they fought for impossible
dreams.

It was too simple an explanation, that once the hunger of the belly
was fulfilled, man would flower, complete in his humanity. It was not
a true one. Not even true in China, where hunger was so normal. For
revolution was not made by the downcast and the downtrodden; its
love and its anger, its exaltation and its heroism were bred and nur-
tured among the privileged themselves. Revolution did not begin as a

thought in the minds of the have-nots, but it was the live spur of conscience among a few that have.

And so man would always transcend himself, though he denied it;
always wanting to believe that his truth, his freedom was the Only
Truth, the Only Freedom; deep need to be absolute, deep need to believe that God was on his side in all his enterprises of existence.

And when there was no beyond to the business of living, no meaning
to life and death, when love began and ended with the mortal creature's need, then life was death in life, bereft of intent, void of ecstasy,
empty and vacant, no glory and no splendor.

And so it was with our love. That for a moment, for a few months,
for a few years, perhaps for the rest of his life, that which Mark sought
was embodied in me. A vision, and an illusion.

Engulfed and hidden away in darkness the *me* I knew, the willful
self submerged, in harmony with a firmament of stars, without want,
feeling or word. Aware at last of that for which our words and our
desires, our illusions and our reality are but an awkward ill-fitting
shell, and, lo! the shadow of that which has no name cast forever upon
the battered wall of our humanity.

In that state of being, with terror and with exultation, I gave up
Mark Elliott's life, his growing living spirit, now believing himself
totally mine, in better hands than mine. For he would move and grow,
and one day the human limitations which each one of us bears, and
imposes upon one another, would chafe him. Then he would see me as
I am, apart from his dream, an empty shell, and he would be sad.

And thus I knew at last that I did love Mark. And that was enough.

We might go on. Together or apart, it did not matter. Intent folded
in one word, fastened to our hearts, the word of love. And this word
would be as a roof above our heads, water for our thirst and food for
our hunger, knowledge within our blood, part of all our thoughts and
deeds, touching all loveliness and misery, a glory and a splendor to last
us all our lives.

And so I came down from the mountain, breathless and broken,
knowing what I had not known, not seeming to love what I loved. I

came down to live, for life is sweet, and to do much wrong — to possess, and to dispute, to scheme and to tangle — but always I remembered the mountain. I came down to go on with Mark for a little while, growing and watching this lovely thing between us grow and live, filled with tenderness and joy, although there was no hope, no hope in time or space in this world. Already relinquished, and so part of each other in the only way there is.

"Have pity, have pity. Mercy upon us."

The blind soldiers were still in the garden, faces lifted to the wide sky, sticks thrust in front of them. Ah Sun, worn out with expostulation, grumbling at himself, thrust coins into their hands.

"Suyin," said Fiona, "I didn't know you were here, sitting in the dark. Why don't you turn on the light? Have you had tea?"

Fiona was back from a walk on the hills with the dogs — Tattybogle and Lolo, and Niko who immediately started chewing the Bokhara carpet and was chased out, and Dainty, Dalmatian Dainty, with a power of emotion too vast for her body, who had given her heart to James and Fiona and was insanely jealous of Lolo.

"Come and sit near the fire," said Fiona, "you look frozen in that corner. Did you have a nice day?"

"Very. Mei enjoyed herself very much."

"Are you feeling all right, Suyin?"

"I've had a letter from Mark, Fiona."

"Oh." Fiona sipped her tea. "How is he?"

"He's very well." His letter in my hand, a treasure after the long acrid journey, the bitter road, thirst and hunger all the way, and the desolation at night; and all of these as nothing to me, unworthy, so unworthy of this magic wealth in my hand.

I found a passage to share with Fiona. "I have just returned from an audience with Bao Dai. I had been asked not to ask him any questions about political, military, or economic affairs, which limited the field somewhat. We spent the first half of the interview talking about *la chasse,* especially *la chasse au tigre,* and the second half talking about yachting. His Majesty has considerable personal charm."

"How amusing," said Fiona. "Such fun to be a correspondent. All these wonderful travels. Very strenuous, too, I should think."

Fiona was discretion itself.

"Mark is coming back to Hong Kong, he doesn't say when," I added.

"Oh, how nice!" said Fiona, happy for me. "That will be lovely, Suyin. Do ask him round to dinner. James and I would love to see him again."

"I will, Fiona. Thank you very much, Fiona."

I was typing a particularly incomprehensible record one dull afternoon when the telephone rang.

"For Dr. Han," said the office boy.

It was Mark at the other end of the wire. "Suyin. How are you?"

"All right."

"The Hungs told me where you work. Can I come to you now? I'm dying to see you."

"Not now. I'm living with Fiona and James Manton. Come there at seven."

The secretary of the department, my only friend there, a Chinese girl very much like Maya in understanding and charm, said to me: "Why don't you take the afternoon off?"

"Oh no," I said, "oh no." I typed on. I could not see the words at all.

Then it was evening, and I was home, dressed in my blue silk dress, and Mei in pale blue velvet with the pearl buttons, given to her by Anne Richards. I brushed and brushed her hair, and tied two ribbons for her. She was very pleased. "I'll show Mark my Chinese composition; I got 90 for it," she said, taking her writing book out of her drawer.

I put on lipstick, and Mei looked on. "You are quite pretty tonight, it's because you're happy, *I* know," she said. "I hate it when you look tired and old. I want you to be young always."

My daughter and I stared at each other, two women understanding each other very well.

We went downstairs to the drawing room. Fiona and James were there, and they had asked a few friends for a drink. "Why, how beautiful you are, Mei," said Fiona. Mei smiled, very pleased, showing the dimple in her right cheek. "You look quite nice too," she answered condescendingly.

We sat among the lamps and the flowers and the carpets and the dogs, the rich warm room with the fire burning, and all so pleasant, glowing with peace and friendliness. The doorbell rang.

"I'll go," said Fiona, and went to the door. "How nice to see you back in Hong Kong," I heard her say. "Come in."

So Mark walked in, more beautiful than I remembered, bringing this great gentleness with him always, and stood speaking to Fiona and to James.

And then it seemed they were waiting for me to say something. I looked and all was lost, there was nothing else.

"Happy New Year," I said.

"Happy New Year, Suyin," said Mark.

Then Mark walked past me, not looking, to Mei, who showed him her composition, for she loved him too. I turned my back on him, suffocated, and James came to me, and held my arm a little, and made small talk; James, always thoughtful, ever forgetful of himself in his great understanding of others, made small talk of the weather.

"It's warmer today," said James, "spring will soon be here. But according to the Chinese calendar it's here already, isn't it?"

"Yes," I said. "It's here already. Spring is come home."

# All Your Houses

*March 1950*

As ONE FALLS IN LOVE AGAIN, ONE GOES BACK TO THE Church.

I thought of Suzanne as I went to Father Low. In his waiting room three plain wood chairs had small holes pierced in their seats for ventilation. The yellow walls held forlorn rusty nails. A bare wooden crucifix stood on the table. Outside the windowpanes the tennis court cut across a hill and a harbor pink with sunset.

"Your visit may be a manifestation of Divine Grace," said Father Low, as he came in breathless from tennis and a quick shower. "You may be trying to come to the Faith."

I shook my head. "We Chinese start life with the moral precepts of Confucius. Our growing imagination wanders with Tao into the Realm of Nothing as It Seems, and we often wind up existence by acquiring merit as Buddhists. In between, many of us become some kind of Christian or other."

Father Low winced. "The Faith goes well with a Chinese background; ancestor veneration does not disturb us. We have many converts in China and in Hong Kong."

The Catholic Church is in truth a powerful spiritual influence in the East, and in Hong Kong is most active in all works of welfare. Tuberculosis, orphans, tenements, shelters, relief, schools — there is no constructive effort for the betterment of the community in which the

Church does not share. It has many converts among the students. Cut off from China, unsatisfied with the pallid Protestant confusion of the many sects, frustrated by the desiccating cynicism of the life wholly given to the pursuit of money which prevails among the Overseas Chinese, appalled by the advent of communism, their young spirits yearn for an ample faith, a magnificent conclusion to give substance to the impotent material reality of existence.

Of the six Chinese medical residents at the Hospital, five had been Catholic converts, the sixth myself. They were very ardent and zealous converts, and treated me, the renegade, with holy and determined contempt.

But I had not come to discuss religion with Father Low. "I've come to talk about something else."

"Love, perhaps," said Father Low, smiling. He had much experience of people.

"I am in love with someone," I said, sticking to the point.

"I thought you were in love with China," said Father Low, still smiling.

As a child wards a blow I put my elbow up.

"Father, what is this which drives one on, and will not let go? For I have now lost everything from within. Everything is no longer what is, but means something else. All desires are but multiple-colored shadows thrown upon the ground of something which stands in the sun and has no shape, within hand reach and never caught. Nothing is as it was. What does it mean?"

"The end of all," said Father Low, sounding not a bit surprised. "It is the Love of God."

"I wish you would not say this to me," I replied. "They are terrible words to hear. I am a woman, obdurate, clinging to sight and smell and feel, suspicious of abstractions. Why did you not speak instead of choices between good and evil, contraries such as freedom and oppression, truth and lies, as the newspapers do? They always make complicated things simple, as if these momentary processes of history through which we live were eternal verities, to endure forever."

"Newspapers," said Father Low, "tackle incomprehensible issues with moral platitudes, and bandy world disasters about like toy balloons. Perhaps they are bewildered, too. We all are. And you are afraid."

"I don't want to be pushed out of normality, to be cast out of ordinary living. I want to have, like everyone else. I want to love a man, to belong somewhere, to live a full life. I don't understand your Christian God. But perhaps this man I love would understand what you mean."

"Some are born to seek God," said Father Low.

"All his life," I went on, wrapped in Mark again, feeling him in every mote of my flesh, "he has wanted a singlehearted devotion, a steady passionate flame to burn him free. And now he thinks he has found it in me. And it is not, it is not me. I alone know how much it is not me. He will know it, too, one day, and feel betrayed. I cannot bear to betray him to himself."

"Mark Elliott," said Father Low, "is a Christian gentleman. He is that attractive composition, a mixture of gentleness and honor, courage and sweetness of character, which is bred in England. A cool spot in the desert, a soft, even-tempered voice, the sanity of birdsong amidst the ravings of the multitudes. I misquote," he added to himself.

"Perhaps it's all me," I said. "Perhaps I've made it all up in my mind."

Abruptly, nothing. Gone the madness, the meaning; ripped off the cloak of dream and small nakedness left; a stale, sour taste upon the tongue, confusion in the head and a sense of the ridiculous. Two people in love, driven to excessive emotion by difficulties and restraints, snared in a tangle of events, hemmed and riddled with compunctions and hesitations and torn loyalties and aspirations. All the rest cunning coinage of my brain. Nothing.

Father Low was speaking. "So few people know this driving intent beyond emotion, this strenuous urge towards the Absolute of joy and sorrow, the integrity which is God. I think you must both be very happy people. You have escaped indifference and mediocrity."

"Alas," I said, very bitter, "what is happiness?"

"Happiness," said Father Low, "is the positive acceptance of the Will of God."

"God is cruel," I replied, suddenly hating, cold and dark inside. "See what He does to us. He gives us to each other in a storm, then takes it all away, flaunts the derision, the futility of possession. And now I cannot go to China wholehearted, for I cannot deny what I have known, revile what I have loved, hate what has made me live; there will always be Mark, a little laugh below the thunder, keeping me from the swarm passion, from the goose-step voice, from hatred and acquisition and so many things which make up conformity. Yet now I cannot have Mark. Not in the way people have and keep and possess. Not with any integrity."

"Beyond the rose garden, beyond the honey country. . . . Oh, dear," said Father Low with a little sigh, "how lucky you are!"

It was now the floating twilight when hearts open and the intricate mind tired of its own deviousness utters through an unknown mouth surprised words, and listens to them in wonder.

"Why should this happen to me? I cannot bear it. Yet it has happened. You who talk easily of the Will of God, have you tried it? Have you tried accepting the intolerable, the inhuman and the unknown?"

"Was it so difficult then?" said Father Low with great candor and simplicity. "Goodness, I must pray, I must try to understand, with God's help."

We walked slowly to the garden gate together, going down the gravel path between two hedges of azalea in bloom, talking of sin and saints, and China, and how God fulfilled Himself through his creatures in many strange ways, for good and evil were in His hands. And we were both at peace, and fearless, for in that moment between the hedges we both belonged, subjects of the Realm that is beyond time and space.

No amount of evil within this world would shake Father Low's belief, his charity, his humility. His Faith was to him alive and tangible in all the ways of matter and spirit, the Tree of Life itself.

And side by side with my pugnacious earthy roots was another affirmation, old as humanity, always denied, always to return. From this safe anchorage upon nothingness, I would find the strength to walk alone, cast out of pace with all the herds, walking my own way, alone. From now on vain would be all external trammels, all forms of servitude and conformity. They would never cage completely the spirit within.

Father Low's last words to me were: "Remember, in my Father's House are many mansions." He thought I might one day come to the Church.

But I felt then that I would not.

"Ever since our liberation," wrote my Third Uncle, "your aunt and I have lived quietly in our old house. With so many mouths in Our Family of three hundred relatives we are not wealthy. Consequently, we need not fret unduly. May your heart therefore be at peace for us.

"I have contributed all my savings to the National Bonds, and your aunt has joined a Woman's Association to render her mind progressive. Inquiry into many matters is necessary to a supple intelligence, and I am taking a course in New Thinking, and in Self-Criticism. It is only the very wisest and the very stupidest who do not change.

"In spite of these things moving heaven and earth, our health remains unchanged, and Our Family continues in harmony and peace with each other. This is due to the virtue of our ancestors, who practiced forbearance and temperateness in gesture and in speech. Alas, it is not so with other families, now divided against each other by hasty ignorance and ill-considered thinking. To lose one's virtue of courtesy is not to belong to the new era. But there are now many opportunists, fawning as hungry dogs upon a new master.

"I shall now tell you about our railway. Forty years ago a railway was planned between Chungking and the capital of our province. Forty years the plans lay idle while warlords fought, rebellions and wars laid waste, and corruption fattened on the fruits of Heaven. I remember well those days forty years ago when your father, a young man, came back from Europe with his foreign wife, your mother. He was filled with eagerness and the new Western knowledge of machines. He had learned to build railways, and thought to build us one in our province.

"It could not be, for at that time the very streets of our city were divided so that one side belonged to one dominion, and the other to another man, and no creature's life was safe. Your father could not build anything, and went away to the North, and for forty years we had no railway, only plans.

"How his heart would now rejoice, for at last the railway is built, after forty years. Thus when honesty is re-established, all things prosper, in the climate of peace.

"Although I am old, and many things are strange to me, the energy of the young does not disturb me. Your cousins are working in the fields for the spring planting instead of loitering to amuse themselves in idleness. Second Brother, Fifth Sister, have gone to the North to study in the Great Universities. Eighth and Ninth Sons have joined the New Army. Tenth and Eleventh Daughters are learning Russian as well as English; they say it is far more difficult. I bade them remember that one foreign language is much like another, as all foreigners look alike to us. If Russia will help us to build this land of ours from waste and poverty and desolation to something worthy, then I will also learn Russian. It seems strange that after so many years of advice, help and money from the other foreigners we should have reached this state of turmoil. I for one never believed in foreigners, and maintain that our strength lies in our own virtue. As for a man, so for a nation.

"There is now food enough for all, and the children are happy. No longer do prices rise as the Great River in spring flood. We who are old have been lucky to see these changes and our country put to right at last.

"There are, among many good things, some which seem childish, excessive and beyond the limits of forbearance. We who were once privileged find ourselves dispossessed and suspected. Many a man once powerful now walks in fear of his past deeds.

"New things learn forbearance only with time. Pride must not be too high, desire too freely indulged, self-will too entire, nor joy excessive. But the young do not know their limitations, and devour the earth with the fury of their burning spirit which clamors for perfection in all things and all peoples. However, they are building a new heaven and a new earth, and it is a big thing. I am old, and must be content.

"For man is formed by action of heaven and of earth, of sensibility and of reason. All elements, their qualities and defects, their passion and inertia, are in him, to move in harmony within. And the heart of man cannot be known entirely, for heaven and earth it is to him, the beginning and end of all things in his own life. And in the interaction of these elements arises a rhythm, the principle of virtue which governs him and also the stars and the sun in their order. Without this virtue he suffers even from goodness pushed to an extremity of violence, and all is disruption, chaos and confusion, until another balance is attained, and the eternal rhythm reasserts itself, struggling to a new harmony.

"In this struggle the old wisdom is cast out, and man has to learn again that the foundation of justice is mercy, the beginning of knowledge is ignorance, and the wisdom of authority lies in benevolence. But such is the cycle of things, and thus our world walks towards the future, not straight and undisturbed, but as a tree grows, by interaction of rain and drought, heat and cold, light and darkness. And so towards all things we must exercise forbearance and restraint, a vision of inner harmony which fuses the contraries in one, meets opposites as aspects of the same. As in the wheel the empty spaces as well as the spokes fashion its virtue as a wheel, so it is with all things under Heaven, to whom all things are equal. Remember this."

"What beautiful brush writing your uncle has," said Mark. "Do you think I shall be able to meet him one day? I hope so."

"He would like you, Mark. You have one thing in common, one essential virtue, in the Chinese sense of virtue."

"That of loving you, Suyin?"

"Silly! I mean something called forbearance. A temperateness refusing the extreme. That which made the Old Books say: 'Always leave a way of escape to your enemy.' The little flaw which makes and keeps us human. A gentleness of mind which robs violence of its triumph."

"I had hoped, you know," said Mark, "that I would meet him one day. But our worlds seem to be moving away from each other. I do not think I shall be able to go to Peking, my darling, in spite of recognition, in spite of so much clamor for peace. I am afraid now, when each morning I wake to think of you, to know how much I want you. Then I open the paper to find out how much progress has been made during the night to split our world into two irreconcilable fragments."

Outside the window of his room the fringe of a trailing cloud dropped a gray swathe of rain upon one side of the sea. Mark's arms were round me, the beating of his heart in my blood, the mortality of the man encompassing all me; and who wanted immortality when the evanescent, transient flesh, knew this golden beauty, this exultant passion? When the swift radiance blazing briefly was ours, was not its tiny spark enough to brave vast abysses of terrifying darkness, was it not enough to deem ourselves transfigured and fulfilled?

"Oh," said Mark, "what a fool, what a fool is man, Suyin, who clutches at the firmament, forgetting the earth is a star."

# CHAPTER VII

# The Sea-Wet Rock

*March, April 1950*

THE SEA EAGLE HANGS SUSPENDED IN A NEVER-ENDING SKY. Exquisite dominion is his; detached and tranquil he surveys the sea-wet rock.

In that spring a new vision was ours, whole, clear and unperplexed. The thousand contradictions of love and hatred, self-deception and treachery which make up the paradox of man no longer stirred us. We laughed, knew joy and the pain coiled at its heart always, and saw — beyond the shabby, sordid torrent, the flood of fear and greed which seems the very tide of mankind — the shining splendor which nothing can foul, warp, or vanquish, the everlasting glory.

On wings of love, we saw the sea-wet rock.

There go in a great hurry those who go nowhere, creatures of a sightless realm, hopeless and meek in the fierce tender spring.

Lily Wu and her sisters, the havoc-pocked emblems of dreary night-eyed sin, scapegoats plying their honest disrepute up and down the streets of night, smiling, seated framed in the lighted windows of a hotel lobby. Their faces held the glory of God and the depravity of their profession.

A boatload of sailors spilled about the streets. "So long, Bud, see you tomorrow." The frizzy, lipsticked Shanghai whore tugs at the hand of the lanky, fair-haired boy so young, still spotty, quite drunk, pulls him away from his buddy into a taxi, impatiently shouts the address. Efficient Venus hurries off her prey, for time is money on the sea-wet rock.

Of three hundred and sixty-one professions in Hongkong, none are more useful than the Ladies of the Night's Perfume, the girls of the Sanitary Department. Creatures of the night in black, nine hundred of them, scavengers in darkness who keep the city clean.

No one meets them save two moonstruck lovers unable to leave each other, walking the streets at cockcrow. Crouched near their pails beside the sprawled street sleepers rolled in their putrid mats, the ladies wait, in affable familiar converse, courteously shouting at each other of food and children and money. Many are pregnant, a few carry the last child asleep on their back tucked in that square piece of cloth embroidered with good-luck words which is the Chinese baby's cradle. The ladies wait until the city sleeps, then up they stand, swing the bamboo pole over their shoulder, and balancing their pails climb foul stairs into rotten buildings, creep along packed fetid rooms and walls glazed with damp, and everywhere empty the covered vessels of human manure, the fecal produce of the day. Without them Hong Kong would be one massive stench. So, with Rabelaisian wit, we call them the Ladies of the Night's Perfume.

There go the careful people who call their souls their own.

Adeline Palmer-Jones, the pyramid's top, Reality gazing upon Hong Kong from her Peak mansion. Her life wheels smoothly within the orbit of her self-approval, circumcongratulated by admiring satellites.

Voluntary giving is better than not to give at all. Adeline organizes charity. Charity is her profession. And within the hierarchy of her society, she has done much. Her implacable confidence that all is solid and pleasant to God in her world, that the poor are there for the exercise of her benevolence, and that there would be no communism, if there were more Adelines, leaves me without a word.

It is because of the Ladies, and Lily Wu, and the refugees and the squatters and the street sleepers that Adeline is. The poor have her always with them. They justify her existence. She is the apex, they are the base, of the pyramid. They are the obverse of the coin of life on which her features prosper. One is not without the other. They stand equal under Heaven.

There trips Suzanne, joyous and gay, the half-and-half, the Eurasian, and so many like her in Hong Kong.

Suzanne has not recovered from the feeling of a white superiority which the concessions, extraterritoriality and colonialism, have left with her. On the other hand, many other Eurasians in Hong Kong deliberately become Chinese, and dislike their white blood. But whatever side they choose, few of them feel the passions, the fanaticism, the blazing torrid emotions which sweep the mainland beyond the hills. Few have any idea of what a European tradition really means. They cannot live in China, they do not live in Europe, so they are here and here they stay, true citizens of the sea-wet rock.

Here glides Ernest Watts, the Goldfish, the self-complete, walking the sea-wet rock alone, alone wherever he goes.

Confucius said: When a man appears generally disliked, inquire after him diligently, for he is a great man.

Ernest Watts, sitting by me eating fruit salad, taunts me, as I expected.

"All things to all men, Dr. Han. One role after another. The solicitous mother, the demure Chinese matron, the brisk efficient doctor, the passionate poet. . . ."

I smile.

With quiet, deadly aversion, Watts goes on:

"And will you go to Peking then, to hide your broken heart?"

The April night is full and gentle, and Mark's head glows under the light. I shout with inward laughter at Ernest Watts.

Time and again I observe Watts, fascinated by his voice, his knowledge, the passionate integrity of his spirit, his cold scorn of humbug, the devastating irony, tempered and smooth and steely, which crumples his enemies. Time and again I accept his contempt.

Mark says to me:

"Does Watts dislike you?"

Simple as any lover, not understanding, even if I explained, he adds: "Shall I tell him what you mean to me?"

"Oh no, no; never. But you must tell him one day what he means to me."

"What is that?"

"The Goldfish, which sees both sides of his glass tank at once, and is betrayed by the primal fault, the essential weakness, his own vision . . . as we all are, Mark."

Here comes Humphrey Palmer-Jones, repeatedly shaking hands, with Mr. Kam, Mrs. Kam, Master Kam and all the Misses Kam.

Humphrey is business, the core of Hong Kong's existence. He does not own, as does the Princely House of Trade, most of Hong Kong and much of Shanghai and goodness knows what else besides. But he is "solid" too, which means as vulnerable to what happens in China as is all Hong Kong.

Humphrey knows that no clock can be put back. For the last few months he has stopped wishing for the good old days. He must adapt or perish. He will adapt.

He has had losses. Heavy taxes to pay in China. Mr. Parrish has left the firm and gone to Japan, where business with China is far better than from Hong Kong; but Humphrey has begun dealing with New China trade agents, and is impressed with their efficiency. "I have faith and confidence in the future," says Humphrey. But does not go on to explain what the word means.

The sea-wet rock, he knows, lives on borrowed time, but all time is borrowed. In its many worlds, in its diversity, its contradictions oblivious of each other, all that tends to make Hong Kong fall apart, he sees hope for survival, the necessary suppleness to meet change and the days to come.

And so he hangs on, not losing his head, taking hard knocks, not carried away by fear.

With Humphrey, drinking lime juice on the hotel roof, we watch

China Building go up. In the vacant lot next to the Hong Kong and Shanghai Bank a hundred workmen are busy with cranes and pile drivers and trucks, loading unwanted soil. Two hundred women with baskets also load, competing with the machines, and cheaper.

Mark, fascinated always by the stammer of pile drivers and the gestures of working men, looks on with blue eyes wide with pleasure.

Says Humphrey: "They'll have finished it just in time for the Reds to take over." It is a standing joke with him.

There drive the government servants down from their hilltop government flats to their government offices. Limited, enlightened, paternalistic colonial government, whose master strategy is compromise. Slow, slow, and when the old way won't do, concede, compromise, inch by inch, step by step.

Find a formula.

The English way.

Administration is a perpetual headache, alleviated with aspirins of compromise and wet towels of caution. A balance between past and future and so many conflicting interests, vested and otherwise, that all solutions become empirical and temporary.

Tuberculosis. "It's bad, it's worse. This week has three hundred and eighty-seven new cases, and ninety-two deaths, but we've just got to cut the extra subsidies to the patients. Other things come first."

"What other things? Isn't there a surplus in the budget?"

"Tuberculosis may slaughter its thousands, and Hong Kong cannot be defended for more than a few days, but defense comes first."

Administration walks the tightrope, lumbering all the way but never falling off.

In a Chinese school the students dance the Yangko. The school is closed because of "Unsanitary washing arrangements." Compromise.

On all the streets, in all the Chinese bookshops, New China literature spreads its countless red and yellow and blue paper covers, its stars, and its hammer and sickle. Life of Stalin. Life of Mao Tse-tung. Life of Lenin. Marxism explained. Self-criticism. Communist newspapers sell everywhere.

"This is English administration. Freedom of the press. We just quietly deport people who *say* too many things we don't like."

Fish. Administration is trying to break down the vicious middlemen ring holding up the prices. But at the same time there are many influences at work. Headache, compromise, and a lot of wet toweling.

"We cannot afford to make conditions too good in Hong Kong. We keep them bad enough so as not to get out of step with the rest of Asia. Otherwise we'd be swamped with people from the Mainland."

Shanghai factory owners have been using young girls to work the looms at night, doubling their profits. Government closes the factories.

"It is the Chinese themselves who are hardest on their own people. They exploit their own underdogs as no Englishman would dare to do in 1950. Their only concern is to get rich quick. Few of them have any interest in Hong Kong itself."

Colonial administration grinds on, and goes on working.

"We know that nothing lasts forever, but we hope that if and when the time comes to hand over, we shall leave something behind of those principles we have tried to practice: justice, fair dealing and tolerance. We have tried."

And that is true. In its own imperfect, hesitating way, colonial government has given justice, fair dealing, conciliation and a sense of tolerance to Hong Kong. Not always, not all the time, but more than enough to leave something of itself behind, something abiding and too precious to lose. And that colonial administration often has to step between Chinese and Chinese, who are harder and more merciless to each other than any Englishman today could be.

There goes Mr. Kam, in an enormous car, to a big business party at the biggest restaurant.

Mr. Kam is Chinese, and in his bosom surges a swelling pride, which he never voices, to hear of the wonderful things that are being done on the Mainland. His agents have been to Peking, and trade is brisk both with the Mainland and with Formosa. But in spite of all this Mr. Kam would not like Hong Kong taken over just yet. Not yet.

He is a little frightened that the new government will do exactly what it says it will do. He is torn between national pride and personal apprehension. So he sits on both sides, hoping the day may come when there shall be no side.

So does Mr. Kam's brother, who is a rubber planter in Malaya, and contributes a fair sum of money to the terrorists to leave him in peace, as well as staunchly supports the administration. What else can he do? He is so frightened. So many, like him, walk a tightrope, and are deemed untrustworthy because they are torn.

Sen and Rose, communists both, walk up Hollywood Street, once famous for brothels, now full of bookshops, with Mark and I.

Rose breathes fiercely, scornfully expels the polluted air of Hong Kong out of her nostrils. Hong Kong is a sink of iniquity. All the racketeers, the gangsters, the prostitutes, the running dogs, the fawning slaves, the exploiters of the people, the spies and reactionaries and rejects of brave new China are here.

It is quite true. There are also many thousands of refugees driven out by fear, and good people.

Sen keeps a fixed superior smile upon his lips while he and Mark talk politely of Winchester, Cambridge, the boat race in England and the Dragon boat races in China, the Tunhuang caves and Housman. Mark plays the recorder, and Sen the Chinese flute.

"Do you think I shall ever be able to go to Peking?" asks Mark, with that unassuming innocence which deceives so many. "I have sent in another application, but there's been no reply."

"It depends," bursts Rose, "whether you are a *sincere* friend or not."

"Mmmmmm . . ." says Mark.

"The English are perfidious," proclaims Rose, "and the American imperialists are much worse. We must fight their aggressive and degrading culture and stop their warmongers from plunging the world into war." She darts into a bookshop and comes back with the *New China Monthly Review* for Mark.

"People make such a fuss about indoctrination," adds Sen. "Yet we are all indoctrinated in one or another way. You, Mr. Elliott, are completely indoctrinated by your public school education. Your behavior and your reflexes are conditioned by these false feudalistic standards inculcated in you during your youth."

"Mmmm . . ." says Mark, ". . . yes, I hadn't thought of it that way."

Here in Hong Kong Sen and Mark can talk, separated by their convictions, but without hatred and insult, and do not realize that their courtesy achieves what cannot be done elsewhere. For a moment, Mark and I look at each other and hope that the world, after all, is not irrecoverably split, doomed to one or the other economic system. Surely, surely, there is a middle way; tolerance, an equilibrium is possible. It must be.

"We want peace," says Sen. "The Americans want war."

"Couldn't it be reciprocal mistrust?" ventures Mark.

"The English are at least thoughtful," concedes Sen. "I know you too were for recognition, Mr. Elliott. But recognition was purely for trade motives, and it came three months too late. It was an insult to New China."

"I don't think it was quite like that," says Mark. "We're always a bit slow, you know; it is our English weather."

They stop near the temple of the God of War and Literature and look down upon the harbor blue and breezy and crowded with ships, and the loud gregarious people hurrying to and fro, and the web of the gray city, and the cars. Watching the future come and the present go, they stand.

"Yes," says Sen, taking his pipe from his mouth with a careful English gesture, and sweeping the horizon with it, "I think we'll keep all this as it is for a little while. We'll have it back later." He is very patronizing.

"Why not," says Mark, tranquil. "It will come back to you one day. Asia must belong to its own peoples."

## I I

March and April. Six weeks of spring.

Unquenched exuberant madness, laughter rich and thickly poured, rapture leaf-feathered, shadow-trammeled, blossom-studded, bird-molested, sky-encompassed, skimming wind and reckless leaping sun-light and so many young desires.

Thrum of wings, burst of buds, call of cuckoo. Spring is come home.

O sea-wet rock thronged, thronged and swarming with hunger and misery and wealth, want and abundance and waste, vice and purity and corruption, law and justice and privilege, charities and private property and Monopoly and Big Business, rackets and tuberculosis and beauty and horror; window of democracy, Hong Kong, haven of Shanghai racketeers and American missionaries and Chinese pro-fessors and international businessmen and out-of-job Kuomintang generals; refuge of refugees and political exiles, end of the road to so many rejects of the New World and relics of the old order, hotel of men at loose ends and men on the make and men with nowhere else to go; outpost of Empire, Hong Kong, excrescence off China with two million four hundred thousand Chinese, communists and Na-tionalists and nothing-ists and so many sitters-on-the-fence; deep-roaring, bustling market Hong Kong, where life and love and souls and blood and all things made and grown under the sun are bought and sold and smuggled and squandered, spring is come home to you.

There are places on the rock; in the rickety-laddery perilous swarm of vertical streets of the overwhelming poor; in front of festering tene-ments; on the odorous Praya redolent with sweat and crated wood and salted fish and apples and oil and flour and machinery and red peppers and paper and sea-rottenness; up the seaward-brooding hills; in stone and sand, in bracken and elephant grass; head high in humanity, with pulped bad oranges and rotten cabbage and spit and urine and dust; with Bokhara rugs and polished teakwood floors and dulcet voices and teacups; on lonely paths with all the sumptuous city night-stretched at our feet; places where my heart goes wild, wild with memory, wildly lost as ever anything was lost.

Compact and driven, pleasure and pain, ecstasy disbodied, insentient, separate, detached. A momentary capture of oneself entire, alone, aloof from all desire. Silence then, slow and beautiful, on the hills, in the sunlight, in the soft night of spring.

"I have lost myself. It is like a death."

Birdsong. Lovely felicitous birdsong, clear, clear, calling the dawn, the morning. The orioles, the orioles round the Peak singing before the Europeans rise from sleep, and he and I walking in the fine stinging mist sharp on our faces. Dawn treading down the mist, shaping the vulture-swooping castles of cloud, turrets lifting the vast clean vault of heaven higher, higher, and all the birds bursting their hearts with spring.

Listen. The orioles, the bulbuls, the rough magpie, the come-to-the-Peak-haha bird, the parakeets and the yellow-faced flower pecker, and the cuckoo loud and mad.

"If this be madness let us be always mad."

Oh, pain, pain, calling as the orioles call round the Peak in the fine sweet dawn. Pain one with our joy always.

"I have not loved enough, I have not lived enough."

Fever of life running, pounding, hammering, thrusting, leaping, overflowing. Do you see? Did you hear? Can you smell? Feel it! Over-head, underfoot, in the air, about us, beyond. All that men pray for, eyes to see, ears to hear, hearts to encompass, all this ours in the fierce frenzied spring.

"I resent this exclusive preoccupation with you. You never leave me, never. You are always with me."

Tenderness, gentle and deep and strong, keeping me safe from the vigilant cowardice within. When the shadows of terror unbidden arose, then his tenderness. No one had ever treated me so gently.

"What are you frightened of?"

"Terrible things. Shadows. I do not know."

"War? Could war destroy us?"

"War destroys everything. Perhaps war."

Honeysuckle, frangipani, cassia over the gray furry walls creviced with ferns and tapestried with moss, snarled and coiled and tangled with the spreading roots of trees growing straight out of the stone walls, looping and holding the old stone walls of Hong Kong together. Bastions and fortresses of property tree-girdled and moss-bound. Honeysuckle, frangipani, sweet cassia, on the roads of spring.

And the azaleas, flaunting shameless, flaring purple and pink loveliness up the hill opposite prim Government House (part Japanese pagoda, also Mexican patio), up and down the University, climbing all the hills, hurtling down the slopes to the sea, the sea-wet rock drowned in the red folly flaunting and challenging the sky.

"Who wants to be immortal when beauty is so mortal? I had rather be a red flower in your hair."

A blank spring moon, young, mistrustful, hollow-cheeked, star-scurrying, cloud-pursued, wild and hungry moon pressing swiftly upon the long roads of the sky.

We found the first spring irises, tender and small and hidden blue irises, a little wet with small rain, Fiona and James and Mark and I and the dogs walking across the hills in the morning, the hills soaked red with azaleas in bloom.

"Oh, look look," said Fiona, and knelt with cupped hands, and all the dogs stood back, attentive, their ebony muzzles quivering towards her.

It rained a little while, then out sprang the sun. We cooled the beer in torrent water down the rocks, and all the dogs drank.

With Mei and Ginger and many another schoolgirl, friends of Mei, we ambled the small upland paths picking ferns. Below us the wind shivered on the sea, and all the little girls laughed.

One day Oh-no came with us to swim in the sea. She would not believe that it was the sea, and did not laugh. She went into the water to the waist, looked at her hands in the water, and never said anything.

We climbed Lantao, bare, cloud-wrapped, twin-peaked island, a thick cold rain upon it and six friends with us. On the ferryboat, among the cheerful, hawking, spitting, chewing, exclaiming Cantonese, large baskets of cabbage and white turnips and spinach and garlic and peppers and Chinese chives and bitter cucumber and taro. Landing, then five hours through the straddled paddy fields with the gazing water buffaloes stupefied and withdrawn, and the cheerful women shouting greeting under round straw hats; then round the hissing rocky shore, frothy with sea-wrath, then up the mountain through the fog and rain, spouting verse and singing stirring Chinese marching songs. Then the Buddhist monastery near the mountain top, the gay little priest, suave as a good hotel manager, and the hot green tea. And Mark and I going out again into the garden, and standing there with stars of rain in our hair amid the peaceful rows of beans and shallot and cabbage, holding hands, looking at each other, and our feet in the mud, sinking slowly. Then back in to the others, and under the hurricane lamp Mark doing crossword puzzles. I put his socks to dry above the lamp, there was no fire. Next morning one was charred to cinders.

At four in the morning the bronze bell of the monastery, leaping alive with deep bronze baying, and the crouched monks and novices supplicating in grayness before dawn amid the incense, to the great golden compassion, the Mercy squatted quiet on the Lotus of the World. Winged sound struck out of the bell, moving out and on without end. The punctuating wooden rattles and the antiphonal nasal chant, priest, novice, acolyte in orderly suppliant rows beating time with their fingers and their voices. And he and I alive and listening.

"Goodness! how splendid you two look, so golden," said Evelyn Walsingham and then stopped, no longer precise and statuesque and unruffled.

"And now an inch of passion breeds its own inch of dust," I said to Mark.

"How wise the Chinese poet, who never forgets the other side of the gold coin we spend, Janus-faced life."

"To travel is better than to arrive. To wait is joyful dalliance."

"I want to be bound to you forever."

"But we are. Bound and free. Only free people can give themselves, and so I belong to you."

"I shall never hold you against your will, Suyin. You will leave me one day."

"Silly. Never."

"Not for a man, but for the unknown, the challenge . . . or for China, China your bones. And I shall thank God for you, foolish mad woman who do not believe I love you."

"It is you who will be bored, and go away. For I am an illusion. But I shall always be happy. There was you."

"I am an illusion too. You must write."

"Silly. I cannot write."

"You must. But I am afraid that only in my world will you be able to write. In the other, the new strong world of shining service and impersonal sacrifice, you will not write. That is why I want my arm around you. To keep you from hurt. To see you blossom as the spring. I want you to write a book."

"I have no book but you."

"Then will you write a book about me? That we loved each other, and that you were the end of the search for me?"

"That is a lie. You know that there is something else."

"Not yet, not yet."

In the clear sun our sudden immense terror, and dark the whole bright world with this thing nameless coming near, and in love and terror we hid our faces, trembling.

"Not yet, not yet. Life is very sweet."

At evening the gold and blood of sunset, the long muzzled, gray-backed, golden-bellied otters of cloud, swift-gathered for a kill, a terrible death behind the implacable sullen hills. How cruel God who made his creatures so beautiful that they may prey upon each other, spirit and limb and life. God who made the mantis, slim jade murderess with the razor jaws, and the oriole with the liquid golden voice, and the civet cat and the sparrow hawk swift-pouncing, and the bamboo snake, and the sea eagle sky-suspended; hair and feather and scale, claw and dart and beak, each a miracle, that they may end as this sun has done today, in terror and torn flesh and spilt blood and agony.

"We must accept it and tolerate it, though it is intolerable."

And then the night wind, filling the world and the darkness. He and I.

# CHAPTER VIII

# How with This Rage

*May and June 1950*

IN THAT SPRING MY LIFE WAS IN HIS HANDS. LOVE FASTENED to our hearts and never going thence, each day I pushed back the limits of my soul to hold more love of him, renouncing possession to receive love afresh, a new and everlasting wonder.

I found him in everything I touched and saw and knew, till all was reflection and shadow, rooted in knowledge and love of Mark. And so I clutched with fervor the shining momentary now, made it Eternity, and thought myself both honest and clever, squaring accounts with Heaven.

There was tension that spring. Many of Mark's colleagues, correspondents all, some famous and renowned, were gathered in Hong Kong, which they called "Crossroads of Asia" and "Chink in the Bamboo Curtain." They wore set faces, worked day and night, argued night and day. I heard the world arranged and transformed; the mystic appeal of communism disputed and dissected and dismissed; iron and bamboo curtains clanged open or whizzed shut; wars past and future and present fought and won and lost on the eighth floor of the Gloucester Hotel; the great, the mean, the trivial and the world-shaking swept to and fro in gusty anecdote and scandalous reminiscence among the whiskies.

In China the campaign against America gathered volume, motion and intensity; the seizure of the American barracks in Peking provoked resentment in Washington; Formosa, supported, subsidized and poised as a threat to the Mainland, was to Peking rankling proof of the imperialist will to war; insult and denunciation, threat and word misuse; vigorous emergencies in Malaya and in Indo-China; a rude, uncivil, churlish world, manacled by fear.

When Mark left Hong Kong again, for another tour, I stayed, suspended as in a dream. His absence left me full of him.

"Will you wait for me? I am coming to you."

"I'll wait. I shall try to make myself better for you."

"And I for you. Will you go to China?"

"I don't know. If I do, I'll wait for you there. I'll always wait for you in my heart."

"Then I shall come to you in China. Across the Himalayas. I've always wanted to climb them."

We laughed. Foolish, mad, invulnerable in lunacy, having forgotten what I knew the winter before: that no one is invulnerable to repeated suggestion; that I was no different, no stronger, no more able to withstand reiteration than others; and that if I went to China, I might one day look at Mark as a spy, a reactionary, a liar and a hypocrite; his love pollution and error, invasion of my soul. I might revile, confess, beat my breast, and hate that love which had made me live. But now this seemed sheer nonsense to me. Loving Mark was the only thing that could never be taken away. I was so much in love.

And so through May and June, somnambulic to all but to each other, we lived in deprivation which was sweet content.

"I wonder when Mark finds time to write for his paper," said James teasing me, "look at what he expects you to read," and pointed to a pile of airmail envelopes waiting for me on the hall table.

My chief, attracted by an unusually vigorous clatter of my typewriter at the Department, bent over my shoulder one day, only to disappear as, in confusion, I tore a letter to Mark off the roller. I felt that my days of typing records would soon be over.

\* \* \*

And so until that Sunday, sunny and incredibly hot, when François Perrin and Anne Richards took Mei and me to swim at Repulse Bay. The Bay was littered with orange peel and paper bags and screaming children and large Shanghai families draped round the fountains composing family snapshots. "Why are the beach habits of the Chinese and the Americans so alike?" asked Anne.

Anne was back from Formosa, where she had gone a few weeks previously after a cable from the head office of the newspaper for which she no longer worked.

INVESTIGATE BIRTH NEW SPIRIT IN FORMOSA, commanded the cable. EVALUATE POSSIBILITY FREE CHINA RECONQUEST MAINLAND CABLE ONE THOUSAND WORDS.

After three weeks in Formosa Anne sent a cable back:

SORRY SAME OLD SPIRIT STOP RECONQUEST NO NO A THOUSAND TIMES NO.

And then she and the paper parted company.

Anne was going to Tonga Island to paint. "I've heard the Queen of Tonga is wonderful, every ounce a queen. I'd love to do a portrait of her. I want to lie in the sun and just smell the flowers and try to forget China, if I can."

We lunched late at the Bay Hotel, on the veranda. Then it was that a fat bald man sitting at another table bent towards us and said to Anne:

"Have you heard the news, Anne?"

"No."

"Korea," said the American. "The North has invaded the South. They crossed the thirty-eighth parallel last night."

"Oh my God," said Anne, "war."

"The Americans are going in," said the fat man. "Thank God for America. No appeasement. We'll show those damned Russians where they get off."

The next few days were hazy to me. A jumble of jubilation, consternation and prediction assaulted me on every side; I noticed in a few people a sense of release from the boredom of uneasy precarious peace, relief now the issues were clear; in others, wrinkled brows and dubiety and confused arguing; a time for decisions and indecisions; a time for rumor and oracle; a time also for exodus from Hong Kong, for now that the American Seventh Fleet protected Formosa many people went there. "Formosa is safer than Hong Kong, the Americans will fight for us," said the wealthy Chinese.

Confusion and rage and many words. Rubber prices going up and up.

"Do you think," I went round asking anxiously, "it will last a long time?"

Laughter. Scorn.

"Two weeks. They'll be rolled right back to Siberia."

Others said:

"This is World War Three."

"I'm talking of the Koreans," I tried to say once or twice.

"Koreans, pah. Russia is behind it all. They've got Russian tanks and guns, haven't they? Now is the time to throw atom bombs on Moscow, and also on Peking."

Rage and many confusions.

"Our new jets . . . the Russians haven't anything like it. . . ."

The price of gold went up. There was a boom in smuggling. More people were caught with gold bars inside them in a week than in the whole of the previous month.

It was three days before the communist papers in Hong Kong came out with their aspect of the truth, which said that South Korea had invaded North Korea.

"The American imperialist beasts, without waiting for U.N. deliberations, invaded Korea. By this aggression the Americans clearly show their plan of world conquest."

And because, after all, the Chinese are not fools, even the people in the little town in China, when they read the paper, were puzzled. For the first time, their confidence in the new government was shaken.

"We heard two days ago on the wireless that South Korea was invaded by the North. Now our government tells us it is the other way round. Yet the North Koreans are advancing into South Korea. Someone is lying. Why should our People's government lie to us?"

But very soon they were swept up, caught in the fiery resentment of white man interference upon Asiatic soil.

"Why should the Americans try to impose their will on Korea? The Koreans are our brothers. You cannot split a country in two pieces and not expect it to want wholeness again."

And so many people in China were against the Americans, because they felt they had no right to make matters worse and to interfere on the Mainland of Asia.

All I could think of was Mark.

"Please, please God, don't let Mark go to Korea."

But of course it could not be. Four days later his telegram was waiting for me on the rosewood hall table:

SUYIN I AM POSTED TO KOREA ARRIVING B O A C NEXT SUNDAY MARK

So there I was again at Kaitak Airport, with my legs shaking under me, waiting for Mark. Life was made up of repetitions.

And knowing a new dress might bewilder him, I wore my old one.

And then the plane was there, rolling to a standstill. And again I stayed inside the waiting room.

But this time Mark turned round on his heel and came to me, knowing exactly where I was.

"Suyin, how nice of you to come," he said.

"Good afternoon," I replied, vicious and trembling. "So you want to rush off to Korea? Haven't you had enough? You can never resist a war."

"How are you?" said Mark.

"Very well." I swayed on my legs, giddy and staring at my shoes.

"How beautiful you are," he said suddenly, so gently it was utter violence. "Smaller than I remembered. Sit down."

We sat down. I looked at the glass-topped table, and printed a row of fingerprints on it, while he looked at me, absorbed, unsparing, never letting go. In the end we rose and walked out down the road. Half a mile later we were offered a lift.

The man who gave us the lift was German. He wore blue jeans and had blond hair and a slightly bucktoothed smile. "I operate an air company from Hanoi to Hong Kong," he told us. "I was in Hanoi and Saigon in January," said Mark. "Are you in business?" asked the German. "No," said Mark, "I'm a reporter." "Oh," said the German, "there are always a lot of you chaps sitting around on the Rue Catinat in Saigon."

So Mark smiled at me, his blue eyes crinkling round the outer corners, and quoted aloud to himself from a sonnet in French which I had written to him for fun, one day, about *"les journalistes"* . . .

> *qui boivent un apéritif éternel*
> *Rue Catinat sous la voûte du ciel*
> *Indochinois . . .*

The German then appraised me and said to Mark as one man to another: "Your girl friend is nice, she has a good skin. Can she speak any English?"

"Oh, no," said Mark, detached and proprietary, "she can only write it a little."

So I sat, looking demure, and then I sat in the lobby of the hotel while Mark booked a room, and came back to me.

"Room 509," he said. "Come up to me in ten minutes."

In ten minutes I was up, and he was unpacking his small fiber case. There were some books on the table, a few shirts, his blue and white good-luck blanket. I walked to the window and looked out. In the Kowloon railway station just opposite to the hotel a small engine puffed a little smoke and started wheeling away. Mark came and stood behind me, also looking.

"Train to China," he said. "I'll never get on it now."

And then while he bathed and dressed I rang up Fiona.

"Fiona, Mark has arrived. He is going away tomorrow. I am staying with him tonight."

I heard Fiona swallow over the telephone, but all she said was:

"Oh, all right, Suyin. Give him my love, and James's, and . . . best luck to him in Korea."

Then we crossed over to Hong Kong on the ferry, and took a taxi; Mark wanted to go to see our stone, so we went to the House of Wisdom, up the cement stairs, and to Lovers' Lane. And he stood, looking around him. Then down again, and up to the Peak in the taxi. And there we walked along the path that circles the Peak, in the sunset. It had rained while we were in the taxi, and two rainbows spanned the sea between Hong Kong and the mainland. "One rainbow is unlucky," said Mark, "but two must be a good omen."

We stood and watched the rainbows, and a francolin flying between them, and then it was time to go to the Gloucester Hotel, to meet other correspondents.

For correspondents and newspaper people are gregarious and open-hearted, and always have to meet and drink and talk with their own kind, and exchange all-precious "dope." They walk in an aura of modest glamour; for they can say things like: "MacArthur said to me and I said to him," "When I interviewed Mao Tse-tung in Yenan," "Down in Teheran last week. . . ." They impart more than a hint of owning, even if only for a short time, broad areas of a wide world. They have the inside story, the art of debunk, the possession of inside knowledge. Mark lacked glamour, on the whole, for he seldom spoke, and rarely argued, and theorized not at all; and when stories flew about, and ash trays got buried under mounds of half-consumed cigarettes, he would smile a little; and sometimes look at me and whisper: "I simply wag my great long furry ears."

So there we were, back with many correspondents, so many bound for Korea, being greeted happily, and Mark shaken by the hand, and there also were François Perrin and Anne. Once again I thought how much sincerity, idealism and spiritual integrity belonged to those who follow the hard-working, austere trade of journalism. I found them more balanced, less prima donnaish, and more tolerant of fresh ideas, than the people in my profession. True, some were afflicted with *folie de grandeur,* but I had seen too much acute megalomania among my own colleagues to mind the symptoms of their mild and tolerable malady.

Everyone was arguing and talking and smoking, about Russia, and America and Korea, and China. Always, always the talk came back to China. And once again Mark and I just sat, and he whispered to me: "I simply wag my great long furry ears."

"By dint of progress we have retrograded," a young American was saying. "We have built bigger and bigger bombers, faster and faster fighters, as if we were perpetually going to bomb an ever-spreading colossal factory — and now, perhaps we shall find that once again it is hordes and numbers which count, and individual courage. Nobody has thought of war as different, because every war is fought along the lines where the last one left off."

"I predict," said the exuberant François, "that if the Chinese ever come into this Korean business you will see a strange phenomenon. Man power versus machine power, or, as the Chinese say: 'A sea of fire drowned by a sea of men.' It sounds lunatic, but it is not. Let us hope China will not come into this conflict. But if she does, for her it will be a Crusade, to deliver the weaker Asiatic brothers from imperialism. I think the Chinese are dying to prove their mettle; a revolution always arouses national ardors and is consolidated by a successful foreign war."

"What I don't understand," said someone else, "is why the North Koreans have chosen this moment to attack. Strategically, it is a bad moment. The paddy fields are flooded, which makes tank advance difficult. Obviously Russia must have been counting on a quick knockout blow. And I cannot understand why the Peking government was so completely taken by surprise. It took the Chinese propaganda machine three days to print news about Korea."

And so it went on, talk, talk. Rage upon earth, argument, and the mix-up of emotions and moral issues with self-interest and balances of power. And sometimes it seemed to me that no one was really concerned about the Koreans at all, but that what dominated their minds was the conflict between two vast economic powers, to be decided on the Korean battlefield. And some thought this would last a long time, and others that it would soon be over. But no one knew. None of the experts knew. No one knew what was going to happen.

Mark was rather sleepy, and yawned. François took us back to the ferry, talking all the way. Talking of the things that make men live, and the things for which they die.

"How ill we use words," said he, "for we say that a man has died for his belief, when we should say that he lived for it, and then he died. It seems to me that the strength of communism lies in giving people the illusion that their lives have had purpose, and therefore they are willing and glad to die in affirmation of their purpose. *Il faut dire aux hommes pourquoi ils doivent se faire tuer.*"

We went back over the ferry to the hotel, back to Mark's room. He fell asleep immediately. I lay with the joy of holding him in my arms, his head on my shoulder, mine for a few hours. Then I too was sleeping until I felt him stir and turn to me and heard him say: "Oh what a lot of time one wastes in sleep." And then it was dawn, and a knock on the door, because his plane was going in two hours' time.

So we got up and walked to the window and dawn was outside in her usual pink and gray with a sleepy hoot of engines from the railway station and the earliest train champing on its coal.

"We've never had a whole day and night together, we've never been able to look forward to hours, days, the future ahead of us. Either you or I have always had to rush away. And I want so much to stay with you."

"But we've seen the dawn. We've seen the dawn together. It is the best hour."

The room boy brought hot milky tea and Mark packed his fiber case. He had taken our seals with him, those we had carved out of one stone, for love, in the spring.

"I've never given you anything," he said. "I'd like so much to be famous, so that I could give you that. Do you think I shall be famous one day?"

"I don't know, but if you marry me, you might easily become notorious, you know."

Mark laughed and laughed. "The Red Doctor," he mimicked.

And then his case was packed, and we stood looking at each other before leaving the room. "I do want to be free to come to you," he said.

And because of the blindness which was a clearness in me through love, because of that impossible summit which was mine, I heard myself say, and it surprised me to hear it more than it surprised Mark:

"But you are free, and so it is not necessary to make gestures of release."

He merely turned his head and stared through the window, the dawn light between us; then I knew I had only bound him to me a little more, and the utter futility of my own gesture, a betrayal of its own aim.

"Oh wise Psyche," said Mark, half mocking and tender, "you know that if you do not detain your lover, he will never leave you."

We went down in the elevator full of correspondents. Into the lobby, with so many correspondents hurrying up and down and drinking tea and signing checks and collecting air labels. We had more tea, and some of them came to sit with us.

"Well, well, Mark Elliott, of all people. Now we'll all be in this together."

Greetings, and cheerfulness, and much bustling about. It seemed all the correspondents on earth were going to Korea.

"It's the biggest story in the world, and how I loathe the prospect," said David, one of Mark's very good friends, sipping tea with us.

Mark went off to get his luggage weighed and I said to David:

"David, I'm worried about this Korean thing. I don't like it at all. Take care of yourself, and take care of Mark, please."

"You bet I will," said David. "You bet I will."

Then Mark came back. "We're going now," he said. I walked to the entrance of the Air Office with him, and we stood and looked at each other, four yards apart.

"Good-by, darling," said Mark. "Take care of yourself until I come back."

"You take care," I said. "Remember, if something were to happen to you, they might turn you into a hero."

How he laughed! I can still hear his laughter, low, smothered, as he stood there, clutching his typewriter.

"Oh Lord, yes," he said. "I'll try not to let that happen. That would be too awful. But then you'd debunk me, wouldn't you?"

"Yes," I replied gaily, "of course I'd debunk you."

And so he walked away and into the bus, the blue and cream bus, and I went out by another door, and stood on the pavement on the other side of the road, and saw the bus loaded with correspondents and their luggage roll heavily round the corner and away, towards Kaitak Airport where the plane to Tokyo was waiting. It was too far to see anyone inside the bus; I stood and watched it become very small.

Then I went back to the office to type records. Out of the Chinese newspaper, which had produced a large map of Korea, I cut the map, and stuck it with tape above my desk, to follow the war.

# CHAPTER IX

## Land of Morning Calm

*July and August 1950*

*July 13*

THIS IS ONE OF THE MOST UNPLEASANT ASSIGNMENTS I'VE ever been on — Malaya, New Guinea, Indonesia all rolled up in one. It was too much for David, who went back this morning. I see and feel all this unpleasantness, but there is another part of me which can look at them from the technical aspect of doing a job of reporting as well and as fully as one can. I feel transported back eight years ago to the days when I also was a war correspondent in an American command. The difficulties over communications, the emotions which certain events and sights arouse, men afraid, men suffering, innocent people caught up in terrible events which they cannot understand; the contrast between natural beauty and the human actions to which it is a setting, the past a long way away, the future even further . . . I seem to have been through all this before.

And they're such nice people, the Koreans. A lot of them are already getting killed; I sometimes feel there won't be many Koreans left after this "unpleasantness" is over.

*July 14*

David is flying to Tokyo and has promised to mail this letter.

Every night I sleep on the floor, and am acquiring, willy-nilly, your Chinese facility for sleeping pillowless on a hard surface.

And what else is happening to me? I don't know, and probably won't know till much later. I've seen some grim and horrible things, things I've seen and felt before, but instead of becoming hard-boiled about them, they seem to strike me more deeply as I get older.

I feel so desperately sorry for the Koreans. The long files of refugees on the roads. Frightened people. Women with small children. Mothers separated from their children. Children carrying smaller children on their backs. The women make me think of you, perhaps because I have a mental picture of you making the same long journeys in China during the war. And now, through loving you, the Koreans are much less strange to me than my own race. These have now become the "foreigners" to me.

It's humiliating to be involved in defeat, and it's humiliating to be frightened. It's hurtful to one's pride to pull out of a place where there are thousands of men who are under orders to stay and fight and get killed. I pulled out of Taejon yesterday.

On the American side, there's been a hopeless underestimation of the opposition; old fuddyduddy generals, the sort the British army always has to get rid of during the first two years of war, always at the same cost of thousands of men killed; inexperienced ill-trained troops, who've never been under fire before, let alone taken part in a retreat. A young G.I. bursting into tears at his first sight of a dead man being brought in. Men getting out of their foxholes and running. A regimental commander (a wonderful person) standing on a road two miles behind the front sending groups of men back into the lines. "Who gave you orders to come out? Go back." Men so nervy they think every Korean is an enemy, firing at, and sometimes killing refugees. And then the good men, calm and steadfast and rocklike. The G.I.s can be made into good soldiers. They are the same human material who during the last war were made into such superb fighting divisions in New Guinea.

*July 15*
Yesterday I interviewed Syngman Rhee, an old man of 75, the chief of the *émigré* clique which was set up as a South Korean government

some four years back. His foreign minister is also an *émigré,* was thirty-eight years out of Korea, came back last year. The people to whom we are committed now in Asia — Rhee here, Quirino in the Philippines, Chiang Kai-shek and his gang, Bao Dai — what a crew!

The reign of terror in the North. People's Courts (although they're difficult to verify, I think there is a good deal of truth in these reports of killings and eliminations in the North).

And the way the South Koreans treat their prisoners! Truckloads of political prisoners taken up a lonely road to be shot. Jammed kneeling in a truck, groaning, crying. Coming back last night long after curfew I came across a long file of two thousand people being taken to prison. Four across, one hand tied to a long rope, other hand clutching the shirt of the person in front. Quite a lot were women, some with babies on their backs. A horrifying spectacle. Policemen with bayonets on their rifles every ten yards on either side.

Why do human beings do these things to one another?

Coming here, a trigger-happy nervous excited American sentry, who clearly thought he was surrounded by enemies, pointing his gun at us. And at the same time the kindness and easygoing generosity of the Americans.

Shall I see you again? I feel I won't. I can't believe that two weeks ago we were together, and talked, and went for a walk, and loved. I was very happy. Now I can only think of you in metaphorical terms, my door to the rose garden, my still center at the center of the cyclone. I want to see you again. I hope we are meant to meet again. Often I feel that I shall not see you again.

*July 17*

Nicholas, who is my other friend here, set out for the front today to see what he could see. I decided to stay back and to write an article dealing with the three questions: Why did North Korea invade the South? Why was allied intelligence so bad? What role are the Russians playing?

What puzzles me so much is this. Russia does not want an atomic war. She may not have instigated or ordered the North Korean attack, (I do not think so, though all the people I talk to think she did), but she could have prevented a war if she had wanted to. Why did she not?

This affair, of course, has shown up American unpreparedness and weakness, but I'm not sure that it's not the best thing that could have happened from America's point of view. They'll do something about it now. I remember my experiences with them in New Guinea. They put up a lamentable performance at first, and the Australians had to come in and do the job for them. But they jolly well took the lesson to heart, sent a hundred officers straight back to the States, and the next time their troops went into action they did quite well.

The Koreans' own name for their country means Morning Calm. A charming name, isn't it, singularly inapposite at the present time.

*July 20*

In Europe the armies advanced from one castle to another across the face of France and Germany. Here in Korea we proceed in the reverse direction from one primary school to the next. I do all my typing and writing at minute desks designed for children smaller than Mei. My bottom is worn to the bone with bouncing about in jeeps on bumpy roads, and its distressed condition is not improved by sitting at these horribly small cramped desks. The lack of higher education in Korea has been brought home to me in a peculiarly direct manner.

I have yet to sleep on anything but a floor. Last night's floor was one of the hardest to date, one of the most verminous too. I do feel rather tired. I had diarrhea this morning for the first time, but I think it was merely due to having eaten rather green Korean apples given to me by some Korean soldiers, and I didn't want to hurt their feelings, and it's nothing serious.

I came down from the front in a rail coach full of wounded Korean soldiers. A second-class coach, padding ripped from the seats. Improvised stretchers. Seriously wounded brought in on straw mats and put on the floor. Two or three terribly young medical orderlies in charge. The American wounded in the first-class coach just behind were much more comfortable and better looked after. At the same time I imagine these Koreans were in better shape than Chinese wounded in the last war. Sturdy peasant types, tough, uncomplaining, same as the Chinese and the Japanese. No lights after dark. It was curious to be closeted in the darkness with all that suffering.

*July 23*

I have been very depressed and unhappy recently, but two things happened to give me pleasure. First a letter from you, your No. 2. The second was that my friend Prasad arrived this morning. He is a little Malabari with a most distinguished war record; I admire and like him so much. I first met him in '41, and again in '44, '45 and '47. I admired him tremendously for his bravery, his intelligence and honesty, the complete detachment with which he was able to talk about the Indians and the British. For me he was also a gateway. He explained to me the Indian sepoys in all their simplicity, and the Indian officers with all their frustrations and idealisms and complexities.

Prasad for India; my friend An for Korea (I knew him in Japan in 1933), Tomoji Murakata for Japan (he is a doctor now in Hokkaido; I propose to visit him there before leaving Japan), you for China and many other things besides China; all are gateways. I suppose it is only thus, through love, that comes the beginning of understanding.

Goodness knows why Prasad has come over here. It was obviously a wangle. He knew there was a show on and wanted to be in on it. (I can hear you mutter, looking cross and wrinkling your nose: "Just like you, Mark, you can never resist a war.") This being a theater of war, he arrived in all his military panoply — rows of ribbons, full colonel's red tabs, paratroop wings, maroon beret.

Prasad tells me that his wife packed his things beautifully before he left. "She did not forget anything. She even put a copy of the 'Bhagavad-Gita' into my pack."

What book would you choose to put into my pack before I went off to the wars?

*July 24*

What can I tell you about this war, this horrible war? Everyone except myself seems to think that we are winning. Colonel K—— told me this afternoon that in a few weeks it will be all over. An American general in Pusan said that the tide will start turning in two days' time. And so it goes. I seem alone in my pessimism. Who am I to pit my judgment against the judgment of these distinguished people? My consolation is that I shall be glad if they are right and myself wrong.

I have been reading a book called *The Last Puritan,* by George Santayana. I shall send it to you when I have finished. Not that it is easy to sit down to a book, however good. It is not easy to relax. Few people in my profession have the composure to sit down and read quietly when their colleagues are dashing madly around.

I feel un-at-home with Americans in the mass. They make me feel so terribly English and different. So often, in response to my inquiries, they stare at me uncomprehendingly and ask me to repeat what I said. So many of them are fat, and soft and too well fed. And yet underneath there is toughness and idealism, and intense vitality. They have yet to be tempered by hardship and misfortune. They are wonderfully kind and helpful, and the G.I.s especially come out with good remarks. A little Jewish boy from Brooklyn said to me yesterday: "My morale is so low you couldn't dig it out with a steam shovel!"

After my Japanese friend Tomoji Murakata was called up for military service and sent to serve as an army doctor in China in the early years of the China war, he sent a postcard to some mutual friends in Singapore with a single sentence which goes something like this. "My body is healthy and strong, but my spirit and heart . . ."

I was trying to concoct something along these lines to send to you, knowing that you, too, understand the value of emptiness, of negation, the suggestiveness of absence. Japanese is full of grammatical constructions in which the real meaning is contained in the unspoken half of the sentence. Thus if you want to say someone is a real bastard, you say: "He is a charming person, but . . ." So much more meaningful.

I must stop now. I too, like you, feel in a state of suspended animation. There is no future, there is no more past. Only the unpleasant present. There are so many horrible things, so many horrible things crowding in, forcing themselves upon me, however deeply I may bury my head in Santayana.

*July 28*

I am quite *désolé* this morning. I mislaid *The Last Puritan* in the train yesterday, and I still had about 80 of its 600 pages to read. It has saved my sanity these past ten days. It was wonderful amid all this madness and beastliness to be able to slip away and read a few pages of it. I had hoped to send it to you when I had finished it. It took me back to my own youth, made me recall my early loves, made me realize that until I was in my late twenties, it was only males who formed and molded me, only through them that I discovered myself and the world.

Its effect on me has been heightened by the circumstances among which I have read it — the insanity, fear, hatred, lying, suffering, brutality, which knock on my consciousness and force their way in a dozen times a day.

Nicholas may be coming to Hong Kong. You will like him. He is so charming and intelligent. His paper wants him to "evaluate the strategic possibilities of Formosa." What a request to make to a man in the wilds of central Korea! Nicholas and I always operate together when on the same front. I have wanted to talk to him about you, in the way that I want to do to all the friends I am attached to, but it has never happened yet, mainly I think because he is so Europe-minded, and finds little to interest or attract him east of the Balkans.

There are two hundred American correspondents in this theater. Most are keen on chasing up stories of personal heroism, but few spend any length of time here. I feel proud of our little British group, English and Australian.

Please don't be upset or worried if I tell you that we've had casualties among correspondents. Two were killed on the west coast, four lost in an aircraft flying from Tokyo, one lost at Taejon, one missing.

*July 29*

For the past five days I have been with the First Cavalry Division where the heaviest fighting has been taking place.

Wonderful moon at night. Each night a little bigger, rising a little further to the left, taking a little longer to reach the trees on the right. Twice, like a ritual, I read your letter by its light. Last night, wonder of wonders, I not only had a camp bed, but I was able to place it so that it faced the open window and our friend the moon. I couldn't decide if she was full or not.

I don't know how to describe my state of mind. I don't quite know why we are here, and why we have to inflict all these horrors upon these poor Koreans.

I feel like saying: *Mais que diable allait-il faire dans cette galère?* The knowledge and awareness of you gives me a sense of self-sufficiency, almost of invulnerability. "He who has once been happy," or in my case, who has loved and seen the inside of the rose garden, "is forever out of destruction's reach."

But it does not make me invulnerable to what are conventionally known as the horrors of war. I could tell you many things about fear; how infectious it is, how relative it is, how safe a place that is being shelled feels after you have been under small-arms fire; how safe a road with a few snipers feels after you have been shelled. The extraordinary sense of relief afterwards.

I have not become invulnerable, however deliberately I try to an-aesthetize my sensibilities, to the sufferings of the wretched Koreans caught between two armies. The Americans near the front regard any Korean civilian as an enemy and blaze away with their weapons. I

was coming back in a weapon carrier the other day when the driver
spied two old men, with large packs on their backs, plodding through
the ricefields about four hundred yards away. He stopped, and he and
the young soldier behind, young G.I.s probably not yet twenty, started
dashing off towards them with their rifles. It was some minutes before I realized what was in their minds. Then I shouted at them: "Don't
shoot them. They're old men." It was quite obvious, even at that distance, that they were old men. One of them was wearing the curious
black top hat which old Korean men wear. They didn't shoot them,
merely made them unpack their bags, which contained rice. A lot of
these trigger-happy G.I.s would have shot them. I was enormously re-
lieved, although the driver afterwards made it quite clear to me that
he regarded me as an English sissy. I was reminded of that little incident in the *Foxhunting Man* when George Sherston calls out: "Don't
chase him, he's trying to escape," and loses a lot of face with his friend
Dennis.


*July 30*

I wonder if this American intervention is not in effect providing the
basis for a united Korea. The Americans are not making many friends
in Korea. Part of the journey yesterday I traveled in a train containing
American troops. Before the train left, a major announced in the coach:
"Men, this train is only for American troops. If any Gooks try to get
on kick them off." (Gooks is their word for Koreans.) Day after day
with their aircraft the Americans are laying waste towns and villages,
killing fifty civilians for every one soldier. In the village committees
which the communists are setting up there will not be wanting people
with very real grievances, who will stand up and declaim against these
saviors, these allies who have caused more damage and destruction and
suffering than the ostensible enemies.

Do you think in China today there are couples who love each other;
who go through all the motions of conformity while perceiving all the
essential folly and absurdity and lying; who preserve their own inner

integrity only as between themselves, who talk to each other quietly in bed at night, and laugh softly or go for long walks together? Or do they get found out? Do they too, eventually discover that they only love Big Brother?

I wonder if we shall ever see each other again. I have to stay and see this thing through. Curiously enough, I don't feel worried about our future. Although I am unhappy about many things, I am never unhappy about you. In fact it is just the opposite. Obviously if God means us to be together in the future, it will happen. If not . . .

In your letter you said that you were in a "state of acceptance." I hope it is a state in which you are continuing to find positive and beautiful things, in which there is no waste, in which you are learning and growing and deepening.

It is as you said. Love is growing up.


*July 31*

I told Nicholas that I found it very difficult to see this conflict in moral terms, right and principle embodied in the United Nations, naked aggression embodied in North Korea with the Soviet bloc behind her (though there certainly was aggression, and quite openly at that); that I found it difficult not to see the conflict simply in terms of Russia and her satellites versus America and hers; that I rarely used the word enemy in referring to the North Koreans, although it sometimes worked its way in. Nicholas blinked his eyes in the funny way he has and then said in his high-pitched, slightly stuttering voice: "Mark, if you don't mind my saying so, I think that is very woolly-minded of you." He then proceeded to develop a conventional and orthodox line of argument.

What do you feel about this? I find it difficult thinking of the relations between countries in terms of right and wrong, good and bad. Morality, when imported into these relations, is simply an aspect, or a function, of power.

\*     \*     \*

*August 1, Pusan*

The Korean women are not at all beautiful, but sometimes a nose, some freckles, a V of hair, reminds me of you.

I have come down to the port of Pusan with Charles, a young Frenchman with beautiful manners, gently cynical. He said: "I don't like communism, but I confess that I don't like a lot of things that are being done in the name of anticommunism." He told me that some time ago he traveled down from Taejon to Taeju with David on a train. Poor David was so moved with pity for the refugees that he flung open the door of the coach (reserved for American personnel and correspondents), and bade them all come in, spent all the local money he had on buying them apples and melons and rice, distributed all his cigarettes, and nursed a small child on his knee all the way.

Here am I, sitting on the pier, waiting for the Marines to arrive. No less than two bands are here, one an enormous Korean military band, the other composed of Negroes tootling away on their instruments, dying to play some jazz. The Marines will be thrown in where the threat is gravest.

The Negroes just can't hold themselves in and are playing madly away in a sort of jam session, although the transports are nowhere in sight. With this carnival atmosphere on the pier, it is difficult to realize that the North Koreans are less than forty-five miles west of here, and advancing steadily.

The Negroes are so happy. They tootle away, and then burst into a terrific march. They're now playing "Colonel Bogey."

*August 3*

Charles and I came back last night. We slept on the floor of a freight car; G.I.s, Negroes, Koreans, sprawled over the place — a pervasive fecal smell, boots kicking you in the face at night. Charles is charming, laughs gently, doesn't fuss or get impatient. We had a bottle of whisky which David sent over from Tokyo, and that helped.

The Americans dislike this country which strikes them as being very dirty (though it's much cleaner than China). Those who fought in Europe remark on the absence of *bistros,* and pretty girls, and pleasant things to be found behind the lines on the European fronts.

Some G.I. remarks I overheard:

"I'd give you fifteen cents for this whole country — if you gave me twelve cents change."

"What the hell are we fighting for anyway?"

"I wish someone would sit down and explain to me what this goddam war is all about."

It is as François said:

*"Il faut dire aux hommes pourquoi ils doivent se faire tuer."*


*August 4*

The cicadas sing away crescendo and then diminuendo almost into complete silence. In the jungle too you get that cycle of sound.

But my heart is heavy, a purely professional malaise. Perhaps it is time that I went to Tokyo for a few days' change of scene.

Do you think we shall ever be together again? Sometimes we've woken up together, and seen the dawn, but we've never been able to wake up with the whole day ahead, let alone the whole week, or the whole future. Still, we've been very lucky, and perhaps God will still be good to us.

We've just had an air briefing. I so hate them. The smugness, the relish with which the briefing officer describes how parachute fragmentation bombs were dropped on towns, how villages were strafed and fires started. And so on. He speaks with much obvious pride, with a peculiar slow emphatic pleasure when describing the bloodier episodes.

"An unquestionably record day . . . the bulk of the slugging was in this area. . . . Many small towns in this area were knocked flat. . . . Some North Koreans had taken refuge in this tunnel. They really worked — the boys over the tunnel. Had napalm bombs. Dropped one at one end. Smoke began to come out at the other end. Then they dropped another one at the other end."

Dreadfulness. Dreadfulness.

And in this world, Suyin, they say that you and I are mad, because we love and dream and cannot hate.

A pilot reported: "North Koreans lying dead all over the area, like confetti. Trucks and vehicles driving over the dead bodies. The whole area strewn with bodies. At first I didn't know what these white objects were. I made a low strafing pass. I saw dead North Koreans in white." How did he know they were *North* Koreans? Only civilians are dressed in white in Korea. It sounds very much as if they were refugees on the roads.

The stupidities, the beastliness, the hatred, the hurt; how does the Superior Person react to them, Suyin? It's no good running away. It's no good becoming blunted, as most people do. I suppose it is part of what we must see steadily and whole, the folly and imbecility of mankind, at the same time refusing to accept them. You deal with suffering; but you can do something about it. I can only stand and watch.

*August 5*

Please do not worry about me. I am not unhappy. Indeed I am often happy. The human organism is such a wonderfully adaptive one. There is always you, my chiefest and most abiding source of happiness. There are friends, who mean much more under circumstances like these; there is a moon, and a River of Heaven; there are the satisfactions of the technician; there are books and poetry, sunrises and sunsets; eating, drinking, smoking, washing the dust off under a hose; all things from which conscious pleasure derives; there are flashes of beauty in the faces of people. If I continue this catalogue much longer I shall convince myself that Korea is a veritable hedonists' paradise.

*August 6*

Why have I been writing to you every day? Because I feel the time may come when I shall not be able even to write to you.

Another friend arrived yesterday. He is reading Thucydides' *History of the Peloponnesian War*. Apropos of nothing he said to me: "I am afraid this is the end of our world, Mark."

And it is your world too, Suyin, though you have the entrée to many, while I am limited to one. The chief reason it makes me sad is not because some hideous impenetrable curtain might come crashing down and separate us — but rather because I do want you to write these books I know you have inside you, and I don't see how you are going to be able to do them except in my world.

But let us not dwell on this, for is it not a thought allied to possessiveness, which we are both agreed is the source of so many evils? You have the essential me, and I want to give the inessential to you too. Perhaps if we do not ask Him too importunately, still less demand anything, or expect it as a right, God, who has already been so good to us, will still be good.

It is curious, this life of suspended animation which you speak of as your present state, the nothingness of the past and the future, the narrow tightrope of the present. What are you waiting for? What is going to happen? Do you know?

*August 8*

Three sights in war always upset me: prisoners, refugees, the wounded. All for the same reason: the indignity of their condition. Today we passed a truck containing ten North Korean prisoners, young men with shaven heads, hands tied with straw ropes to the sides of the truck, labels round their necks. The wounded too have labels tied round their necks.

Is the fundamental difference between the philosophies of the communist and noncommunist worlds that in one men are allowed to be individuals and in the other merely organisms with labels tied round their necks?

But perhaps this packed and crowded and hungry world has become such a complicated place, the organization of its economic life so difficult, that labels in both worlds are inescapable. I do not know. Do you?


### August 9

Prasad, who has just been in to see me on his return from Tokyo, says everyone there is very optimistic about the Korean war.

The destruction and suffering in Korea are already on such a scale that in the minds of ordinary Koreans, and of educated professional people like doctors and teachers, they easily transcend the ideological issues. American aircraft are systematically razing all Korean towns of any size to the ground. Taejon and Kimchon are flat. Soon it will be Taeju. Some very terrible incidents have occurred when young pilots have strafed refugees. The rice is ripening in the fields. Harvesting is due soon. Who is going to do it? Intelligent Koreans see this merely as a struggle between two world powers competing for supremacy. It was Korea's misfortune to be the testing ground, her tragedy that the Korean people are paying the price. They are appalled by the vengeance which the North Koreans would wreak on the South Koreans, although the Northerners have recently become more moderate, and are behaving much more as did the Chinese when they came to power last year; they are even more appalled by the prospect of even greater vengeance which the Southern Koreans would wreak on the North.

If I go and interview the Korean foreign minister, he will give me a grandiloquent statement. Privately he is bitter. An edge is lent to his bitterness by the knowledge that his government is so dependent on the Americans. It is so galling, as the Chinese in Formosa are finding it, to have to accept money and help from others.

Korean towns always have lots of seal carvers, because every Korean, like every Chinese and every Japanese, has to have a seal. Charles and I spent some time in a shop and I found myself giving him a long discourse on seals. I told him too how if a man and a woman love each other, in China, they had seals made with names of their own choosing, seals from the same block of stone, the man's name in relief, the woman's carved into the stone. He asked me what sort of names they chose and I said, trying to appear nonchalant: "Oh, names like Wing of Spring and Beautiful Wing." He said: "How I wish that I could have come East when it was still possible to go to China."

*August 10*

The pleasure of seeing friends again, a whisky and gentle leisurely talk in the dark, no moon but lots of stars and the River of Heaven flowing brightly, and then sleep, sleep with my magic good-luck blanket spread over me. Comforts are very relative, and pleasures and delights are only waiting to be plucked out of the air.

But now I must turn and write a piece for my paper. Shut the door on one world, open the door on another. Who is to say which is the real one? I suppose both are, or both equally illusory.

We are both of us, don't you think, Suyin, rather prone to be moonstruck in the sunshine?

*August 11*

Shall I give you a thought for the day:

"In this world men must be saved by their lack of faith."

It was quoted to me by Nicholas this morning.

I went up to the front with Prasad. We talked about India, and once again I thought how, if I cannot work in China, then I would like to be in India.

B. arrived today, arrogant, pugnacious, amusing for a time. The first thing he said to me was: "Excuse me, but are you proud or ashamed to work for your paper?" There seemed no point in taking umbrage. I laughed and said: "Neither I suppose. I've never worked for anyone else." I confess I do not feel terribly drawn to the diehard Tory views he puts forward. He was saying rude things about our "giving India away." He has already seen all the bigwigs, including General MacArthur. Nicholas told me that he and MacArthur "seemed to have made a mutually favorable impression on each other."

*August 12*

Quite the nicest thing you have said to me is that you will always be waiting for me in your heart. The same thought has come to me many times while I have been over here. What is love? Do you know? You gave me some answers, but you also gave me many questions.

Last night in bed I was trying to remember that poem of Francis Thompson, "In No Strange Land." Most of it came back to me. I expect you know it. Let me write out a few lines for you:

> The angels keep their ancient places: —
> Turn but a stone and start a wing!
> 'Tis ye, 'tis your estrangèd faces
> That miss the many-splendored thing.

No wonder that I appear very self-contained, carrying inside me the love of you, an ever-running fountain of happiness, watering and making fertile my whole existence. God has been so good to us. Somebody once said to me that it was a "tragedy not to be loved." Surely the real tragedy is not to love?

Oh Suyin, I am so happy. We have not missed, you and I, we have not missed the many-splendored thing.

# CHAPTER X

## *A Many-Splendored Thing*

*August 1950*

ALL THROUGH JULY AND THE FIRST TWELVE DAYS OF AUGUST I lived a suspended existence, laden with unformed apprehension, awaiting I knew not what. Only one cable from Mark, which said: DO READ LAST PURITAN BY SANTAYANA A WONDERFUL BOOK IS MOON WAXING IN HONG KONG MARK.

I hold nothing of the heat-enameled, cloud-bloated July save Peter Dixon's visit. Peter Dixon and his wife, Kay, a Siamese friend of mine, had asked Mei and me to stay with them in his Bangkok house, on our way to Hong Kong from England nearly two years ago. It was Peter Dixon who first said to Mark, all of a year and a half ago:

"When you get to Hong Kong, do ring up Dr. Han. She's a Chinese doctor, quite brainy."

So Mark carefully eschewed doing so. A brainy Chinese female doctor is an appalling combination.

Peter came to tea at Conduit Road.

"My, you look wonderful, Suyin. Kay would be surprised. You've changed. Why, you're beautiful now."

"It's Mark," I said.

"I know," said Peter. "Mark told me when he was in Bangkok in February this year. I was very surprised, you know. You were both so conventional. So inhibited even, both of you."

"It's Mark," I said.

"I know it is," said Peter. "He's changed too. And now you. Goodness," he added, suddenly wistful, "I wish I could feel like that. We're very fond of each other, Kay and I, but at our age, of course . . ."

"It's Mark," I explained. Peter is one year younger than Mark and three years older than I.

"Don't keep on saying: 'It's Mark, it's Mark,'" replied Peter, a little irritably. "I suppose it's never happened to either of you before."

"Not to me," I said. "It's Mark."

Then Peter talked about what he called the "practical" view, and how impossible it was to wait years for Mark. He gave me good advice. I nodded and listened and smiled and said: "Thank you so much, Peter. I'll think about it."

I came down to breakfast that Sunday morning feeling cross, on edge; Mei was eating already and Fiona had just fed the dogs and came and sat with her bandanna round her head. "Phew! What a hot day. Tattybogle won't eat his chow. Have the papers come yet?"

Every day we read the papers for the war news. James also listened to the one o'clock news.

"Fiona," I said, "I'm feeling so jittery. So many correspondents have been killed or missing."

"Oh, Suyin, the papers said there are two hundred and seventy correspondents in Korea. There's safety in numbers, you know."

Ah Sun brought in the *Sunday Herald* rolled up, and I started on my toast. Fiona unrolled the *Herald*. No sooner had the paper stopped its unfolding noise than Fiona gasped once and said:

"Suyin . . ."

"What?" I said. "What is it?" I looked at her. She had a horrible fixed stare upon her face. Her mouth couldn't shut.

"What," I said. "Mark?"

"Yes. Oh don't look, Suyin." She put her hand flat snap on the paper. "Dead or prisoner?" I said.

"Dead. Oh, Suyin, Suyin . . ." And her voice broke.

"It's not true," I said angrily. "Why, it's ridiculous. Give me that paper."

In big letters, right in the middle of the front page.

"Fiona, it's not true. It's a lie. Fiona, it's a lie."

"It's true, Suyin," said Fiona.

Mei had stopped eating and was looking at me, so I said:

"Mark is dead, darling."

I walked out of the dining room. It seemed to me that I was making a lot of noise. I opened a door very noisily, then I was in the drawing room, looking round. There was the empty striped chair. I sat watching the chair, watching. If I looked long enough, I would not miss him, he would be there.

But he did not come, and then I knew it would always be like that, the empty room, the vacant chair, and I would sit and stare and wait and he would not be there.

And life went by, softly, softly.

And then the doorbell rang, the telephone rang, and in they came with their voices and their tears, some of those who had laughed with him, and eaten with him, and loved him.

And Father Low said a mass for Mark next morning with only Fiona and me there.

And Mei wrote in her diary: "I had a friend who wanted to marry my mother and my mother wanted to marry him. But it couldn't be done and now he is dead, which is a pity."

And the next day Mark's letters began to arrive. One by one they came, one by one. Twenty-one of them from Korea.

And that was all.

# PART FOUR
# Conclusion

# The End and the Beginning

AFTERWARDS, AS HAPPENS WHEN A MAN IS SAFELY DEAD, they spoke of his courage, his nobility; how he walked through the bullets of war as for an afternoon amble, and his name was a legend for bravery. They said how cool and even-tempered he was, and how his presence quietened those that were with him. They spoke of his gentleness, his tolerance and his understanding. They deplored the fate that had wasted his gifts when they were so much needed.

His friends came back from the wars, and they said many fine things about him. Among them was David; and now David was eager that I should not do anything to sully a memory grown sacred, a little superhuman to him. He would write a book about Mark. It would be Mark's life. It would be a good book. I would read it one day, and discover what Mark had done in such and such a year, where his feet had carried him, what friends had met him, and laughed with him. For, after all, I had only known Mark for a year and a month and a few days.

David thought it best if I should quietly pack my things, leave Hong Kong, and go back to China to bury myself in medical work, and forget Mark. He thought it a very bad idea that I should write a book. "It would be . . . sacrilege, don't you think?" said David.

And suddenly I realized that in David's eyes our many-splendored thing, Mark's and mine, was an offense. David had not understood Mark. But he would write a good book about him. Mark would be such a recognizable, immaculate, superhuman part of speech all through it.

I realized that people bring to what they see and hear and feel the inner weather of their souls and the complexion of their minds. And so in my book, the moralist would find enough to wax righteously indignant, the politician would cull perverse propensities to fit his political verdicts, and the pompous and the humbug — what a good time they would have, exhibiting their outraged feelings of propriety, their delicate sense of privacy, their offended reticence! I was grateful to David for pointing all this out to me. But I went on writing this book. I could no longer stop myself.

So I stayed in Hong Kong, on the sea-wet rock; it was the only place where I could write this book. I could not write it in China, and I could not go anywhere else. So here I stayed, took another job, and worked by day, and wrote by night.

At night then I become again haunted, companioned by his gentle ghost, my hand in his, following him, safe in darkness and in silence, with Mark. And the fishing fleet comes swinging gaily out upon the sea, and our friend the moon goes to sleep. I sit and dream.

I deem it strange and wonderful that my love should have been a stranger, a man so gaily encountered, by luck, a transient on an island of transients. And that because of this love, light as a bird on the wing and terrible as the last day of the world I should have been pulled out of a frozen, inhuman sleep into life. And now there is no going back from life.

Now there will always be Mark, a little laugh below the thunder of the loudspeakers, the sanity of birdsong amid the ravings of the multitudes. Mark and the gentleness of his eyes and his hands holding me still, keeping me safe from so many things:

From intolerant faiths and infallible beliefs, from hatred and cynicism and bitterness, from the swarm-passion and the goose-step voice, wherever they may be, keeping me safe from those foes of the human soul.

For he was gentle, and his tenderness encompassed me. And there is not anything in the world stronger than tenderness.

And because of what happened, Mark died a happy man.

"Lucky, lucky Mark," said François, "how I envy him! He died as we would all die, feeling young, invulnerable, and that life had been worth living, wrapped in a splendid love. This is how I would die. *Il a toujours eu de la chance, Mark!*"

It made me happy, though perhaps François said it also to console me. For at that moment Adeline Palmer-Jones, in pale blue with a lot of sequins, had just placed her arm publicly round me, and drawn my reluctant body within the redundant softnesses of her being, and talked about a "terrible, terrible, tragedy."

Dear Adeline. She meant so well. But she had far less of the understanding heart than Lily Wu.

I met Lily, alone for once, as I wandered down the Praya, and she saw my eyes, and seized my hand.

"It is true, then, what I read in the papers? He is dead. You must not weep. You must laugh, as you laughed when you were together with him. You must be happy now, always, to please him. He would not like to see you cry."

And so I dream, content since I must be content, and fulfilled, dreaming thus, as if I were waiting for him.

As if at any hour of the day — at noon, under the high calm sun he loved so well, at night under the River of Heaven — he might be back. As if I might meet him strolling along the Praya, smiling and blue-eyed as the sea. Or walking up the gold-speckled gravel of the drive I might see him, walking towards me, his hair blown over his forehead by the sea wind, coming joyful towards me between the sea and the hill.

Look, says the child, look. For a moment I stood on tiptoe, and grasped with both my hands at the sky. Look. In my empty enchanted hands I hold fabulous treasure; the immense nothingness of heaven, the vacancy of space, and time's fleet magic. Look how it has transformed me. For I am now crowned with negation, mantled with absence, throned on nothingness, empress of exceeding glory, the splendor and wealth of love and death.

I sit and dream, as if . . .

As if my dream were reality. For now, like Mark, I do not know what is reality and what is dream. And if it is a dream, then I have dreamed a wonderful dream to shield me from the night, and the breath of heaven itself cannot blow my dream away.

I have dreamed a wonderful dream; of life, and love and death, of laughter, and tears, and good and ill, and all these things which are equal under Heaven, which equalizes all things.

A wonderful dream, my many-splendored thing.

*Begun in Hong Kong September 1950.*
*Finished in Hong Kong July 1951.*